# Plastic Design in Steel

## A GUIDE AND COMMENTARY

By a Joint Committee of the
Welding Research Council and the
American Society of Civil Engineers

## ASCE-WRC

**Second Edition**

*PUBLISHED BY ASCE*

American Society of Civil Engineers • 345 East 47th Street • New York, New York 10017

# JOINT COMMITTEE (FIRST EDITION)

## WELDING RESEARCH COUNCIL

Structural Steel Committee

Subcommittee on Welded Continuous Frames and their Components—Lehigh University

A. Amirikian
Lynn S. Beedle
J. M. Crowley
F. H. Dill
Samuel Epstein
Gerald F. Fox
LaMotte Grover
William H. Jameson
Bruce G. Johnston
Jonathan Jones (Deceased)
T. C. Kavanagh
R. L. Ketter
Carl Kreidler
H. W. Lawson
Nathan M. Newmark
Emmanuel Pisetzner
R. M. Stuchell (Deceased)
John Vasta
T. R. Higgins, *Chairman*

## AMERICAN SOCIETY OF CIVIL ENGINEERS

Engineering Mechanics Division

Committee on Plasticity Related to Design

Frank Baron
John M. Biggs
Daniel C. Drucker
John D. Griffiths
William J. Hall
T. R. Higgins
Harry N. Hill
Eivind Hognestad
Robert L. Janes
Bruce G. Johnston
William H. Munse, Jr.
Egor P. Popov
John B. Scalzi
Paul S. Symonds
Bruno Thürlimann
George Winter
Douglas T. Wright
Lynn S. Beedle, *Chairman*

---

---

ISBN: 0-87262-217-7

# JOINT COMMITTEE (SECOND EDITION)

iii

# CONTENTS

## FOREWORD TO THE FIRST EDITION (1961)

The evaluation of a considerable amount of research work has demonstrated the applicability of plastic analysis to structural design. For the type of structure to which its application is intended, plastic design results in an over-all balanced design, and a more economical use of material than conventional methods. In comparison with allowable stress ("elastic") design methods, plastic design is a simpler design technique. As a consequence designers have chosen the plastic design method for more than 2,000 structures built in the United States and abroad.

This Manual documents the applicability of plastic analysis to the design of structural steel beams and frames. Theoretical considerations involved in the plastic theory and in certain secondary design problems are presented. Experimental verification is provided, and approximations in the form of design guides are suggested.

In 1959, the American Institute of Steel Construction published a report entitled "Plastic Design in Steel" which illustrates the procedures of the plastic method of design with specific reference to building construction. It supplies information to supplement clauses in a specification for plastic design. Appropriate reference is made to this valuable design aid. The recent books which should be consulted for a much fuller discussion than space permits herein are listed at the beginning of Appendix III.—References.

This Commentary is based on a series of preliminary reports prepared for the Welding Research Council and the American Society of Civil Engineers by a research group at the Fritz Engineering Laboratory, Department of Civil Engineering, Lehigh University, Bethlehem, Pa. The staff members at Fritz Laboratory included: L. S. Beedle, G. C. Driscoll, Jr., T. V. Galambos, R. L. Ketter, T. Kusuda, G. C. Lee, T. Lee, L. W. Lu, A. Ostapenko, and B. Thürlimann. The organizations that supported the research projects out of which the preliminary reports were prepared were the following: American Institute of Steel Construction, American Iron and Steel Institute, Column Research Council, the Department of the Navy (Office of Naval Research, Bureau of Ships, Bureau of Yards and Docks), and the Welding Research Council.

Although much of the experimental and theoretical work was performed at Lehigh University, the WRC-ASCE Joint Committee has broadened this Commentary by including the results of research at other institutions

ix

both in the United States and abroad. The inclusion of this information and of certain unpublished data is gratefully acknowledged.

The Joint Committee notes with sorrow the passing of one of its members, Jonathan Jones, Hon. M. ASCE. Mr. Jones' critical review of the manuscript constituted a distinct contribution to this document.

The Joint Committee recommends that this Manual be read carefully by all structural engineers.

# FOREWORD TO THE SECOND EDITION

Since publication of the First Edition in 1961, there have been notable developments in plastic design of steel structures. A substantial amount of literature has been published as a result of the research work completed since the first publication. Formal recognition has been given to plastic design in building specifications; it is now "Part 2" of the AISC Specifications for buildings, and many of the provisions of Part 1 (Allowable-Stress Design) were affected by the research on the plastic behavior of structures. There has been significant application of the method, not only to low buildings, but also to a number of multistory frames. The substantial amount of research on multistory frames and on higher-strength steels resulted in a summer conference at Lehigh University in 1965 which brought into focus a number of the new problems and many of their solutions.

The ASCE Structural Division Committee on Plastic Design therefore took steps to prepare a revision to this Manual. The contents are extended, as are its recommendations, to reflect the developments since the beginning of this decade.

The objective of the committee was to prepare a modest revision. The basic approach is still the simple plastic theory but with modifications where necessary to extend its applicability. In addition to covering low unbraced frames, the Manual is expanded to include braced and unbraced multistory frames. Steels with a well-defined yield plateau are considered, the upper limit of the yield stress being 65 ksi. The scope is also limited to planar structures. The loading is considered to be primarily static; however, some attention is given to repeated loading effects that are characteristic of those associated with earthquakes.

The Ad Hoc Committee for the preparation of this Second Edition is made up of the members of the original two committees of WRC and ASCE, of designated members of the present Committee on Plasticity of the Engineering Mechanics Division, of the ASCE Structural Division Committee on Plastic Design, and of Lehigh University investigators.

This Manual results from a series of drafts prepared by certain members of the Ad Hoc Committee, and subsequently reviewed by the membership of three major committees listed earlier. Authors of the original drafts were Messrs. P. F. Adams, S. C. Batterman, L. S. Beedle, L. D. Carpenter, W. F. Chen, J. H. Daniels, G. C. Driscoll, Jr., J. W. Fisher, T. V. Galambos, W. C. Hansell, L. C. Lim, L. W. Lu, B. M. McNamee,

xi

A. Ostapenko, and E. P. Popov. In addition the committee had the help and advice of the following overseas representatives: M. G. Lay (Australia), H. Beer (Austria), C. Massonnet (Belgium), F. F. Faltus (Czechoslovakia), D. Sfintesco (France), O. Steinhardt, U. Vogel (Germany), O. Halasz (Hungary), H. Tanaka, M. Wakabayashi (Japan), K. Basler, B. Thürlimann (Switzerland), E. R. Bryan, J. Heyman, M. R. Horne (United Kingdom), V. A. Baldin, V. N. Nasonov (USSR), and M. Marincek (Yugoslavia).

The committee recommends this Manual for study by all structural engineers.

### Ad Hoc Committee

| | |
|---|---|
| H. Allison | J. Heyman |
| J. F. Baker | T. R. Higgins |
| S. C. Batterman | M. R. Horne |
| E. R. Bryan | B. G. Johnston |
| W. F. Chen | M. G. Lay |
| J. H. Daniels | S. L. Lee |
| G. C. Driscoll, Jr. | L. C. Lim |
| D. C. Drucker | L. W. Lu |
| T. C. Fan | C. Massonnet |
| M. N. Fialkow | B. M. McNamee |
| J. W. Fisher | W. H. Munse |
| G. F. Fox | A. Ostapenko |
| Y. Fujita | E. P. Popov |
| T. V. Galambos | D. Sfintesco |
| K. H. Gerstle | B. Thürlimann |
| J. A. Gilligan | M. Wakabayashi |
| W. J. Hall | L. S. Beedle, *Chairman* |
| W. C. Hansell | |

# CHAPTER 1.—INTRODUCTION

## 1.1 STRUCTURAL DESIGN

An engineering structure is satisfactorily designed if it can be built with the required economy and if, throughout its useful life, it carries its intended loads and otherwise performs its intended function. In the process of selecting the members for a steel frame structure it is necessary, first, to make a general analysis of structural strength and, second, to examine certain details (usually covered by codes or specifications) to assure that premature local failure does not occur.

The design of a steel frame can be based on a number of criteria, any one of which may actually constitute a "Limit of Structural Usefulness." These are:

1. Hypothetical attainment of a specified minimum yield-point stress (such designs are frequently based on allowable stress).
2. Attainment of maximum plastic strength (assuming idealized behavior).
3. Excessive deflections.
4. Buckling and instability.
5. Fatigue.
6. Fracture.

Item 1 in conjunction with Items 4 and 5 was, for many years, the basis for structural design which used the "allowable-stress" concept. Certain provisions also are included in specifications which are intended to assure that the capacity is not otherwise limited. Under certain adverse conditions steel may fracture in a brittle manner; and although no specific rule has been available, the occurrence of such fractures has been reduced by proper attention to material, design details, and fabrication procedures.

Strictly speaking, a design based on any one of the six criteria given above could be referred to as a "Limit Design," although the term usually has been applied to determination of maximum strength according to Items 2 and 4. "Plastic Design," as an aspect of limit design, embraces primarily Item 2 (attainment of maximum plastic strength), and is applicable to continuous beams and building frames 1 story to 2 stories in height (hereafter referred to as "low" buildings) as well as to independently braced buildings of greater height. It is based on the maximum load the structure will carry, as determined from an analysis of strength in

1

the plastic range (that is, a plastic analysis). Whereas "allowable-stress design" is performed by assuming *working loads* and an *allowable* stress, plastic design is based on the concepts of *factored* loads, obtained by applying appropriate load factors to the working loads, and on *limiting* (or capacity) moments, shears, and axial loads.

## 1.2   PLASTICITY AND DESIGN—SOME ADVANTAGES AND LIMITATIONS

It has long been known that an indeterminate steel frame has a greater load-carrying capacity than that indicated by the allowable-stress concept. Such frames are able to carry increased loads above the yield value because structural steel has the capacity to yield. Although the allowable-stress concept is satisfactory for simple structures, its extension to indeterminate steel structures has overemphasized the importance of stress rather than strength as the basis of engineering design. Furthermore, it has introduced a complexity that is unnecessary for many structures.

Indeed, there is no basis for an assumption that at no time should the stress in a steel structure go beyond the elastic range. As a matter of fact, it is necessary to consider plasticity in all structural design (1.18). An actual structure is a complex body with an extremely complicated state of stress. It is an assembly of many individual members joined together to form a working unit. The individual structural elements, such as the beams and columns, come from the mills with residual stresses which are often over one-third the yield stress. In connecting the parts local stresses are produced by welding, by other fabrication and erection methods, and by misfits. There are over-all assembly stresses. The structure is sometimes pierced by many holes, reinforcements of all kinds (such as cover plates and stiffeners) are present, and many secondary stresses arise owing to continuity of the structure. Because of the deformations caused by the loading, bending and torsion may occur in what are assumed to be simple tension members, and axial force and torsion may occur in beams. As a consequence of these factors (the combination of unknown initial stress, stress concentration, and redistribution due to discontinuities of the structure), it is inevitable that local plastic flow will take place in any kind of design. An examination of actual load-deflection curves presented subsequently will demonstrate this conclusively.

Numerous examples have been given elsewhere in which the benefits of plasticity are used consciously or unconsciously in allowable-stress design (1.2, 1.19). Two of these are cited here. In the design of round pins, specifications permit an allowable stress which is higher than the allowable stress for I-beams. This is possible because of the large plastic reserve of strength in pins. Also, a reduction of the negative moment is permitted at points of interior support in continuous beams. This is to recognize the moment redistribution which results from ductility.

From the foregoing it is evident that local yielding undoubtedly will occur in most steel frames by the time full service loads are reached. Furthermore, parts of these structures will enter appreciably into the plastic range before reaching their assumed limit of carrying capacity.

This situation will also exist in a structure designed on the basis of plasticity. Nevertheless it is important to note that at working load, the plastically designed structure is normally in the so-called "elastic" range. A plastic design is based on a load which is equal to the working load multiplied by a load factor. Local inelastic deformations at working load may develop at first loading, just as such deformations may develop in a structure designed by the allowable-stress method. With either method of design, when the working load is removed from the structure a permanent set remains, and with it a corresponding system of residual stress. The change in stress and strain from this residual state produced by subsequent reapplications and removals of the working load would then be purely elastic.

Knowledge of the ductile behavior of steel also permits the designer to eliminate costly details intended to provide actual hinges that would be required only if the construction material were brittle. With modern welding techniques, splices are often less expensive than mechanical hinges or other details that would allow more or less free rotations. With a knowledge of behavior in the plastic range, the designer will realize that the elimination of hinges simply results in a stiffer structure with a strength at least equal to (and usually greater than) that calculated for the same structure with hinges. The saving in fabrication costs that result from a better design of details based on an understanding of ductile behavior may be very great indeed.

An exact plastic design which considered strain hardening would be a formidable task. However, if the behavior of structural steel is idealized (see Chapter 2), so that it is either completely elastic or perfectly plastic, then there is obtained a simple and yet reasonably satisfactory approximation termed plastic design (more precisely "plastic limit design," but referred to hereafter by the shorter term). Within this simplification, the structure is assumed to reach its maximum predictable strength at a definite load called the "plastic limit load." This load is sometimes also referred to as "collapse load." It is emphasized, however, that a structure carrying the computed limit load is seldom in a state of real collapse. For this reason, the term "plastic limit load" or "plastic load" will be used throughout this Manual. For a large majority of continuous beams and low building frames, a design based on a reasonable load factor against the plastic limit load provides a more appropriate structure than a design based on allowable stresses and elastic stress computations.

As was intimated at the outset, there are several design factors to which consideration must be given beyond the selection of members on the basis of plasticity. One such factor is the effect of repeated loading, in which case additional consideration should be given to the possibility of fatigue failure or excessive deformation. Another is the occurrence of buckling before full plasticity is reached and, in general, any other factor that greatly increases the weakening or strengthening effect of deformation prior to failure. Brittle fracture is another consideration of importance both to allowable-stress and to plastic design. Plastic limit load computations for continuous frames are based on the assumption that "plastic hinge moments" are developed at points of maximum moment in the structure and maintained during further loading. Thus design criteria for the stability of members and details, which under allowable-stress design merely guard against the initiation of buckling prior to first yielding, require reexamination in plastic design where plastic buckling must be controlled during hinge deformation. The magnitude of the deflection at working load may constitute still another design criterion. All of these problems are discussed in more detail subsequently; however, it is emphasized here that, in principle, the problems of plastic design are no different from those which exist in any design procedure.

Plasticity concepts were applied to the design of building frames as early as 1914 (1.20, 1.21). Basic tests verifying the concepts of plastic design were reported in 1927 (1.22). Since then, significant contributions have been made to the plastic theory of structures both in the United States and abroad (1.1 to 1.11, 1.23 to 1.30). Plastic design techniques have been in wide use in the United States and Britain since the middle 1950's (1.31), and specifications in many other countries now permit the use of plastic design. The scope and use of plastic design is summarized in Table 1.1 (1.32). Because of its importance in engineering application, plastic theory is now discussed in elementary books on Mechanics of Materials and Structural Design (1.12 to 1.17).

It is emphasized that plastic design is not a technique that is intended to replace all other design procedures. Factors such as buckling, fatigue, and deflection limitations may become the design criteria. As an example of a limitation that comes about because of column buckling, most trusses would be excluded from plastic design (with the exception of the Vierendeel type); the method discussed herein requires that "hinges" form, and chord members would not exhibit the necessary deformation capacity in compression. In ordinary building construction, limitations such as fatigue and buckling are usually the exception and not the rule. Therefore plastic design is finding considerable application in continuous beams and low building frames where the members are stressed primarily in bending.

TABLE 1.1—PLASTIC DESIGN STATUS

| Country[a] (1) | Current plastic design specification or code (2) | Type of specification or code (3) | Application | | |
|---|---|---|---|---|---|
| | | | Beams and girders (4) | Low buildings (5) | Braced multi-story frames (6) |
| USA | AISC—Part 2 (1969) | Detailed specification | Extensive | Extensive | A few |
| Australia | (SAA) AS CA1, 1968 | Detailed specification | Many | Many portal frames | Aware of none |
| Austria | ONORM B4600 (1964) | General provisions | Extensive | A few | Aware of none |
| Belgium | Addendum to NBN1 | Detailed specification | A few | A few | Aware of none |
| Canada | CSA S16 (1969) | Detailed specification | Extensive | Extensive | A few |
| Czechoslovakia | CSN 73 1401 Sect. 23–26 | General provisions | A few | A few | Aware of none |
| Denmark | Danish Engineering Society: Steel Construction Code | Alternate method | A few | A few | Aware of none |
| France | "Not Prohibited" | — | None | None | None |
| Germany | DIN 1050 Sect. 3.2, 5.33 | General provisions | Many | A few | Aware of none |
| Hong Kong | BSS 449 (1959) | General provisions | Aware of none | A few | None |
| Hungary | Hungary Design Code (draft form) | — | A few | Aware of none | Aware of none |
| India | I.S. 800 (1962) ISI Handbook (draft form) | General provisions Detailed specification | A few | A few | Aware of none |
| Italy | CNR-UNI 10011/67 | General provisions | Many | Aware of none | Aware of none |
| Japan | Structural Standards of Architectural Institute of Japan (draft form) | Detailed specification | A few (a few pedestrian bridges) | None | None |
| Mexico | Mexico Building Code Federal Electric Commission under study | General provisions Detailed specification | Many | Many | A few (also some unbraced) |
| Netherlands | | Detailed specification | A few | A few | None |
| South Africa | BSS 449 (1959) | General provisions | A few | Nearly all frames | Aware of none |
| Sweden | SBN 67 | General provisions | A few | A few | None |
| Switzerland | SIA No. 161 | Alternate method | A few | A few | None |
| United Kingdom | BSS 449 | General provisions | Many | Nearly all frames | A few braced multistory frames on the basis of "open" specifications "up to the designer" |
| USSR | SNiP, II-B. 3–62 and II-A. 10–62 | — | Extensive | Information not available | Information not available |
| Yugoslavia | under study | — | Some | Some | Aware of none |

[a]Europe—Task Group on Plastic Design is working on draft of a specification

Research effort since 1958 has been directed primarily toward the extension of plastic design methods to tall multistory frames whose behavior and strength are significantly affected by the axial forces present in the members (1.33). Plastic design methods are now available for laterally braced multistory frames, and extensive work is under way on the development of practical methods for the design of unbraced frames. A summary of the design concepts for braced and unbraced frames is given in Chapter 10. Application of these concepts to the design of a braced 11-story apartment building has been reported (1.34).

Computer programs have been developed for performing optimum (minimum weight) designs based on plastic concepts (1.35, 1.36, 1.37). It is anticipated that the use of computers will make it possible to obtain solutions for many highly indeterminate structures which would be difficult, if not impossible, to analyze by manual methods.

# CHAPTER 2.—BASIC PRINCIPLES

## 2.1 BEHAVIOR OF MATERIAL AND STRUCTURAL ELEMENTS

Plastic design takes advantage of an important and unique property of structural steel, namely its ductility. Evidence of this ductility may be seen by examining a stress-strain curve obtained from a simple tension or compression test. This curve may be represented in idealized form by two straight lines, as shown in Fig. 2.1. Up to the yield-stress level the material is elastic. After the yield stress has been reached the strain increases greatly without any further increase of the stress. From this it follows that the initial attainment of a maximum fiber stress equal to the yield value does not result in failure of a beam. Rather, the section has a plastic reserve in strength which depends on the shape of the cross section.

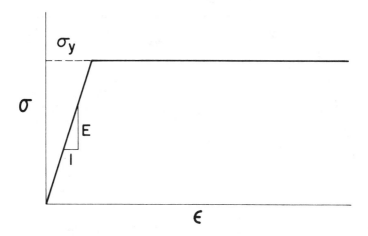

FIG. 2.1.—STRESS-STRAIN CURVE FOR UNIAXIAL TENSION OR COMPRESSION

Fig. 2.2 shows the stress distribution at five stages as bending moment is applied to a member of rectangular cross section. It is assumed that each fiber behaves as shown in Fig. 2.1, and that plane sections before bending remain plane after bending. The moment-curvature relationship for this beam is shown in Fig. 2.3; the numbered points correspond to the five stages in Fig. 2.2. Stage 2 corresponds to the yield moment, $M_y$, and stage

7

5 corresponds to the plastic moment, $M_p$. The exact shape of the moment-curvature diagram between stages 2 and 5 depends on the cross-sectional form, but the moment rapidly approaches the value of the full plastic moment corresponding to stress distribution 5 (Fig. 2.2). The "rapid approach" to this limiting plastic moment is an important feature of simple

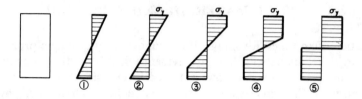

FIG. 2.2.—SUCCESSIVE STAGES OF STRESS DISTRIBUTION

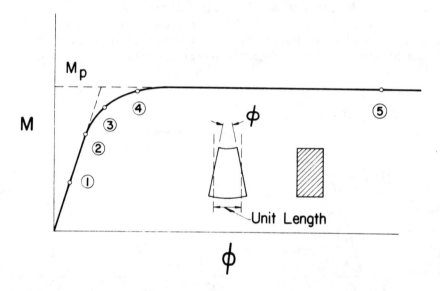

FIG. 2.3.—MOMENT-CURVATURE RELATIONSHIP FOR BEAM OF REC-TANGULAR SECTION IN BENDING

plastic theory. In most calculations the moment-curvature relationship is approximated by two straight lines as shown partly dotted in Fig. 2.3.

The process of successive yielding of fibers as bending moment is increased (stage 2 to stage 5 in Fig. 2.3) is called *plastification* of the cross section. At the section(s) where yielding occurs, relatively large rotations are possible without a significant increase or decrease of moments; in other words, "plastic hinges" develop. The plastic hinge thus formed permits *redistribution of moments* in statically indeterminate beams and frames. Thus, further increases of the loads are carried by other less heavily stressed parts of the structure, until a sufficient number of plastic hinges is formed and the structure starts to behave as a mechanism. Thereafter deflections increase rapidly while the loads remain practically constant. In other words, the plastic limit load has been reached.

In summary, a structure will reach its plastic limit load as determined by simple plastic theory only if the sections or connections where plastic hinges are to form attain the predicted moment and subsequently are able to undergo sufficiently large rotations under substantially constant moment. An exception, of course, is the plastic hinge which forms last, for which no inelastic rotation is required after the plastic moment has been reached.

## 2.2  PLASTIC THEORY
**Conditions.**
In the elastic analysis of an indeterminate structure under static loading, three conditions must be considered:

1. *Continuity*—the deflected shape is assumed to be a continuous curve, and thus "continuity equations" may be formulated with due regard to boundary conditions.
2. *Equilibrium*—the summation of the forces and moments acting on any free body must be equal to zero.
3. *Limiting moment*—the moment at first yield is the limiting moment.

In plastic analysis three similar conditions (or modifications thereof) must be considered. With regard to continuity of slope, the situation is just the reverse: theoretically, plastic hinges interrupt such continuity, so the requirement is that sufficient plastic hinges form to allow the structure (or part of it) to deform as a mechanism which is compatible with the remaining constraints. This could be termed a *mechanism* condition. The *equilibrium* condition is the same as in elastic analysis. Instead of initial yield, the limit of usefulness is the attainment of plastic hinge moments at each of the sections involved in the mechanism motion. The *plastic-moment* condition states that moments in excess of the plastic bending strength cannot be resisted. The three conditions that must be satisfied in plastic analysis are, therefore:

1. Mechanism condition.
2. Equilibrium condition.
3. Plastic-moment condition.

When all three of these conditions are satisfied, then the resulting analysis for the plastic limit load is correct, because the two limit theorems basic to the plastic method are satisfied. These theorems will now be discussed.

**Plastic Limit Theorems.**

A general treatment of structures requires consideration of some basic plastic limit theorems which have provided concise and rigorous formalization of intuitively known concepts of structural failure (1.26, 2.1–2.6). According to the concepts discussed in Art. 2.1, structural steel may be idealized as an elastic-perfectly plastic material (Fig. 2.1). Therefore when changes in the configuration of the structure due to deformation are neglected (as is done in most elastic solutions), it can be shown that failure occurs under constant load and at constant stress. In Art. 2.1 this was stated in a different way, namely, that the plastic limit load is reached when a sufficient number of sections have attained their "limit" or "plastic hinge" moment. Only plastic strains take place as deformation occurs at constant load.

The theorems are:

---

**PLASTIC LIMIT THEOREMS**

I. *Upper Bound.*—For any compatible pattern of plastic deformation, the structure cannot stand up if the rate at which the external forces do work exceeds the rate of internal dissipation.

II. *Lower Bound.*—If an equilibrium distribution of stress can be found which balances the applied load and is everywhere less than or equal to the yield stress, the structure will not fail. At most it will just have reached the plastic limit load.

---

Theorem I is a formal statement of the fact that if a path to failure exists, the structures will fail. Thus a load determined for an assumed pattern of mechanism motion will always be greater than (or at least equal to) the true plastic limit load. The theorem, therefore, deals with upper bounds on, or unsafe values of, the plastic load. The minimum upper bound is the correct plastic load itself.

Theorem II is a statement of the ability of the material to adjust itself to carry the applied load if at all possible. It gives lower bounds on, or safe values of, the true plastic load. The maximum lower bound is the true plastic load itself.

The lower-bound theorem leads to the following important corollaries (2.6):

1. Initial stresses, deformations, or support settlements have no effect on the plastic limit load provided the geometry is essentially unaltered.

2. Except for its effect on dead load, addition of material without any change in the position of the applied loads cannot lower the plastic limit load.
3. Increasing the yield strength of the material in any region cannot weaken the structure. Conversely, decreasing the yield strength cannot strengthen it.

Continuous beams and low building frames are simple enough to permit "exact" calculations of the plastic limit load. This Manual is devoted primarily to the design of such structures, using the plastic limit load, determined by the application of the foregoing theorems, as the basis. For beams and for framed structures, the limit theorems can be stated as follows:

---

**PLASTIC LIMIT THEOREMS**

I. *Upper Bound.*—A load computed on the basis of an assumed mechanism will always be greater than or equal to the true plastic limit load.

II. *Lower Bound.*—A load computed on the basis of an equilibrium moment distribution in which the moments are nowhere greater than $M_p$ is less than or equal to the true plastic limit load.

---

For complicated structures it may well be that "exact" plastic limit loads cannot be found, due to involved geometry of parts or of the complete structure. The above theorems enable the bracketing of the answer closely enough for practical engineering purposes.

An actual, and therefore three-dimensional, building frame usually is treated as a collection of two-dimensional frames subjected to statically equivalent loads. This procedure disregards part of the strength of the actual structure. By the lower-bound theorem, such a design is on the safe side as compared to a design of the three-dimensional structure (excluding any possible instability effect).

The simplicity of plastic analysis opens the way to direct plastic design, as contrasted with the trial-and-error procedure which is normally necessary in allowable-stress design of indeterminate structures. Some steps that have been taken along these lines are given in Chapter 3.

There are numerous methods by which the plastic limit load for a continuous steel structure can be determined. In the "mechanism method," a mechanism is assumed and the resulting virtual-work equations are solved for the plastic limit load. This value is correct only if the plastic moment condition is also satisfied. In the semigraphical ("statical" or "equilibrium") method, an equilibrium moment diagram is drawn such that the moment is nowhere greater than the plastic moment, $M_p$. It thus automatically satisfies the lower-bound theorem. The resulting load is correct only if sufficient plastic hinges were assumed to create a mechanism (thus satisfying the upper-bound theorem).

## 2.3 ROLE OF STRAIN HARDENING

The limit theorems described above and the plastic analysis methods to be presented in Chapter 3 assume that the material becomes perfectly plastic when the stress reaches the yield stress. Most structural steels, however, strain harden under continued straining (see Figs. 5.1 and 5.2). The effect of strain hardening, in general, is to improve the load-carrying capacity of the structure and to reduce the deformations in the plastic range. Therefore, the actual strength will be somewhat higher than that predicted by the limit theorems.

The influence of strain hardening in continuous beams has been studied both theoretically and experimentally (2.7–2.12). The moment redistribution process occurring in beams and the actual load-deformation relationship were examined in detail in these studies. The trilinear moment-curvature relationship, as shown in Fig. 2.4, has been found to give good agreement when compared with test results (2.6, 2.9). Methods which account for strain hardening have been proposed for analyzing beams and framed structures (2.13, 2.14, 2.15, 2.16).

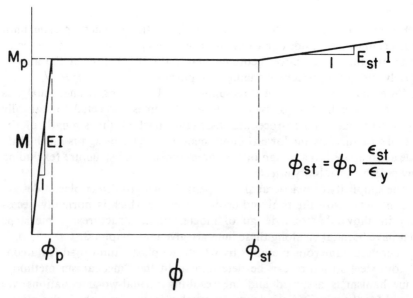

FIG. 2.4.—IDEALIZED MOMENT-CURVATURE RELATIONSHIP (WITH STRAIN HARDENING)

From these studies the following conclusions have been reached:

1. Strain hardening causes a moment redistribution pattern different from that predicted by elastic-plastic theory (2.8, 2.12). This is illustrated in Fig. 2.5 for a three-span beam. The solid lines show the

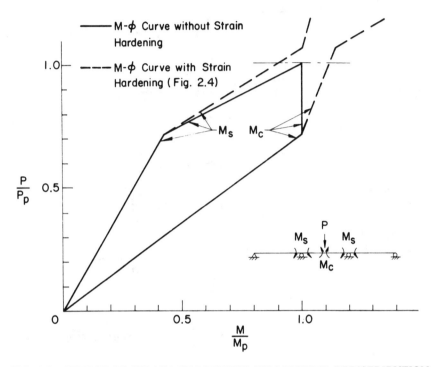

FIG. 2.5.—EFFECT OF STRAIN HARDENING ON MOMENT REDISTRIBUTION

variation of the midspan and support moment according to the elastic-plastic theory, and the dashed lines show the effect of strain hardening. At the plastic limit load the support moment is less than the plastic moment, and the midspan moment is greater.

2. As a consequence of the above, strain hardening tends to increase the stiffness of a structure, and, thus, to reduce the inelastic deformations at a given load. This is illustrated in Fig. 2.6 for the three-span beam of Fig. 2.5 (2.11, 2.12). As shown by the dotted line, the slope of the load-deformation curve in the elastic-plastic range is steeper when strain hardening is included in the analysis. Also, the curve including strain hardening tends to rise above the corresponding elastic-plastic curve. It will not, of course, continue to rise indefinitely, because eventually the beam will fail by instability. It has

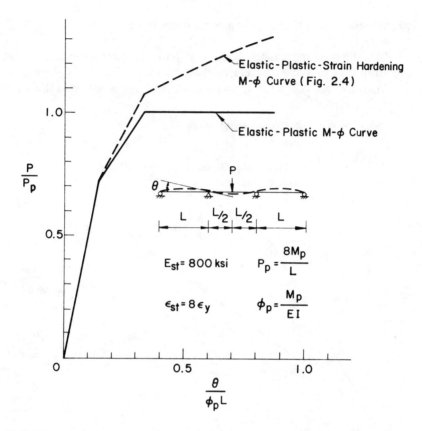

FIG. 2.6.—EFFECT OF STRAIN HARDENING ON LOAD-ROTATION CURVE

also been observed that plastic hinge rotations actually will be smaller than those predicted by elastic-plastic analysis, and that the order of hinge formation may be different (2.16).

3. It has been demonstrated both theoretically and experimentally that strain hardening is needed to achieve moment redistribution and the attainment of the plastic limit load (2.7, 2.9, 2.11). Steels such as ASTM A36, A441, A527, A572, and A588 are suitable in this regard. A member fabricated of a material which exhibits very limited strain hardening will experience very high local strains at the critical sections, and this will lead to early instability or, if this is prevented, to fracture of the material.

The effect of strain hardening in analysis and design is considered further in Chapters 5, 6, 8, and 9.

**STRAIN HARDENING**
1. Materials which exhibit strain hardening can be used in plastic design (ASTM A36, A441, A527, A572, A588, and other steels with similar mechanical properties).
2. The plastic limit load of structures can be computed with sufficient accuracy without considering the effect of strain hardening.

# CHAPTER 3.—ANALYSIS AND DESIGN

The purpose of this chapter is to state the important assumptions of the plastic theory and to show the essential features of plastic analysis and design. All of the available methods developed for structural engineering applications can be classified into two groups, those based on the upper-bound theorem and those based on the lower-bound theorem. It is not intended herein to present a complete discussion of all the methods; Refs. 1.1 through 1.6, 1.8, 1.9, 1.10, 3.1, 3.2, and 3.3 may be consulted for this purpose. However, brief outlines of the frequently encountered methods most illustrative of the two groups are presented in Art. 3.2 (based on upper bound) and Arts. 3.3 and 3.4 (based on lower bound).

## 3.1 CONCEPTS AND ASSUMPTIONS

The important concepts and assumptions with regard to the plastic behavior of structures according to the "simple plastic theory" are as follows:

1. The structure and the loads are all in the same plane, and each member has an axis of symmetry lying in that plane.
2. The material is ductile. It has the capacity of undergoing large plastic deformation without fracture.
3. Each member cross section has a maximum resisting moment (the plastic moment, $M_p$), a moment that is developed through plastic yielding of the entire cross section (plastification).
4. Because of the ductility of steel, rotation at relatively constant moment will occur through a considerable angle; in other words, a plastic hinge will form.
5. Connections proportioned for full continuity will transmit the calculated plastic moment. This condition is idealized as a plastic hinge at a point.
6. Plastic hinges will first form at sections where the moments under elastic condition reach $M_p$. With these sections rotating at constant moment, additional loading will be accompanied by a redistribution of moments in the structure, so that plastic hinges will appear at some other locations where the moments under elastic conditions were less than $M_p$.
7. The plastic limit load is reached when enough plastic hinges have formed to create a mechanism.

17

8. The deformations are small, and therefore the equilibrium equations can be formulated for the undeformed structure (as in ordinary elastic analysis). Similarly, virtual-work expressions for mechanism displacement are based on small deflections.
9. No instability will occur before the attainment of the plastic limit load.
10. The influence of normal force and shearing force on the plastic moment is not considered.
11. The loading is proportional, that is, the ratios between different loads remain constant during loading.

The experimental verification of some of these assumptions is presented in Chapters 5 and 8. Other assumptions may need implementation to assure that the appropriate requirements are met, and this is the concern of parts of Chapter 4 and of Chapters 6 and 7.


## 3.2   MECHANISM METHOD

The mechanism method is based on the upper-bound theorem. As is intimated in Art. 2.2, its objective is to select from all the possible modes of failure the one that corresponds to the lowest possible plastic limit load. A check of the moments should be used to verify that the plastic-moment condition is not violated ($M \leq M_p$). In essence, therefore, the method gives a solution that is the correct value of the plastic load only when it also satisfies the plastic-moment condition. An example follows.

*Analysis of Rectangular Portal Frame.*

It is required to find the plastic limit load for the structure shown in Fig. 3.1(a). All members are of uniform moment capacity, $M_p$.

The first step in the mechanism method is to find the position of possible plastic hinges. These hinges may form at points of peak moment, that is, where the shear passes through zero, for example, at such places as concentrated load points, connections, etc. Therefore, the possible plastic-hinge locations are at sections 1, 2, 3, 4, and 5.

The next step is to select for investigation the various possible failure mechanisms. Three of these are shown in Figs. 3.1(b), (c), and (d). Mechanism 1 corresponds to the action of vertical load $P$ and is called a "beam" mechanism. Mechanism 2 corresponds to the action of the horizontal load $P$ and is often referred to as a "sway" or "panel" mechanism. Mechanism 3, on the other hand, is a combined mechanism representing the action of both loads. It is a combination of mechanisms 1 and 2 and does not require a plastic hinge at section 2.

The correct failure mechanism will be the one which results in the lowest loading, because any greater loading would lead to the violation of the plastic-moment condition. The loading that corresponds to each mecha-

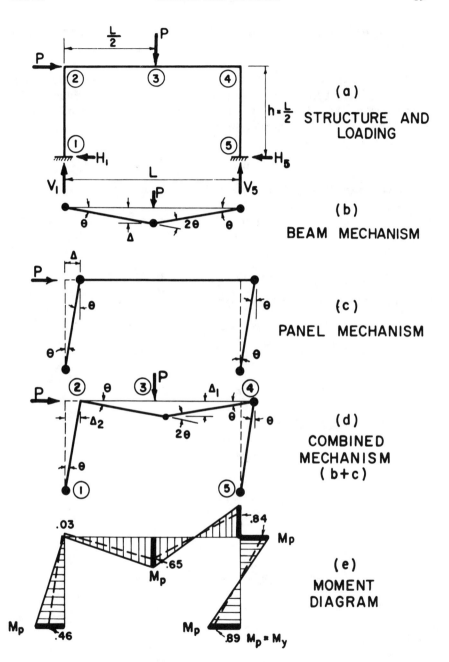

(a)
STRUCTURE AND
LOADING

(b)
BEAM MECHANISM

(c)
PANEL MECHANISM

(d)
COMBINED
MECHANISM
(b+c)

(e)
MOMENT
DIAGRAM

FIG. 3.1.—MECHANISM METHOD OF ANALYSIS APPLIED TO A FIXED-BASE
RECTANGULAR PORTAL FRAME

nism may be computed by applying a virtual displacement (one that satisfies the constraints on that mechanism) and then using the upper-bound
theorem. Referring to Fig. 3.1(b), the beam is allowed to move through a
virtual displacement, $\Delta$. The value of $P$, obtained by equating the *external
work*, $W_E$, done by the load as it moves through this displacement to the
*internal work*, $W_I$, absorbed at the plastic hinges as they rotate through
corresponding angles, is greater than or equal to the plastic limit load.
According to this procedure

$$W_E = W_I \ \ldots\ldots\ldots\ldots\ldots \ (3.1)$$

For mechanism 1 the external work is given by

$$W_E = P \Delta = P \frac{L}{2}\theta \ \ldots\ldots\ldots\ldots \ (3.2)$$

The internal work is given by

$$W_I = M_p\,\theta + M_p\,2\,\theta + M_p\,\theta = 4\,M_p\theta \ \ \ldots\ldots \ (3.3)$$

Equating Eqs. 3.2 and 3.3 according to Eq. 3.1

$$P \frac{L}{2}\theta = 4\,M_p\,\theta$$

and

$$P_1 = \frac{8\,M_p}{L} \ \ldots\ldots\ldots\ldots \ (3.4)$$

Similarly, for mechanism 2

$$P \frac{L}{2}\theta = M_p\,(\theta + \theta + \theta + \theta)$$

and

$$P_2 = \frac{8\,M_p}{L} \ \ldots\ldots\ldots\ldots \ (3.5)$$

For mechanism 3

$$P\,\Delta_1 + P\,\Delta_2 = M_p\,(\theta + 2\,\theta + 2\,\theta + \theta)$$

$$P \frac{L}{2}\theta + P \frac{L}{2}\theta = 6\,M_p$$

and

$$P_3 = \frac{6\,M_p}{L} \ \leftarrow \boxed{P_p} \ \ldots\ldots\ldots\ldots \ (3.6)$$

Since the lowest value is $P_3$, this is assumed to be the true limit load.

To make sure that some other mechanism was not overlooked and that $P_3$ is the true plastic limit load, the plastic-moment condition should be checked. An efficient way of doing this is to construct the moment diagram for the entire structure. The complete diagram is shown in Fig. 3.1(e), the moment at each section being determined by statics (the moments are plotted on the tension side of the member). It is found that $M \leq M_p$ throughout, and thus the answer determined above is verified. It is only a coincidence that the moment at section 2 is equal to zero.

The dotted line in Fig. 3.1(e) traces the moment diagram at the stage at which the hypothetical yield moment would first be reached in the frame— namely at section 5, where the moment is shown as $M_y$. The first plastic hinge would form there, followed by hinges at sections 4, 3, and finally at section 1.

If the problem were to design the frame for the loads $P$, the required section would be found from Eq. 3.6 as

$$M_p = \frac{PL}{6} \dots\dots\dots\dots\dots\dots (3.7)$$

By using the principles illustrated in the example much more complex frames can also be analyzed.

## 3.3  STATICAL METHOD

The statical method of analysis employs the lower-bound theorem and is suitable for continuous beams and for frames in which the number of redundants is one or two. As described in Art. 2.2, the objective of this method is to find a possible moment diagram in which the plastic-moment condition is not violated ($M \leq M_p$). To make sure that this also gives the maximum possible load, a sufficient number of plastic hinges must be formed to create a mechanism. An example follows.

Suppose it is desired to determine the load, $w_p$, that may be carried by a beam of given constant moment capacity in a multispan structure. One of the interior spans, AC, is shown in Fig. 3.2(a).

As the loading, $w$, increases from zero, there are peak moments at the two supports and a peak moment within the span. Unless the structure and loading are symmetrical about span AC, the moments at the two supports will be unequal, and a typical moment diagram at the elastic limit is shown in Fig. 3.2(b). The maximum moment within the span is not at the span center line but is near it. As the load increases still further, the greater end moment (C) attains $M_p$ and a plastic hinge forms there. As the load increases still further, the other support moment (A) attains $M_p$, and the maximum moment within the span increases as shown by curve 2 in Fig. 3.2(c). Since there is a hinge at each end of the span, the point of maximum moment has shifted to the center of the span and the moment curve 2 is

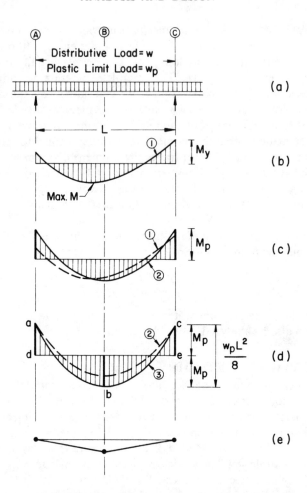

FIG. 3.2.—STATICAL METHOD OF ANALYSIS APPLIED TO A CONTINUOUS BEAM

symmetrical. Any of these load values gives a lower-bound solution. The true plastic limit load will be reached only when a mechanism develops in the span. In the example this is attained when a plastic hinge finally forms at midspan. The moment diagram at the plastic load is shown by curve 3 in Fig. 3.2(d), and the corresponding failure mechanism in Fig. 3.2(e).

The maximum ordinate of the determinate moment diagram must be $w_P L^2/8$. Thus, referring to Fig. 3.2(d)

$$\frac{w_p L^2}{8} = M_p + M_p \quad \dots \dots \dots \dots \dots \quad (3.8)$$

and

$$w_p = \frac{16\,M_p}{L^2} \quad \ldots \ldots \ldots \ldots \ldots \ldots (3.9)$$

As described in Art. 4.6, the plastic moment of any beam cross section may be computed from a knowledge of the yield-stress level and the cross-section geometry. Thus the plastic load, $w_p$, is determined.

For design, that is, if the required plastic limit load is given by the terms of the problem, the required $M_p$ for the beam may be calculated and the beam selected. It will be seen from Fig. 3.2(d) that the plastic design for a uniform, restrained beam may be expressed as follows:

> Draw the determinate moment diagram for load $w_p$ on a beam of the same span but with hinged ends. Draw a new base line for zero moments (a "fixing line") at the midheight of this curve. Equate the three maximum moments thus found to $M_p$.

This completes the solution for an interior span of a continuous beam with restraining moments at least as great as the strength of the beam selected. The same reasoning as followed previously for a uniform load will lead to the same solution method for other types of loading, such as partial uniform or concentrated.

Of course, where a smaller beam adjoins an interior span, or in the case of an end span with simple exterior support, or in the case of nonprismatic section, the fixing line would not be drawn at midheight of the determinate moment diagram. Its position should reflect the member moment capacity at the points of peak moment. In essence, then, the failure moment diagram is drawn in such a way that a mechanism forms. Curve 3 of Fig. 3.2(d) satisfies this requirement, of course, because the three plastic hinges at a, b, and e result in the mechanism shown in Fig. 3.2(e).

In plastic design of continuous beams and frames it is unnecessary to consider the elastic distribution of moments such as that shown in Fig. 3.2(b), or the behavior under increasing load. A systematized procedure for the general case would simply involve the construction of a determinate moment diagram [corresponding to curve abc of Fig. 3.2(d)], which is then combined with a redundant moment diagram (adec) in such a way that a mechanism is formed.

Although the statical method is quite simple when applied to continuous beams, it is inefficient for frames with more than one degree of indeterminacy. For such frames recourse should be made to other methods, such as the moment balancing method described in Art. 3.4.

## 3.4  MOMENT BALANCING METHOD

The moment balancing method is best suited for designing rectangular frames of one or more stories. It is akin to the statical method but has considerably greater versatility (1.25, 3.4).

The aim is to find in the structure a distribution of bending moments which is in equilibrium with the applied loads. The required member sizes then can be determined from the bending moment distribution. In an actual design, it is possible to find many such distributions; the one which results in the lowest total weight of the structure is frequently adopted for final design, because it is usually associated with maximum economy. This design criterion will be used in the illustrative example.

The method involves the following steps:

1. Select a distribution of bending moments such that equilibrium requirements of each member and of individual stories are satisfied—only the joints may not be in equilibrium.
2. Balance the moments at the joints to bring them into equilibrium (joint balance). The relative distribution to the individual members depends on the judgment of the designer as influenced by the design objective.
3. Restore equilibrium in the members by adjusting the within-span moments to the loads acting on each member (carry-over).
4. Restore story (or sidesway) equilibrium by adjusting the column end moments (sidesway balance). As in step 3, the relative distribution is arbitrary.
5. Step 4 may lead to the unbalancing of joint moments. If necessary, repeat steps 2, 3, and 4 until all requirements of equilibrium are satisfied and a distribution of moments is achieved which apparently satisfies the design objective (such as minimum weight.) Try out several combinations and select the one that best meets the objective.

An example illustrating the application of the method in plastic design is given in Fig. 3.3. It is required to provide a design for the single-story two-bay frame loaded as shown in Fig. 3.3(a). The steps involved in the design are shown in Figs. 3.3(b) through (j).

Step 1 results in a moment distribution in equilibrium with all the loads as given in Fig. 3.3(b). It is convenient to select in this step moments corresponding to a mechanism in each member: for example, sidesway moment = 4 kips × 15 ft = 60 kip-ft would be equal to the sum of column end moments with 10 kip-ft assigned to each end, Fig. 3.3(b). Moments at the joints are not in equilibrium.

The results of step 2 are shown in Fig. 3.3(c), in which only the column moments were modified in order to balance the joints. The girder moments were kept unchanged, and consequently there was no need to use step 3 of the prior tabulation. To restore sidesway equilibrium disturbed in step 2 ($-30$ kip-ft at point 2, $-5$ kip-ft at point 11, and $+5$ kip-ft at point 9, a total of $-30$ kip-ft), the column end moments are modified as shown in Fig. 3.3(d). Moments at the bottom of the center and right columns were increased by 15 kip-ft. All the equilibrium requirements are now met and a possible design is obtained.

Assuming that each member has a constant plastic moment capacity over its length, an indication of the total weight of the material required for the frame may be computed from

$$W = \sum_{i=1}^{n} M_{pi} L_i. \quad\dots\dots\dots\dots\dots (3.10)$$

in which $W$ = the weight function; $M_{pi}$ = the plastic moment required for member $i$; and $L_i$ = the length of member $i$. [A more accurate formula is $W = \sum_{i}^{n} (M_{pi}/d_i) L_i$, in which $d_i$ = the depth of the member $i$ (see Ref. 3.5).] For the moment diagram of Fig. 3.3(d)

$$W = W_{\text{girders}} + W_{\text{columns}} = (20 \times 20 + 15 \times 40)$$
$$+ (20 \times 15 + 25 \times 15 + 25 \times 15) = 2{,}050$$

Fig. 3.3(e) shows that for the members selected according to the diagram of Fig. 3.3(d) only beam mechanisms will form. This is an indication that there may be other more economical solutions.

Starting with the final distribution of Fig. 3.3(d), a trial modification of the end moments in the left span is given in Fig. 3.3(f). The left end moment is reduced by 10 kip-ft and the right end moment is increased by 5 kip-ft. Joints 3 and 11 are next balanced (step 2) as shown in the same figure. The midspan moment is adjusted in Fig. 3.3(g) from 20 kip-ft to 22.5 kip-ft to be in equilibrium with the load in the span (step 3). Fig. 3.3(g) also shows the balancing of the sidesway unbalanced in steps 1 and 2 by a 15 kip-ft clockwise moment. The bottom column end moments are selected to be all equal. The weight function for the resultant moment requirements is $W = 1{,}775$, which is considerably smaller than that of the first design. A check on the mechanism formation [Fig. 3.3(h)] shows that only one beam mechanism would form. Thus a more efficient moment distribution is still possible.

The most obvious adjustment is to make the maximum moments in the left girder equal to each other by rotating the determinate moment diagram of the left span about its left end until the midspan and the right-end

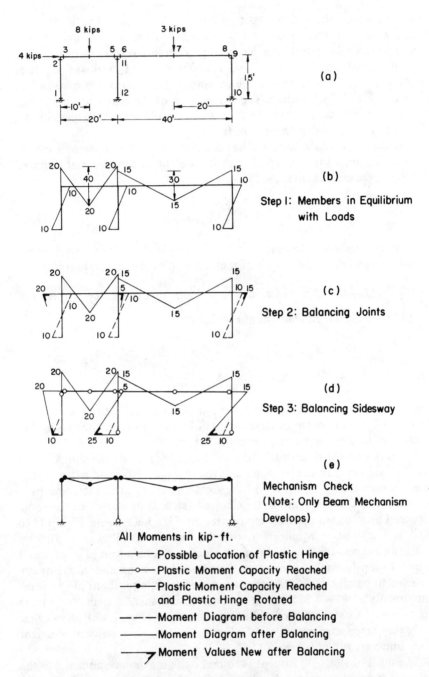

FIG. 3.3.—MOMENT BALANCING METHOD APPLIED TO THE DESIGN OF A SINGLE-STORY, TWO-BAY FRAME

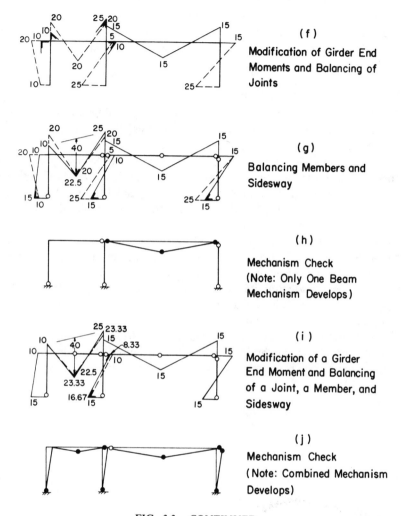

(f)

Modification of Girder End
Moments and Balancing of
Joints

(g)

Balancing Members and
Sidesway

(h)

Mechanism Check
(Note: Only One Beam
Mechanism Develops)

(i)

Modification of a Girder
End Moment and Balancing
of a Joint, a Member, and
Sidesway

(j)

Mechanism Check
(Note: Combined Mechanism
Develops)

FIG. 3.3.—CONTINUED

moments are both equal to 23.33 kip-ft. Results of such an adjustment
and of subsequent balancing of the middle joints and of the sidesway are
shown in Fig. 3.3(i). The weight function becomes $W = 1,766$, and the
mechanism, now a combined one, is shown in Fig. 3.3(j).

Further improvements are still possible; for example, a solution with
$M_1 = M_2 = 2.5$, $M_4 = M_5 = 27.5$, $M_6 = M_7 = M_8 = M_{10} = 15$, and $M_{11} = M_{12} = 12.5$ gives $W = 1,600$.

Although moment balancing is most suitable for design, it can also be
used for analysis by striving for final moments at the same ratio to each
other as are the moment capacities in the given structure.

In practical application of the method many simplifying techniques can be employed, such as a tabular arrangement analogous to that used for conventional moment distributions, and the use of charts when girders are subjected to distributed loading (1.33).

## 3.5 OTHER METHODS

The three previous articles have presented, in simplified form, the important steps in three methods of plastic analysis. Refs. 1.1 through 1.6, 1.8, 1.25, 1.33, 3.1, and 3.2 may be consulted for complete systematized procedures of analysis and design using these methods.

In addition to the methods described, other techniques are available for determining the plastic limit load of a structure. One of these is the "method of inequalities." Refs. 3.3 and 3.5 present the details of this method.

Just as in allowable-stress design, for which the engineer has available certain charts, tables, and formulas with which to analyze standard cases, it has also been possible to develop convenient design aids for the rapid selection of member sizes on the basis of the plastic limit load. The designer may use such techniques to shorten the design time even further, but discussion of these aids is outside the scope of this Manual. Some of these techniques have been illustrated on practical design examples in Refs. 1.3 and 1.33. Computer programs have also been developed to facilitate the use of plastic design methods, and often to accomplish optimization of the total weight. Such methods are given in Refs. 1.36, 1.37, 3.6, 3.7, 3.8, 3.9 and 3.10.

# CHAPTER 4.—GENERAL PROVISIONS

## 4.1 INTRODUCTION

This chapter will describe some of the basic conditions that should be satisfied in establishing a plastic-design procedure. This includes questions about types of construction, materials, structural ductility (avoidance of brittle fracture), the yield-stress level to be used, the plastic moment, the loads and forces that would be considered as applied to the structure, and the load factor. In each case the suggested provision will be given first, followed by pertinent discussion.

## 4.2 TYPES OF CONSTRUCTION

Plastic design is applicable to the following types of planar structures:

1. Continuous beams.
2. One- and two-story, single-span and multispan continuous building frames.
3. Multistory tier buildings with sidesway prevented by walls or internal bracing systems, or both.

Plastic design is not recommended as a substitute for allowable-stress design for structures that are essentially pin-connected. It is intended for use in structures which depend on continuity for their ability to carry the computed maximum load.

The necessary continuity may be achieved by welding, bolting, or riveting. The background and justification for design guides for the use of such connecting devices are discussed in Chapter 8.

## 4.3 MATERIAL

Material with the characteristics of ASTM A36, A441, and A572 structural steels should be used, with modifications when needed, to assure weldability and ductility at lowest expected service temperature.

It is not intended to specify any particular steels, but to indicate that the important property required of a material is ductility at service temperature. Plastic design can be applied to building structures fabricated from steels exhibiting stress-strain characteristics similar to those of the three steels given above (4.1). This would also include A588.

## 4.4 STRUCTURAL DUCTILITY

Fabrication processes should be such as to retain ductility. At plastic-hinge locations, unfinished sheared edges and punched holes in tension flanges should not be permitted. Subpunched and reamed holes for connecting devices would be satisfactory if the reaming removes the cold-worked material.

In design, triaxial states of tensile stress set up by geometrical restraints should be minimized.

This provision, together with Art. 4.3, is intended to help assure that brittle fracture will not prevent the formation of a plastic hinge. The assumption of ductility is an equally important aspect of allowable-stress design, and numerous design assumptions rely on it.

In plastic design the engineer should be guided by the same principles that govern the proper design of welded, bolted, or riveted structures designed by the allowable-stress methods, since ductility is important to both. Thus the proper material must be specified to meet the appropriate service conditions, the fabrication and workmanship must meet high standards, and design details should be such that the material is as free to deform as possible (4.2).

With respect to fabrication, because of the severe cold working involved, punched holes and sheared edges should not be permitted in parts that might be subjected to stresses approaching the yield stress in tension at ultimate load. Punched holes *would* be permitted here if they were given sufficient reaming to remove the cold-worked material. In Ref. 4.3 the effect of various edge conditions on the brittle failure of steel is described.

## 4.5 YIELD-STRESS LEVEL

| Steel | Normal stress, $\sigma_y$ | Shear stress, $\tau_y$ |
|---|---|---|
| ASTM A36 | 36 | $\dfrac{\sigma_y}{\sqrt{3}}$ |
| ASTM A441 | 42, 46, 50 | |
| ASTM A572 | 45, 50, 55, 60, 65 | |

As an example, a yield-stress level of 36.0 ksi corresponds to the minimum yield point permitted in a mill-type acceptance test of ASTM A36 steel. Such a test differs from the test conducted in the laboratory for many reasons, one of the most important of which is strain rate. An extensive investigation into the yield-stress level of ASTM A7 steel* (nominal yield stress = 33 ksi) has been conducted using as the test specimen a complete cross section of a rolled wide-flange shape (4.4). The loading was performed in a manner that simulates "static" loading. By such a test procedure it was possible to include such effects as differences in web and flange strength, strain rate, and size, since representative cross sections from the very smallest to the largest rolled shapes were included in the program. Ref. 4.5 describes results from studies of the influence of strain rate of steels up to 100 ksi.

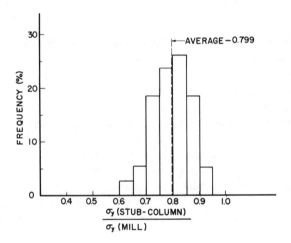

FIG. 4.1.—FREQUENCY DISTRIBUTION OF THE RATIO $\dfrac{\sigma_y\,(\text{Stub-Column})}{\sigma_y\,(\text{Mill})}$

According to data available at the time, this investigation showed that the most probable value of the yield-stress level of ASTM A7 steel is 34.1 ksi, with variations ranging from 24.6 ksi to 43.0 ksi. (According to the usual acceptance test, the most probable value of the yield point would be 42.6 ksi.) Fig. 4.1 shows the histogram of the ratio of yield-stress level determined from a stub column test as compared with the yield-point value obtained in a mill-type acceptance test.

The yield-stress level of other structural steels based on the stub column tests has not been systematically and thoroughly investigated. For these

---

*Although A7 steel has been replaced by A36 steel, the former is frequently referred to in this Manual because of the earlier research work.

steels the data on the yield-stress level have been collected primarily from tension tests rather than from stub column tests. These determinations have shown that the static yield-stress level is close (4%) to the specified minimum yield point (4.6, 4.7, 4.8).

In summary, it is evident that the minimum yield point permitted in acceptance tests is very close to the average basic yield-stress level of this material. Thus the factor of safety includes the possibility of variation below this average value, because the design is actually based on an average, not a minimum. This situation has always existed in design, and therefore represents no departure from past practice.

## 4.6  PLASTIC MOMENT

$$M_p = \sigma_y Z \dots \dots \dots \dots \dots \dots \dots \dots \dots \dots \dots \text{(4.1)}$$

in which $\sigma_y$ = yield-stress level and $Z$ = plastic modulus.

It was pointed out in Art. 2.1 that the formation of plastic hinges is of basic importance to plastic design. Fig. 2.3 shows the characteristic moment-rotation curve of a beam of rectangular cross section under bending, and the moment at "stage 5" shown in Figs. 2.2 and 2.3 is called the plastic moment. It is computed according to Eq. 4.1.

The plastic modulus, $Z$, is a geometrical function analogous to the section modulus. It is the modulus of resistance to bending of a completely yielded cross section, and is calculated by taking the combined statical moment about the neutral axis of the cross-sectional areas above and below that axis.

For sections symmetrical about the axis of bending, the neutral axis is coincident with the centroidal axis. If the section is unsymmetrical or if, in a built-up or hybrid section, $\sigma_y$ is not the same in the tension and compression flanges, the neutral axis must be determined so that

$$\int \sigma_{y_c} dA_c = \int \sigma_{y_t} dA_t \dots \dots \dots \dots \dots \text{(4.2)}$$

in which $c$ = compression and $t$ = tension.

The plastic moment may be expressed by

$$M_p = \int_A \sigma_y \, y \, dA \dots \dots \dots \dots \dots \dots \text{(4.3)}$$

Eq. 4.1 is the special form of Eq. 4.3 for a section with uniform yield point.

As will be evident in Chapter 5, it is frequently observed in tests that the moment-deformation behavior is not exactly like that shown in Fig. 2.3 (see Fig. 5.5, for example). Because of strain hardening, the resisting moment is greater than the value computed according to Eq. 4.1. However, no present simple theory can take this additional reserve in strength into account without undue complications.

For material whose characteristics are not similar to those of the steels mentioned in Art. 4.5, but which exhibits continuous strain hardening, it might be desirable to arrive at a semiempirical value for the "plastic hinge" moment. Studies would have to be made on the particular material (including bending tests and tests of indeterminate structures) to arrive at a suitable approximation for the plastic moment.

The plastic theory can be extended to determine the moment-carrying capacity in the positive bending region of a composite section of concrete slab and steel beams (4.9–4.13). For such a section, the plastic moment can be computed according to Eq. 4.3. It is assumed that the concrete has no tensile strength. A simplified stress-strain relationship is also assumed for concrete under compression. Its average compressive strength is taken as 0.85 $f'_c$, in which $f'_c$ = the ultimate cylinder strength. Two equations for the plastic moment are derived depending on the location of the neutral axis at failure: namely, when the neutral axis lies in the slab (Case I), and

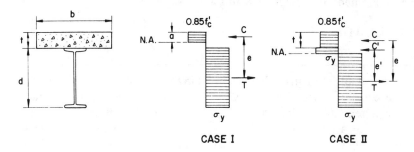

CASE I　　　　　　　　CASE II

FIG. 4.2.—STRESS DISTRIBUTION AT PLASTIC MOMENT OF A COMPOSITE STEEL AND CONCRETE SECTION

in the beam (Case II), as shown in Fig. 4.2. These equations are, for Case I

$$M_p = A_s\sigma_y\left(\frac{d}{2} + t - \frac{a}{2}\right) \quad\ldots\ldots\ldots\ldots (4.4)$$

and for Case II

$$M_p = Ce + C'e' \quad\ldots\ldots\ldots\ldots\ldots (4.5)$$

in which

$$a = \frac{A_s\sigma_y}{0.85 f'_c b}. \quad\ldots\ldots\ldots\ldots\ldots (4.6)$$

$$C = 0.85 f'_c\, bt \quad\ldots\ldots\ldots\ldots\ldots (4.7)$$

$$C' = \frac{A_s\sigma_y - 0.85 f'_c\, bt}{2} \quad\ldots\ldots\ldots\ldots (4.8)$$

and $A_s$ = total area of the steel section. For Case II, the values of $e$ and $e'$ are dependent on the geometry and steel cross section.

The attainment of the plastic moment for a composite beam is possible only if the steel beam is provided with an adequate number of mechanical shear connectors, so that the horizontal shear force from the slab can be effectively transmitted to the steel beam. The natural bond between steel and concrete is unreliable, because it is greatly influenced by the surface conditions of the steel beam. For the type of unencased composite beam shown in Fig. 4.2, natural bond is usually not considered.

In the negative moment region, it is the usual practice not to count on the tensile strength of concrete to increase the moment-carrying capacity of the composite beam. Instead, the plastic moment is computed based on the geometrical and mechanical properties of the steel beam only. However, tests have shown that some inclusion of the contribution made by the reinforcement to the plastic moment may be possible (4.14, 4.15, 4.16). Research on this aspect is still continuing, and it may be expected that the contribution of reinforcement could be included in the computation of the plastic moment of composite beams at the supports.

## 4.7  LOADS

The loads to be provided for (working loads) should be those that are customary for the particular type of construction. These loads are increased by a load factor to obtain a design ultimate loading. Members are selected on the basis of their plastic strength to resist the most critical condition of such loading. The design ultimate load can be expressed as

$$P_u = F P_w \dots\dots\dots\dots\dots\dots\dots(4.9)$$

in which          $F$ = load factor;

$P_u$ = design ultimate load or factored load; and

$P_w$ = allowable (working) load.

A margin of safety is achieved in allowable-stress design by the use of allowable stresses obtained from a stress level, assumed to represent failure, which has been reduced by a "factor of safety." In plastic design, safety is achieved by multiplying the given service loads by a "load factor" as discussed in Art. 4.8.

The use of plastic design does not involve any changes in the magnitude of the service loading, $P_w$, specified for a given structure. The difference is that, in the case of plastic design, members are selected so that the plastic limit load of the structure will be equal to or greater than the design ultimate load, $P_u$. In allowable-stress design, the members are so selected that allowable stresses will not be exceeded at service load, $P_w$. (As used here, $P$ is the critical combination of given independently variable loads used as the basis for the design by either method.)

The loading conditions that would be investigated for building construction are:

1. Dead load plus live load.
2. Dead load, plus live load, plus wind or earthquake forces.

In calculating the total load acting on the girders and columns in multistory frames, advantage can be gained by making use of the provisions for live-load reduction factors in standard building codes, one of which is USASI A58.1 (4.17).

It is assumed that the live loading is static and proportional, even for the characteristic fluctuations of live load found in buildings. For unusual conditions, deflection stability would be investigated (see Art. 6.4).

In the design of structures to resist the dynamic loading resulting from blast forces, plastic-design concepts generally are used. However, selection of the loading and the type of design are largely a matter of judgment, and are based on studies of vulnerability and consequences of failure. In making the design it is necessary to consider the nature of the loading, increased dynamic yield strength of the material, effective load duration, distribution of mass, effective mass, and natural period of the structure, as well as other factors not commonly considered in usual structural design.

In designing for earthquakes, most building codes provide for the application of equivalent lateral static loads to produce a desired level of earthquake resistance. In conformity with such practice, the specified loads can be multiplied by a load factor to yield design ultimate loads.

Concepts of plastic analysis are currently being used for design to resist earthquake forces, using procedures that take into account the elastic-plastic response of the structure as a function of time. The variation and random nature of earthquake loading require that consideration be given to loading approximations used in the design, as well as to many of the factors noted above as of importance in designing for blast forces. Greater refinement in design procedures using these concepts must await further study. Results of experiments on the behavior of steel beam-to-column connections and steel frames subjected to repeating inelastic strains are now (1970) available. They are presented in Art. 6.4.

## 4.8  LOAD FACTORS

| | |
|---|---|
| Dead load plus live load | $F_1 = 1.70$ |
| Dead load plus live load plus wind or earthquake forces | $F_2 = 1.30$ |

The factor of safety implicit in allowable-stress design and the load factor used in plastic design are not concerned only with the possibility of overloading. Other factors which influence the selection of an appropriate margin of safety are:

1. Approximations and uncertainties in the method of analysis.
2. Quality of workmanship.
3. Presence of residual stresses and stress concentrations.*
4. Underrun in physical properties of material.
5. Underrun of cross-sectional dimensions of members.
6. Location and intended use of structure.

Depending on the type of structure and its intended use, the importance of any one of the foregoing factors, as compared with the others, can vary somewhat. One might arrive at a precise over-all load factor, $F$, in each case if sufficient statistical data were available to weigh properly the importance of its various constituent parts; but any resulting departure from current practice would be equally applicable to the stresses specified for use in allowable-stress designs. Since such statistical data are not available, it would seem consistent to draw on the vast experience gained from allowable-stress design to obtain a single average value of the load factor, applicable throughout the range of building construction.

Such a value can be obtained by considering the plastic strength of simple beams in the light of the allowable stress for which these beams were proportioned, there being no necessity for requiring any greater margin of safety merely because the structure is redundant. For simple beams the load factor is equal to the ratio of the design ultimate load, $P_u$, to the working load, $P_w$; thus $F = P_u / P_w$. Since here the bending moment varies linearly with the load, and for the case in which $P_u = P_p$ and $P_w = P_a$

$$F = \frac{P_u}{P_w} = \frac{P_p}{P_a} = \frac{M_p}{M_a}$$

---

*While this factor contributes to uncertainty as to the precise stress level, the discussion in Art. 1.2, 5.1, and 5.3 shows that it may not influence the maximum load-carrying capacity (excepting column buckling and the danger of brittle fracture).

Substituting for $M_p$ and $M_a$

$$F = \frac{\sigma_y Z}{\sigma_a S} = \frac{\sigma_y}{\sigma_a} f$$

in which $f$ = the shape factor.

The allowable working stress for "compact"† beams in building design, according to Part 1 of the current AISC Specification (4.18), is 0.66 of the specified yield stress of the steel used. Restated, the load factor against the guaranteed maximum capacity of these beams has not exceeded

$$F = \frac{\sigma_y}{0.66\sigma_y} f = 1.50 f \ldots \ldots \ldots \ldots (4.10)$$

The formulation of a satisfactory load factor is therefore dependent only on the determination of a shape factor representative of the simple beams now in service.

The variation of the shape factor for wide-flange beams and columns, and for American Standard beams, is shown in Fig. 4.3. For wide-flange shapes normally used as beams listed in the "section economy" table of the AISC Manual of Steel Construction (4.18), the shape factor varies from 1.10 to 1.18, with an average value of 1.134 and a mode (most frequently observed value) of 1.12. For wide-flange shapes normally used as columns that appear in the "column" tables of Ref. 4.18 the shape factor varies from 1.10 to 1.23, with an average value of 1.137 and a mode of 1.115. The shape-factor distribution of American Standard beams is shown in the lower portion of Fig. 4.3. The minimum is 1.14 and the maximum is 1.23, the average being 1.18. Using the mode of 1.12, therefore, Eq. 4.10 becomes

$$F = 1.50(1.12) = 1.68 \text{ rounded to } 1.70$$

The factor of safety can also be examined from the standpoint of values inherent in the design of different kinds of structural members. Table 4.1 (4.19) shows the magnitude of the factor of safety based on the designated design criterion and in accordance with the AISC Specification (4.18); it also shows the major structural elements, the design ultimate load, $P_u$, according to the selected limit of usefulness, the allowable load (or moment) according to the Specification, and, finally, the computed factor of safety.

The comparison of the factors of safety for three of the structural elements listed shows a relatively consistent development: a factor of 1.67 for tension members, 1.67 for "short columns," 1.92 for "long columns,"

---

†According to the 1969 edition of the AISC Specification, a "compact shape" is one that meets the requirements of Sect. 1.5.1.4. "Plastic design" sections (Part 2) have somewhat more restrictive width-thickness ratios.

TABLE 4.1—FACTOR OF SAFETY FOR SELECTED STRUCTURAL ELEMENTS[a]

| Structural element (1) | Design criterion (2) | Design ultimate load, $P_u$ (3) | Allowable load, $P_w$ (4) | Factor of safety (Eq. 4.10) (5) |
|---|---|---|---|---|
| Tension members | Unrestricted plastic flow | $\sigma_y A$ | $0.6\,\sigma_y A$ | $\dfrac{\sigma_y A}{0.6\,\sigma_y A} = 1.67$ |
| Beams | Hypothetical first yield (slender shapes) | $M_y = \sigma_y S$ | $M_w = 0.6\,\sigma_y S$ | $\dfrac{\sigma_y S}{0.6\,\sigma_y S} = 1.67$ |
| | Unrestricted plastic flow (compact shapes) | $M_p = \sigma_y Z$ | $M_w = 0.66\,\sigma_y S$ | $\dfrac{\sigma_y Z}{0.66\,\sigma_y S} = \dfrac{1.12^b}{0.66} = 1.70$ |
| Columns | Maximum load (instability) | CRC column formula | Depends on $L/r$ | $\dfrac{L}{r} = 0,\ F = 1.67$ |
| | | | | $\dfrac{L}{r} \geq 126\ (A36),\ F = 1.92$ |

[a]Based on AISC Specifications (4.18)
[b]$Z/S = 1.12 =$ average value for all shapes in the AISC Manual

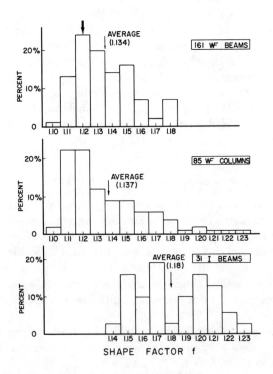

FIG. 4.3.—VARIATION OF SHAPE FACTOR FOR WIDE-FLANGE BEAMS AND COLUMNS AND AMERICAN STANDARD BEAMS

1.67 for slender beams, and 1.70 for compact shapes. Accordingly it is recommended that a load factor of 1.70 be used for plastically designed structures under gravity load. In the case of gravity loading in combination with wind or earthquake forces, allowable-stress design specifications permit a one-third increase in computed stresses. Consistent with this

TABLE 4.2—LOAD FACTORS FOR PLASTIC DESIGN IN VARIOUS COUNTRIES

| Country (1) | Assumed shape factor (2) | Dead load + live load (3) | Dead load + live load + wind or earthquake forces (4) | Number of load factors (5) |
|---|---|---|---|---|
| | | (a) Single Load Factor | | |
| USA | 1.12 | 1.70 | 1.30 | 2 |
| Australia | 1.15 | 1.75 | 1.40 | 2 |
| Belgium | 1.12 | 1.68 | 1.49 (1.12 for extreme wind) | 3 |
| Canada | 1.12 | 1.70 | 1.30 | 2 |
| Germany | — | 1.71$f$ | 1.50$f$ | 2 |
| India | 1.15 | 1.85 | 1.40 | 2 |
| Mexico | 1.12 | 1.70 | 1.30 | 2 |
| South Africa | 1.15 | 1.75 (portal frames) 1.50 (multistory braced frames) | 1.40 | 3 |
| Sweden | — | 1.57 | 1.34 | 2 |
| United Kingdom | 1.15 | 1.75 (portal frames) 1.50 (multistory braced frames | 1.40 | 3 |
| | | (b) Multiple Load Factors[a] | | |
| Czechoslovakia | 1.20 (maximum) | $[F_1 D + F_2 (L_1 + L_2)] \dfrac{1}{k}$ | $[F_1 D + F_2 L_1 + 0.9 (F_2 L_2 + F_3 W + 1.4 S)] \dfrac{1}{k}$ or $[F_1 D + F_2 L_1 + 0.8 (F_2 L_2 + F_3 W + 1.4 S + E)] \dfrac{1}{k}$ | Several |
| Hungary[b] | 1.05 | Proposal 1: (single load factor) 1.2–1.5 depending on combinations of $D$, $L_1$, and $L_2$. | | 3 |
| | | Proposal 2: (multiple load factor) many possible combinations | | 4 |
| Japan[b] | — | 1.2 $D$ + 2.1 ($L$ + $S$) or 1.4 ($D$ + $L$ + $S$) (normal condition) ($D$ + $L$) + 1.5 $E$ or ($D$ + $L$ + $nS$) + 1.5 $E$ (under earthquake) ($D$ + $L$) + 1.5 $W$ or ($D$ + $L$ + $nS$) + 1.5 $W$ (under typhoon) | | 6 |
| USSR | — | $F_1 D + F_2 L$ or 1.2 $L_3$ | 1.40 | Several |
| Yugoslavia | 1.12 | $D$ = 1.49, $L$ = 1.68 + Additional Combinations | | Several |

[a]The following symbols are used:
$D$ = dead load
$L$ = live load
$L_1$ = regular (long-time) live load
$L_2$ = irregular (short-time) live load
$L_3$ = movable concentrated load
$E$ = earthquake load
$f$ = shape factor
$S$ = maximum snow load
$W$ = wind force
[b]Under study

$F_1$ = 1.1–1.3
$F_2$ = 1.2–1.4
$F_3$ = 1.2–1.3
$k$ = 0.87 for $\sigma_y$ = 34.3 ksi
$k$ = 0.80 for $\sigma_y$ = 51.4 ksi. For

| $n$ | A period of snowdrifts |
|---|---|
| 0 | less than one month |
| 0.5 | one month |
| 1.0 | three months |

allowance, the value of $F$ for combined dead, live, and wind or earthquake loading would be $(3/4) \times 1.70 \approx 1.30$.

The variations in the types and values of load factors recommended for plastically designed steel structures elsewhere in the world are listed in Table 4.2 (1.32). Countries using a single load factor are Australia, Belgium, Canada, Germany, India, Mexico, South Africa, Sweden, the

United Kingdom, and the United States. Other countries, such as Czecho-slovakia, Hungary, Japan, USSR, and Yugoslavia, adopt a system of multiple load factors in which the load factors are adjusted according to the nature and frequency of the loads. Where the single load factor is used, the value for gravity load ranges from 1.70 (USA, Canada, and Mexico) to 1.85 (India).

# CHAPTER 5.—VERIFICATION OF PLASTIC THEORY

The purpose of this chapter is to show that the actual behavior of large-scale structures under test verifies the predictions of plastic theory. It is not intended to present the results of all tests on both small- and large-scale structures, because a comprehensive survey of such tests (up to 1964) has been given in Ref. 1.30.

This chapter includes three articles. In Art. 5.1 it is demonstrated that structural steel exhibits the ductility assumed, and that plastic hinges will form and allow the necessary redistribution of moment. Art. 5.2 presents the results of continuous-beam tests. Finally, Art. 5.3 shows how tests of rigid frames verify plastic theory. The various structures which are referred to in this chapter were fabricated of ASTM A7 steel unless otherwise indicated.

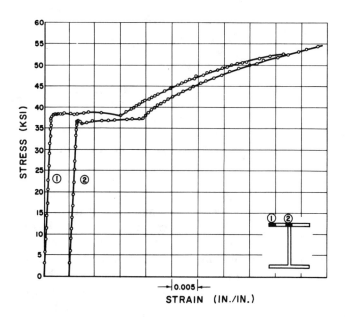

FIG. 5.1.—STRESS-STRAIN RELATIONSHIP OF TENSILE SPECIMENS OF ASTM A7 STEEL (5.1)

## 5.1  BASIC CONCEPTS

**Ductility of Steel.**

Fig. 5.1 shows the tensile stress-strain curves obtained from two coupons cut from two separate locations of an 8 **W** 40 beam. They are typical of the behavior of ASTM A7 steel. The steel deforms plastically about 15 times the strain at the elastic limit, and then begins to strain harden.*

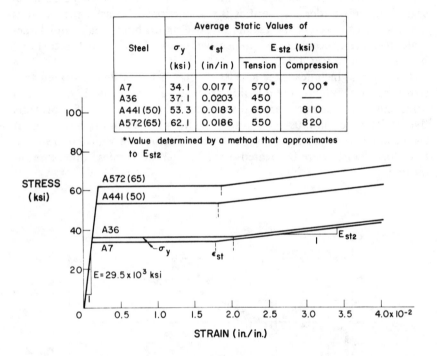

| Steel | $\sigma_y$ | $\epsilon_{st}$ | $E_{st2}$ (ksi) | |
|---|---|---|---|---|
| | (ksi) | (in/in) | Tension | Compression |
| A7 | 34.1 | 0.0177 | 570* | 700* |
| A36 | 37.1 | 0.0203 | 450 | —— |
| A441 (50) | 53.3 | 0.0183 | 650 | 810 |
| A572 (65) | 62.1 | 0.0186 | 550 | 820 |

*Value determined by a method that approximates to $E_{st2}$

FIG. 5.2.—IDEALIZED STRESS-STRAIN RELATIONSHIP FOR FOUR STRUCTURAL STEELS

Although the data are plotted well into the strain-hardening range, the strains shown are still considerably less than those that correspond to the tensile (ultimate) strength. The compressive and the tensile stress-strain relationships are quite similar. In fact, the properties in compression are practically identical with those in tension, except in the region beyond the onset of strain hardening. Fig. 5.2 shows in idealized form the stress-strain relationships for ASTM A7, A36, A441, and A572 steels. Average values of the static yield stress, $\sigma_y$, the strain at the onset of strain hardening,

---

*ASTM-A7 requires an elongation in 2 in. of not less than 24% at failure, an elongation that is more than 200 times the maximum elastic value. (See discussion in Art. 4.5.)

$\epsilon_{st}$, and the strain-hardening modulus in tension and compression, $E_{st2}$, of the four steels determined by laboratory tests, are tabulated in the inset (4.4, 4.6, 4.7). The stress-strain curves are consistent with these values. The methods used in obtaining them are described in detail in Refs. 4.4, 4.6, 5.2, and 5.3. Briefly, for the tension specimen the static yield-stress level is determined by stopping the testing machine for at least 5 minutes

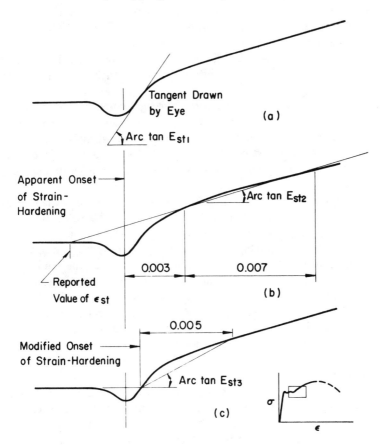

FIG. 5.3.—SKETCH DEFINING $E_{st1}$, $E_{st2}$, AND $E_{st3}$

when the specimen is loaded to a strain of 0.5%. The yield-stress level so obtained is lower than that defined in the CRC Guide (5.2) or ASTM Standards because of the strain-rate effect as discussed in Art. 4.5. The strain-hardening modulus, $E_{st2}$, is the slope of a line drawn to pass through the strain points of 0.003 in. per in. and 0.010 in. per in. beyond the apparent onset of strain hardening on the stress-strain curve, as illustrated in Fig. 5.3(b). The intersection on the stress-strain curve of the yield stress level in the plastic range with the simplified strain-hardening line gives the strain-hardening strain of the steel.

The strain-hardening modulus, $E_{st}$, depends very much on the selection of that portion of the stress-strain curve in the strain-hardening region where the slope is taken. Some approaches used in evaluating $E_{st}$ are briefly reviewed below.

The value $E_{st1}$ is the instantaneous value as measured by a tangent to the curve at the apparent onset of strain hardening [Fig. 5.3(a)]. It represents the upper bound of the $E_{st}$ values.

The value of the strain-hardening modulus, $E_{st2}$, has been defined earlier. Tests have shown that this exhibits the least scatter of experimental values (4.6, 4.7).

The value $E_{st3}$ is obtained by using the average value in an increment of 0.005 in. per in. strain after the onset of strain hardening (5.2). The onset of strain hardening is defined, in this instance, as the strain corresponding to the intersection on the stress-strain curve of the yield-stress level in the plastic range with the tangent to the curve in the strain-hardening range [Fig. 5.3(a)].

It has been observed that even with the same method of measurement, there is still considerable scatter in the value of $E_{st}$. The values tabulated in Fig. 5.2 represent the averages available at the present time.

In addition to the complicated situation of having more than one definition of $E_{st}$, the tensile value of $E_{st}$ is not the same as the compressive value. Tests have shown that the value of $E_{st}$ is somewhat higher in compression than in tension (4.6, 4.7). An examination of $E_{st2}$ values given in the insert of Fig. 5.2 will support this. Also, it has been observed that the compressive values of $E_{st}$ are not subject to as much scatter as the tensile values for the steels for which plastic design is applicable. It is in the problems involving compressive stress that the $E_{st}$ value is most frequently used (see Arts. 6.2 and 6.3).

The values of $E_{st2}$ for the four steels given in Fig. 5.2 are suggested as a basis for calculations not only because they exhibit the least scatter of experimental values, but also because they define the average slope of the part of the stress-strain curve into which most steel members are strain hardened.

### The Plastic Moment and the Plastic Hinge.

As a demonstration that the plastic moment is attained through plastification of a cross section, Fig. 5.4(a) shows a typical $M$-$\phi$ curve obtained from a beam, part of which is in pure bending (5.4). The dotted line is the idealized curve and the solid line through the circles shows the results of a test. The theoretical stress distributions (according to the simple plastic theory) at different stages of bending are shown in Fig. 5.4(b). Below these, in Fig. 5.4(c), are shown the corresponding stress distributions as

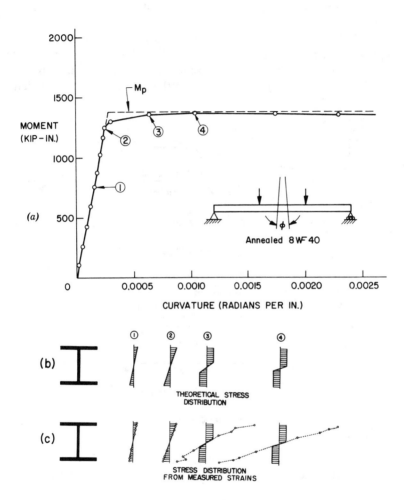

FIG. 5.4.—EXPERIMENTAL VERIFICATION OF THE MOMENT-CURVATURE RELATIONSHIP AND THEORETICAL AND COMPUTED STRESS DISTRIBUTIONS (5.4)

determined from SR-4 strain-gage measurements. It will be seen that plastification of the cross section *does* occur, and that the bending moment corresponding to this condition is the full plastic moment as computed from the equation $M_p = \sigma_y Z$.

Although there will be inevitable minor variations from the result shown in Fig. 5.4(a), the many tests conducted on rolled shapes indicate that hot-rolled wide-flange beams meeting the requirements outlined in this Manual will develop the strength predicted by the plastic theory, and that a

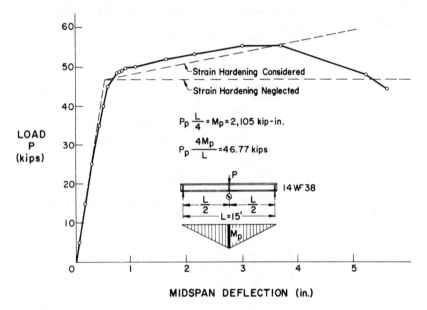

FIG. 5.5.—LOAD-MIDSPAN DEFLECTION RELATIONSHIP OF A 14 **WF** 38 BEAM (A7 STEEL) (5.5)

plastic hinge (characterized by rotation at near-constant moment) does actually form.

To be sure, a somewhat unrealistic loading condition has been taken, since "pure moment" is a condition not likely to be encountered in actual structures. Usually there will be a gradient in moment, as when a single concentrated load is applied to a beam. In such a case the deformation tends to be concentrated under the load point (the point of maximum moment). Because the plastic deformation is more localized, the strain-hardening region is reached at a lesser deflection; consequently, the beam develops a moment greater than the plastic moment (4.8, 5.5, 5.6, 5.7, 5.8).

Typical of the behavior of a beam under moment gradient is that shown in Fig. 5.5. The theoretical load-deflection curve, with and without the inclusion of strain hardening, is shown by dashed lines. The results of a test of such a beam are shown as a solid line. As a result of the strain-hardening phenomenon there is an increase in load-carrying capacity as the deformation continues beyond the yield level. The decrease in measured resistance, which occurred after a large hinge rotation at the center, resulted from local buckling of the flanges followed by lateral buckling.

Thus strain hardening improves the moment-carrying capacity of a beam, as discussed in Art. 2.3. Although it is disregarded in the plastic theory (except for checking a beam for stability against buckling), this additional reserve strength is still present in most ordinary structures, and contributes to an actual factor of safety that is greater than the value assumed in the plastic theory.

**Redistribution of Moment.**

From the previous section it is seen that plastic hinges may be depended upon to form at connections and at concentrated-load points. Development of the plastic moment is one of the sources of reserve strength in

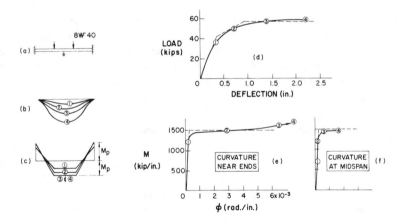

FIG. 5.6.—REDISTRIBUTION OF MOMENT AS REVEALED BY TEST ON A FIXED-END BEAM

structural steel beyond the elastic limit. Another source is the redistribution of moment in continuous structures.

Fig. 5.6 portrays the redistribution process as predicted theoretically and as obtained experimentally. A test was made on a continuous beam to simulate the condition of third-point loading on a fixed-end beam (5.1);

thus experimental data were available to compare with the theoretical predictions. The behavior of the beam at the following four stages of loading is shown:

Stage 1—at the computed elastic limit.
Stage 2—after the plastic hinges have formed at the ends and the load has increased towards its plastic limit value.
Stage 3—when the theoretical plastic limit load is first reached.
Stage 4—after deformation has been continued through an arbitrary additional displacement.

Fig. 5.6 shows (a) the loading, (b) the deflected shape at the four stages, (c) the moment diagram, (d) the load-deflection curve, and the moment-curvature relationship near the ends (e) and at the center (f).

In the elastic range (stage 1) it can be seen that the beam behaves just as assumed by the theory, the moment at the midspan being one-half the moment at the fixed ends [Figs. 5.6(c), (e), and (f)]. As the moment at the ends approaches the yield moment, the curvature, $\phi$, begins to increase more rapidly; a plastic hinge begins to form [Fig. 5.6(e)]. Because of this "hinge action," the additional moments due to increase in load are distributed between the ends and the midspan in a different ratio beyond the elastic range than before. As long as the beam is elastic, the increase in moment at the midspan corresponding to a load increment is one-half the increase at the ends. However, after a plastic hinge forms at the ends, most of the increase of moment occurs at the midspan; the moment increment at the ends is small [Figs. 5.6(e) and (f)]. This is the process known as redistribution of moment.

As a result of plastification at the ends, the beam actually behaves somewhat more flexibly than before [Fig. 5.6(d)]. At stage 2 the elastic-moment capacity near the midspan is practically exhausted. It is evident from Fig. 5.6 that substantially all of the moment capacity has been absorbed when stage 3 is reached (plastic limit load). Beyond this, the beam simply deforms as a mechanism with the moment diagram remaining largely unchanged, the plastic hinges at the ends and midspan rotating further.

Clear evidence is therefore available that redistribution of moment occurs through the formation of plastic hinges, allowing the structure to reach (and usually to exceed) the theoretical load predicted by simple plastic theory.

Incidentally, Fig. 5.6(d) illustrates the gradual transition from the elastic to the inelastic range that is typical for continuous steel beams and frames. Theoretically, upon first loading the structure should remain elastic up to stage 1. However, because of the combination of unknown initial stress conditions and discontinuities, local plastic flow takes place at a lower

load than that which corresponds to stage 1. But there is no effect what-
ever on the plastic limit load as long as buckling is prevented.

## 5.2 CONTINUOUS BEAMS

Fig. 5.7 shows the results of continuous-beam tests in which the members were fabricated from rolled sections. The structure and loading are
shown to scale at left. Next, the size of member (or members) is indicated.
To the right is a bar graph on which is plotted the percentage of predicted
maximum strength exhibited by the test structure. A test result plotted to
the "100%" line shows that the structure reached the load predicted by the
simple plastic theory. The shaded portion of the bar chart represents the
reserve strength beyond the elastic limit, since the end of the unshaded
portion of each bar graph is the computed elastic limit (on a nondimensional basis), and the end of the shaded portion is the observed maximum
strength.

Particularly remarkable among the continuous beam tests of Fig. 5.7 is
one described in Ref. 1.22 and shown as the next to last structure. In this
experiment, before the vertical load was applied, the center support was
raised until the allowable stress was just reached, with the result that application of the first increment of external load was, in fact, a load greater
than that allowed by the specifications. Despite this, the computed plastic
limit load was attained. The observed maximum load in this test was
within 3% of that of the two structures shown immediately above in Fig.
5.7.

The continuous beams shown in Fig. 5.8 were tested to show that members of otherwise inadequate strength may be cover-plated to achieve the
desired load-carrying capacity.

## 5.3 FRAMES

The structures shown in Figs. 5.9 and 5.11 are typical of some of the
frames tested in the United States as part of the experimental verification
of the plastic theory. The gabled frame in Fig. 5.9 had a span of 40 ft and
was fabricated of 12WF36 rolled shapes (5.5). The 3-story, 2-bay braced
frame (5.10) shown in Fig. 5.11 was fabricated of 12B16.5 girders and
6WF20 and 6WF25 columns. It had an over-all height and span of 30 ft. The
frames were tested with combined horizontal and vertical loads. Not only
was the computed plastic limit load reached, but each frame absorbed considerable plastic deformation while sustaining a load slightly in excess of
$P_p$.

Figs. 5.10 and 5.12 show the load-deformation curve for the gabled
frame and for the 3-story, 2-bay braced frame, respectively. The dashed
line corresponds to the predicted behavior based on theory, and the series
of open circles connected by the solid line represents the observed behav-

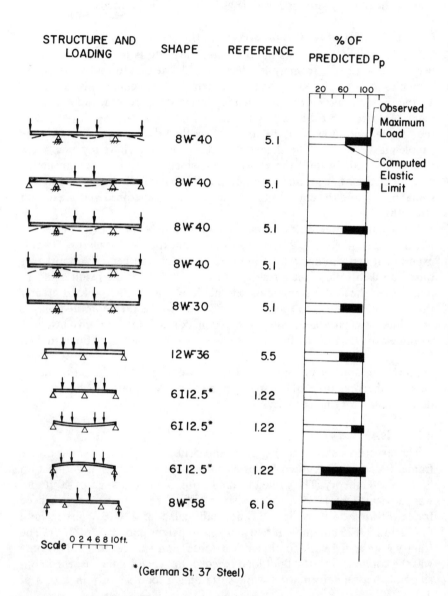

| STRUCTURE AND LOADING | SHAPE | REFERENCE | % OF PREDICTED $P_p$ |

FIG. 5.7.—SUMMARY OF CONTINUOUS BEAM TEST RESULTS SHOWING CORRELATION WITH PREDICTIONS OF PLASTIC THEORY

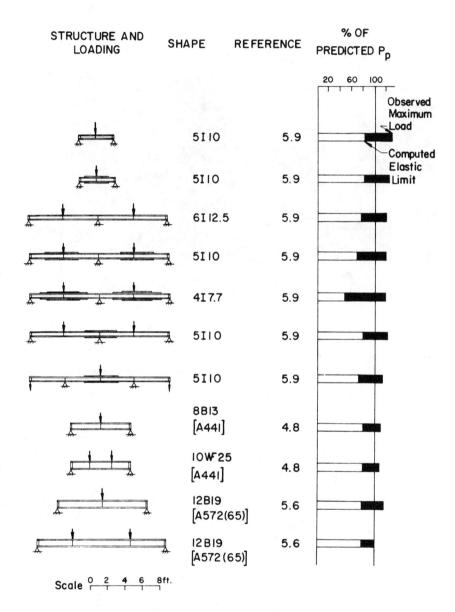

FIG. 5.8.—SUMMARY OF BEAM TEST RESULTS SHOWING CORRELATION WITH PREDICTIONS OF PLASTIC THEORY

FIG. 5.9.—TEST OF A 40-FT SPAN GABLE FRAME

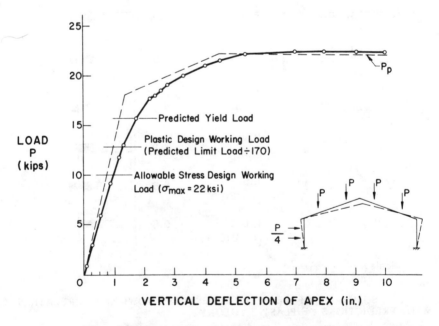

FIG. 5.10.—LOAD-CENTER DEFLECTION DIAGRAM OF TEST FRAME SHOWN IN FIG. 5.9

FIG. 5.11.—TEST OF A 3-STORY, 2-BAY BRACED FRAME (A36 STEEL)

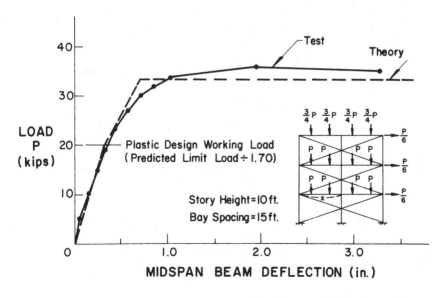

FIG. 5.12.—LOAD-BEAM DEFLECTION OF TEST FRAME SHOWN IN FIG. 5.11

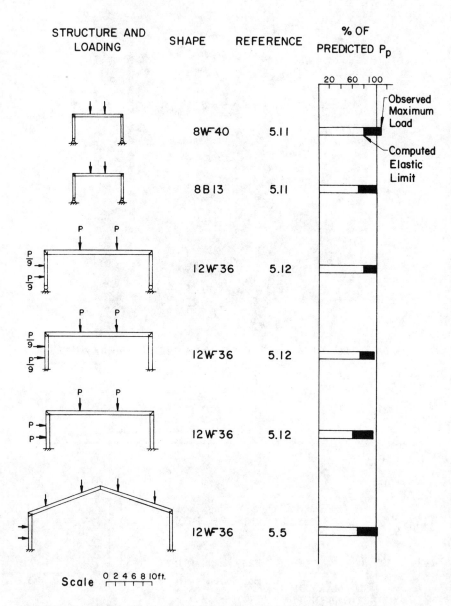

FIG. 5.13.—SUMMARY OF FRAME TEST RESULTS SHOWING CORRELATION WITH PREDICTIONS OF PLASTIC THEORY

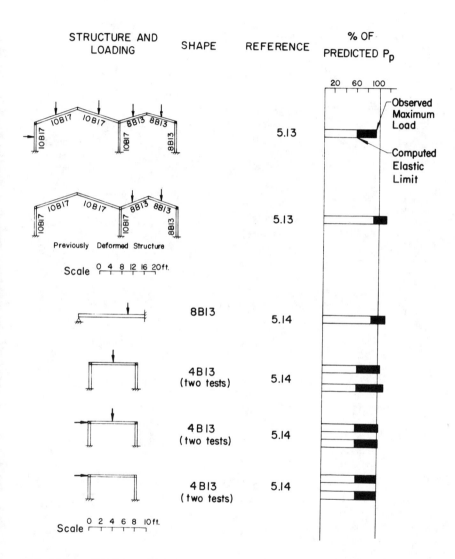

FIG. 5.14.——SUMMARY OF FRAME TEST RESULTS SHOWING CORRELATION WITH PREDICTIONS OF PLASTIC THEORY

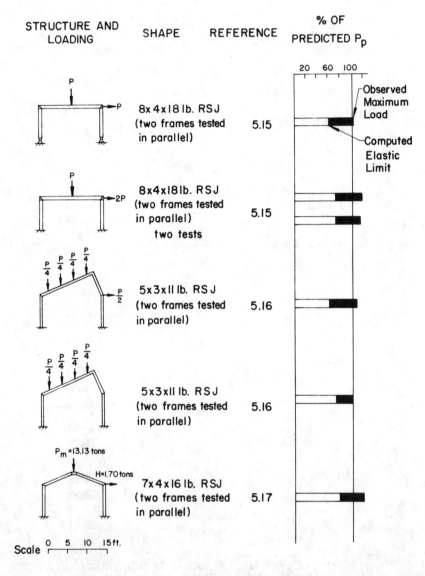

FIG. 5.15.—SUMMARY OF FRAME TEST RESULTS SHOWING CORRELATION
WITH PREDICTIONS OF PLASTIC THEORY (BRITISH B.S. 15 STEEL)

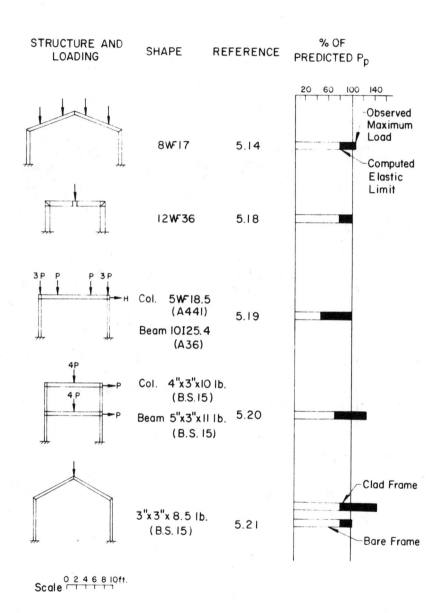

FIG. 5.16.—SUMMARY OF FRAME TEST RESULTS SHOWING CORRELATION WITH PREDICTIONS OF PLASTIC THEORY

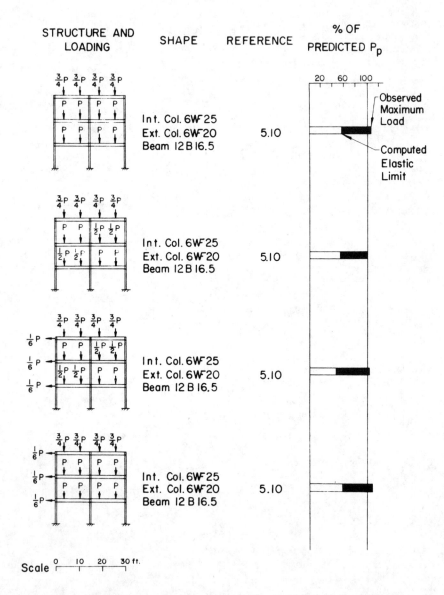

FIG. 5.17.—SUMMARY OF BRACED-FRAME TEST RESULTS SHOWING COR-
RELATION WITH PREDICTIONS OF PLASTIC THEORY (A36 STEEL)

ior. These results demonstrate once again that inelastic action (due to local effects) commences at a load considerably less than the predicted yield value. They also show that the plastic limit load is not affected by such initial conditions.

It is of interest to note that at maximum load the excess of actual deflection above the computed value for both frames was no greater than that observed at the predicted yield load. This means that the methods for com-

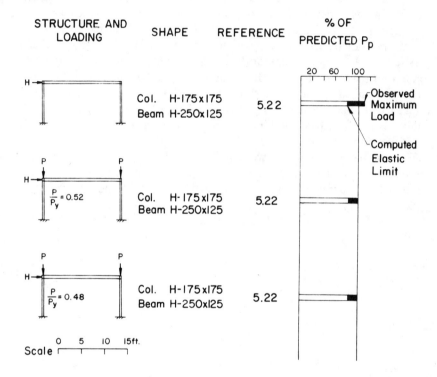

FIG. 5.18.—SUMMARY OF FRAME TEST RESULTS SHOWING CORRELATION WITH PREDICTIONS OF PLASTIC THEORY (JAPANESE SS41 STEEL)

puting such deflections are as dependable as the elastic deflection calculations.

Figs. 5.13 to 5.18 show frames tested both in the United States and abroad, and represent some of the structures which have been tested to maximum load capacity prior to 1970. As before, the unshaded portion of each bar graph represents the loading range up to the computed elastic limit. The shaded portion represents the reserve strength beyond the elastic limit, the end of that part being the observed maximum load. Good agreement is observed at maximum load, except for those cases in which strain hardening accounted for an increase; it is better, in fact, than the agreement between the predicted load at first yield and the observed value. In Fig. 5.13 testing of the fourth frame was interrupted, so that the fifth test might be carried out on the same structure with a different proportion of horizontal to vertical load.

Of particular interest is the test of a sheeted gable frame shed (5.21), as shown at the bottom of Fig. 5.16. This shed was built from seven gabled frames clad by corrugated steel roofing. Vertical loads of equal magnitude were applied to the apex of every frame. The five intermediate frames failed simultaneously at a load which was 45% higher than the predicted plastic limit load for a similar frame but ignoring the cladding effect. Similar tests were performed on two bare frames. The maximum load that could be applied to each bare frame was 1.02 times the predicted plastic limit load. These tests demonstrate the presence of additional strength in a gabled frame due to the cladding effect of the metal roofing, which is disregarded in the plastic theory.

The notable agreement between plastic theory and the results of these tests demonstrates the applicability of the plastic method to structural-design problems involving continuous steel beams and building frames.

# CHAPTER 6.—ADDITIONAL DESIGN CONSIDERATIONS

In the application of plastic theory to design, just as in the case of allowable-stress design, there are many important factors to be evaluated. Those considered in this chapter include shear force, local buckling of flanges and webs, lateral instability, and repeated loading. The problem of column buckling is treated in Chapter 7. The background of research is described, including the important assumptions and steps of pertinent theoretical analyses. Experimental correlation is given, and approximations for design use are discussed.

## 6.1  SHEAR FORCE

### Statement of the Problem.

Simple plastic theory is based on the concept of the attainment of the full plastic moment at certain sections of a structure, followed by adequate rotation at this constant moment value as the applied load increases. It must be recognized, however, that the magnitude of the moment at which large inelastic rotations occur is not constant under all circumstances. In calculating the full plastic moment, $M_p$, as $\sigma_y Z$, it is assumed that the member is stable and is subjected to pure bending; thus axial thrust and shear force are both ignored.

Since plastic hinges usually occur at positions where shear and axial force are present, it is of importance to be able to predict the changes in the values of the plastic moments due to these causes. In most practical cases the influence of shear force will be very small. In some special cases the combined influence of shear and axial thrust is important.

### Previous Research.

The effect of transverse shear force was considered in Ref. 6.1 for the case of a beam of rectangular cross section bent about one of its axes of symmetry. An approximate solution was obtained which is valid for shear forces less than a certain limit. This solution was also extended to an I-section bent about the axis normal to the web (strong axis).

The latter solution was modified in Ref. 6.2 to determine a lower bound (which is valid over the full range of shear forces) on the value of the full plastic moment in the presence of shear forces. An upper bound on the full plastic moment when the shear force has its full plastic value was also included. However, in both of these analyses, the conditions of equilibrium at the flange-web junction were not met. Consequently, the lower-bound solutions were not truly lower bounds. Suitable modifications subsequently were presented in Ref. 6.3, in which all conditions of equilibrium were satisfied.

In Ref. 6.4 a semiempirical theory was proposed, which is also valid over the full range of shear forces. An upper bound on the value of the full plastic moment in the presence of shear force was presented in Ref. 6.5 for beams of rectangular and I-section. This upper bound agrees closely with the lower bound of Ref. 6.2 for large values of the shear force. Upper-bound solutions were also derived independently (6.5, 6.6) for a beam of rectangular cross section by assuming a plane-strain state and a rigid-plastic material. Ref. 6.7 demonstrated the lack of uniqueness of interaction curves for shear and moment, explored bounds for a beam of rectangular cross section, and proposed an approximate interaction formula

$$\frac{M_{ps}}{M_p} = 1 - \left(\frac{V}{V_p}\right)^4 \quad\ldots\ldots\ldots\ldots\ldots (6.1)$$

in which    $M_{ps}$ = plastic hinge moment modified to include the effect of shear force;

$M_p$ = plastic moment = $\sigma_y b\, d^2 /4$;

$V$ = applied shear force; and

$V_p$ = $\tau_y bd = (\sigma_y /2)bd$. (In Eq. 6.1, the Tresca yield criterion is used.)

Ref. 6.8 gives the derivation for a general expression which is valid over the full range of shear and is applicable to both rectangular and I-beams. A lower-bound solution was developed for a cantilever beam with rectangular cross section, assuming the plane stress state and allowing warping at the fixed end (6.9). This solution was modified for wide-flange sections, including an extreme case of shear failure (3.1). Independent investigations have been made of the effect of both shear force and axial thrust on the full plastic moment (6.10, 6.11). The theoretical results obtained in Ref. 6.11 are in fair agreement with experimental observations. Lower-bound solutions were also developed in Refs. 6.12 and 6.13 for a cantilever of rectangular or I-section under the combined effect of shear force and axial thrust.

**Theoretical Analysis.**

In most practical situations, wide-flange or I-sections are used. However, the essentials of the problem can be shown by the simple example of a cantilever beam with rectangular cross section of depth $d$ and width $b$ (Fig. 6.1). Von Mises yield criterion is adopted for the combined stress state, so that yielding under pure shear is $\tau_y = \sigma_y/\sqrt{3}$. As the external loading is increased, yielding will commence at the fixed end of the beam and start to penetrate into the cross section [Fig. 6.1(a)]. Within the framework of beam theory, Ref. 6.14 has shown that the shear stress, $\tau$, must

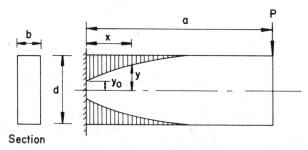

(a) Cantilever ( Yielded Zone Shown
Cross Hatched)

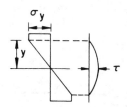

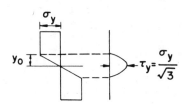

(b) Stress Distribution          (c) Stress Distribution at
at Section x                          Section x = 0

FIG. 6.1.—YIELDED ZONES AND STRESS DISTRIBUTION IN A CANTILEVER
BEAM OF RECTANGULAR CROSS SECTION

vanish in the plastic zones and that its distribution over the elastic portion
is parabolic. Thus the normal stress is still $\sigma_y$ in the plastic zones, and the
shear stress has a maximum value at the neutral axis. This stress distribution is shown in Fig. 6.1(b). It is assumed that the resistance of the elastic-
plastic section will be exhausted when the maximum shearing stress
reaches its yield value. This condition will first be reached at the neutral
axis at the fixed end. The corresponding stress distribution is shown in
Fig. 6.1(c). External and internal moment and shear at this section are
given by

$$M_{ps} = M_p \left[ 1 - \frac{1}{3} \left( \frac{y_o}{\frac{d}{2}} \right)^2 \right] \quad \ldots \ldots \ldots \ldots (6.2)$$

and

$$P = V = \frac{M_{ps}}{a} = \frac{4}{3} \frac{\sigma_y}{\sqrt{3}} b \, y_o \quad \ldots \ldots \ldots \ldots (6.3)$$

By eliminating $y_o$ and substituting $Z = bd^2/4$, Eqs. 6.2 and 6.3 are now combined to give

$$\frac{M_{ps}}{M_p} = \frac{8}{9}\frac{b\,a^2}{Z}\left(\sqrt{1 + \frac{9}{4}\frac{Z}{b\,a^2}} - 1\right) \quad \ldots \ldots \ldots (6.4)$$

Eq. 6.4 gives the desired relationship between the plastic moment, $M_{ps}$, as modified by shear, and the full plastic moment, $M_p$. It can readily be solved for the parameter $a/d$ (length of cantilever/depth of section) for different values of the ratio $M_{ps}/M_p$. The result is shown in Fig. 6.2 for the dashed curve marked "rectangle."

The rectangular cross section of Fig. 6.1(a) can be considered as the web plate of a wide-flange section. Eq. 6.4 still holds true if the appropriate plastic modulus, $Z$, of the wide-flange section is used when yielding due to normal stresses has penetrated into the web of the section, and if the web thickness, $w$, is used instead of the breadth, $b$.

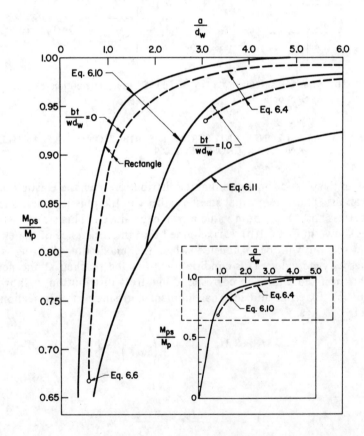

FIG. 6.2.—REDUCTION OF PLASTIC MOMENT BY SHEAR FORCE

Instead of using the tabulated values of $Z$, the plastic modulus of a wide-flange shape may be computed from

$$Z = bt \, d_f + \frac{1}{4} w \, d_w^2 \quad \ldots \ldots \ldots \ldots \quad (6.5)$$

Eq. 6.5 is introduced for use in the following derivation.

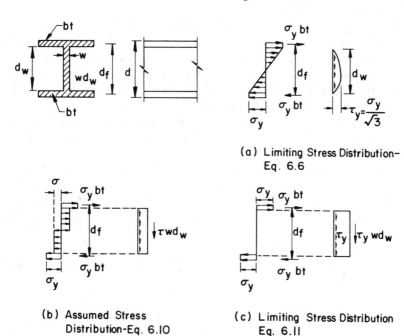

(a) Limiting Stress Distribution–
    Eq. 6.6

(b) Assumed Stress
    Distribution-Eq. 6.10

(c) Limiting Stress Distribution
    Eq. 6.11

FIG. 6.3.—ASSUMED LIMITING STRESS DISTRIBUTION IN A WIDE-FLANGE CROSS SECTION LOADED BY SHEAR FORCE AND MOMENT

Fig. 6.3(a) shows the stress distribution for a limiting case in which the parabolic shear stress distribution spreads to the full depth of the web $(y_o = d_w/2)$, and for which the shear stress on the neutral axis just reaches the shearing yield stress, $\tau_y$. For such a case, by eliminating $a$, Eq. 6.4 becomes

$$\frac{M_{ps}}{M_p} = 1 - \frac{1}{3} \left( \frac{1}{1 + \dfrac{4 bt}{w \, d_w} \dfrac{d_f}{d_w}} \right) \quad \ldots \ldots \ldots \ldots \quad (6.6)$$

Eq. 6.6 can also be obtained directly by computing the moment, $M_{ps}$, from the normal stress distribution shown in Fig. 6.3(a).

In Fig. 6.2 the dashed lines (Eq. 6.4) show the comparable reduction of the full plastic moment due to shear force for ratios of flange to web areas $bt/(wd_w)$ equal to 0 and 1. The case $bt/(wd_w) = 0$ corresponds to a rectangle. A value of 1.05 was taken as the average ratio of $d_f/d_w$. The two open circles show the limiting solutions as given by Eq. 6.6. As indicated on the inset of Fig. 6.2, that portion of the chart for $M_{ps}/M_p > 0.65$ is shown to the larger scale.

It can be verified that the von Mises criterion is nowhere violated in the portion of depth $2y_o$ for which the material is under combined normal and shear stresses. Hence, by limit theorem I, Eq. 6.4 is a lower bound for the maximum load-carrying capacity of the cantilever. It can therefore be expected that members tested under this condition will display a greater strength than that predicted by the theory.

The lower bound can be improved by assuming a uniform distribution of normal and shear stress at the fixed end, as shown in Fig. 6.3(b), which must satisfy the von Mises yield criterion

$$\sigma^2 + 3\,\tau^2 = \sigma_y^2 \quad \dots \dots \dots \dots \dots \text{(6.7)}$$

over the part of the cross section that is under the combined stresses of $\sigma$ and $\tau$. Equilibrium of external and internal moment and shear at the fixed end requires that

$$M_{ps} = \sigma_y\, bt\, d_f + \frac{1}{4}\,\sigma\, w\, d_w^2 \quad \dots \dots \dots \dots \text{(6.8)}$$

and

$$P = V = \frac{M_{ps}}{a} = \tau\, wd_w \quad \dots \dots \dots \dots \text{(6.9)}$$

Substituting for the values of $\sigma$ and $\tau$ in Eq. 6.7 with those from Eq. 6.8 and Eq. 6.9, and solving for $M_{ps}$

$$\frac{M_{ps}}{M_p} = \frac{1 + \sqrt{1 - \left(1 + \dfrac{3}{16}\dfrac{d_w^2}{a^2}\right)\left(1 - \dfrac{1}{16}\dfrac{w^2\,d_w^4}{b^2t^2\,d_f^2}\right)}}{\left(1 + \dfrac{3}{16}\dfrac{d_w^2}{a^2}\right)\left(1 + \dfrac{1}{4}\dfrac{w\,d_w^2}{bt\,d_f}\right)} \quad \dots \text{(6.10)}$$

is obtained.

Another limiting condition on the stress distribution is indicated in Fig. 6.3(c), in which the entire bending moment is taken by the flanges and the shear produces full yielding of the web. Then Eq. 6.10 becomes

$$\frac{M_{ps}}{M_p} = \frac{1}{1 + \dfrac{\sqrt{3}}{4}\dfrac{d_w}{a}} \quad \dots \dots \dots \dots \text{(6.11)}$$

Eq. 6.11 can be obtained directly from Fig. 6.3(c), using $a = M_{ps}/V$. The results of Eq. 6.10 and Eq. 6.11, in which an average ratio of $d_f/d_w = 1.05$ was again taken, are plotted in Fig. 6.2 as a solid curve. These solutions constitute good "lower bounds" from a Strength of Materials standpoint because all of the equilibrium conditions of force, moment, and yielding are satisfied. However, conditions of equilibrium at the flange-web junction are not fully satisfied, and, in addition, the shear stress, $\tau$, does not vanish at $y = (\pm d/2)$ for the case $bt/(wd_w) = 0$ (which corresponds to a rectangular section). Also, it is not shown here that the assumed stress distribution for the fixed-end section could be extended throughout the beam in a satisfactory manner. In a sense, therefore, the solutions of Eq. 6.10 and Eq. 6.11 are not truly lower bounds. When these conditions are taken into account, the analysis becomes more complicated, but the reduction of the plastic moment due to shear force is not affected to any great extent.

The shear force, $V_p$, that produces full yielding of the web [Fig. 6.3(c)] is

$$V_p = \tau_y wd_w = \left( \frac{\sigma_y}{\sqrt{3}} \right) (w\, d_w) \dots \dots \dots (6.12)$$

As an example, using a value of 1.07 for the $d/d_w$ ratio for common wide-flange shapes, the maximum allowable shear force, $V_p$, for A36 steel is

$$V_p = \frac{36.0}{(1.07)\sqrt{3}}\, wd = 19.5\, wd \dots \dots \dots \dots (6.13)$$

in which $V_p$ is in kips and $w$ and $d$ are in inches.

When the maximum shear force at maximum load $V$ is greater than $V_p$ as given by Eq. 6.12, the web may be reinforced, or Eq. 6.11 may be used to predict the modified plastic moment value. When $V$ is less than $V_p$, either Eq. 6.4 or Eq. 6.10 is appropriate; however, it will be seen later from experimental results that the implied reduction in moment capacity does not actually occur, because of strain hardening. Also it has been observed that there is an added strengthening influence under combined loading.

If, in addition to shear, an axial force is also present, a similar method of analysis may be applied. For wide-flange sections with $A_f/A_w = 1.0$ and $d_f/d_w = 1.05$, the problem has been solved in Ref. 6.11. Fig. 6.4 shows the relationship of $M_{pm}/M_p$ to $a/d_w$ for a cantilever beam, the parameter being the magnitude of axial load, $P$. In Fig. 6.4, $P_y$ is the axial yield load $= \sigma_y A$, and $M_{pm}$ denotes the plastic-hinge moment modified to include effect of axial compression and shear force. The curve for axial force equal to zero, $P/P_y = 0$, is the same as that given in Fig. 6.2 for $bt/wd_w = 1.0$ (solid curve). The other curves show the combined influence of shear and axial force as functions of the ratios $a/d_w$ and $P/P_y$.

Ref. 6.12 extended the related work of Ref. 6.7 and proposed an approximate interaction formula for a rectangular section

$$\frac{M}{M_p} + \left(\frac{P}{P_y}\right)^2 + \frac{\left(\frac{V}{V_p}\right)^4}{\left[1 - \left(\frac{P}{P_y}\right)^2\right]} = 1 \dots \dots \dots (6.14)$$

For the case in which no axial force is present ($P = 0$), Eq. 6.14 reduces to Eq. 6.1. When shear force is absent ($V = 0$), Eq. 6.14 reduces to Eq. 7.4, which is an expression for the reduction of the plastic moment of a section due to the presence of an axial thrust. Eq. 6.14 is "exact" when $V = 0$, and the discrepancy between the exact and the approximate solutions never exceeds 5% over the full range of values of $M$, $P$, and $V$.

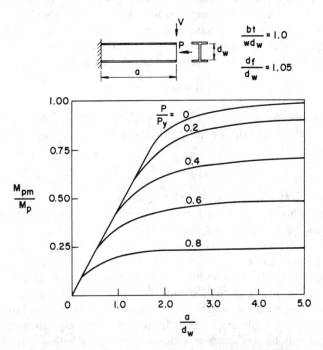

FIG. 6.4.—MOMENT CAPACITY AS MODIFIED BY THE COMBINED ACTION OF SHEAR AND THRUST ON WIDE-FLANGE CROSS SECTION

In practice it is unlikely that high shear forces and high axial forces will occur in combination at points where plastic hinges are expected. If this were to occur, however, Fig. 6.4 could be used to modify a trial design that neglected this unusual combination.

**Experimental Correlation.**

It is not easy to make a precise comparison between the theoretical predictions and experiments, since the effect of shear is quite small for wide-flange sections until the shear force, $V$, approaches the extreme value of shear failure, $V_y$, as given by Eq. 6.12. When $V$ is in the neighborhood of $V_y$ the load-deflection curves for beams show no appreciable horizontal portion corresponding to plastic-hinge action. Instead, it is found that the load-deflection or the moment-rotation curves continue to rise fairly steadily and to such an extent that the full plastic moment, $M_p$, is exceeded; hence no sharply defined failure condition exists.

However, the intersection of two tangents to the load-deflection or moment-rotation curves in the elastic and plastic range provides one pos-

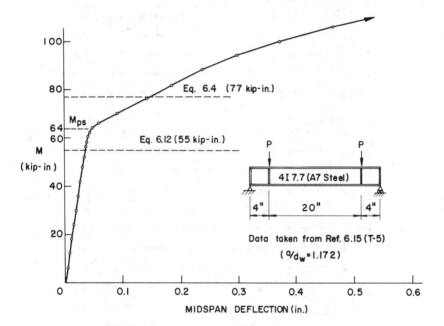

FIG. 6.5.—DETERMINATION OF PLASTIC MOMENT AS MODIFIED BY SHEAR, $M_{ps}$, USING TANGENT INTERSECTION METHOD

sible criterion for evaluating experimentally the modified plastic moment of the section due to shear force. Beyond this value of moment the deflection or curvature of the beam increases more rapidly than before.

The determination of $M_{ps}$ is shown in Fig. 6.5; the test data are taken from Ref. 6.15. In Fig. 6.5 a moment-deflection curve is shown for the test of an A7 steel beam in which the plastic moment was reduced by shear. An experimental value of $M_{ps}$ is obtained by extending the elastic portion of the moment-deflection curve to an intersection with the tangent to this curve in the inelastic range. Predictions from Eqs. 6.4 and 6.12 are also indicated for comparison. The shear force, $V$, in this case is greater than $V_p = (\sigma_y / \sqrt{3}) \, w d_w$ ; hence Eq. 6.12 would be used.

Fig. 6.6 shows, in tabular form, a number of tests which indicate the influence of shear on the plastic moment. The structure and loading are shown at the left. Next is indicated the size of member and the ratio $a/d$ in which $d$ = depth of member and $a$ = ratio $M/V$. For constant shear, $a$ is the distance from a plastic hinge to the point of inflection. Therefore $a$ is

| NO. | STRUCTURES (Span in Inches) | SHAPE | $\dfrac{a}{d}$ | $\dfrac{M_{ps}}{M_p}$ or $\dfrac{M_{max}}{M_p}$ (0 — 0.5 — 1.0) | REF. |
|---|---|---|---|---|---|
| 1 | 4  4  4 | 4 I 7.7 | 1.0 | Observed $M_{ps}$ / Observed $M_{max}$ | 6.15 |
| 2 | 4  4  4 | 4 I 7.7 | 1.0 | | 6.15 |
| 3 | 4  4  4 | 4 I 7.7 | 1.0 | | 6.15 |
| 4 | 4  8  4 | 4 I 7.7 | 1.0 | | 6.15 |
| 5 | 4  20  4 | 4 I 7.7 | 1.0 | | 6.15 |
| 6 | 6  20  6 | 4 I 7.7 | 1.5 | Eq. 6.11 / Eq. 6.4 | 6.15 |
| 7 | 40 40 40 40 40 40 | 12 WF 36 | 2.0 | | 5.9 |
| 8 | 8  8  8 | 4 I 7.7 | 2.0 | | 6.15 |
| 9 | 8  20  8 | 4 I 7.7 | 2.0 | | 6.15 |
| 10 | 24  36  24 | 12 WF 27 | 2.0 | | 6.9 |
| 11 | 24  24 | 12 WF 27 | 2.0 | | 6.9 |
| 12 | 84 56 56 84 | 14 WF 30 | 2.0 | | 2.8 |
| 13 | 53 36 36 36 53 | 8 WF 58 | 2.1 | | 6.16 |
| 14 | 36  36  36 | 12 WF 27 | 3.0 | | 6.9 |
| 15 | 84 56  56 84 | 8 WF 40 | 3.4 | | 2.8 |
| 16 | 84 56 56 56 84 | 8 WF 40 | 3.4 | | 2.8 |
| 17 | 84 56 56 56 84 | 8 WF 40 | 3.4 | | 2.8 |
| 18 | 84 56 56 56 84 | 8 WF 40 | 3.4 | | 2.8 |
| 19 | 48  36  48 | 12 WF 27 | 4.0 | Eq. 6.4 | 6.9 |
| 20 | 60  60 | 12 WF 27 | 5.0 | | 6.9 |

FIG. 6.6.—SUMMARY OF TEST RESULTS FOR BEAMS (A7 STEEL) UNDER COMBINED ACTION OF SHEAR AND MOMENT

sometimes referred to as the length of an "equivalent cantilever beam." To the right is a bar graph on which is plotted the maximum moment corresponding to the observed maximum load and observed reduced plastic moment, $M_{ps}$, due to shear, the latter being determined as described earlier. The theoretical limit according to Eq. 6.4 or Eq. 6.11 (depending on which case is the controlling one) is shown by the dotted line. In the range where the shear force, $V$, is high and greater than $V_p$, Eq. 6.11 is used to compute the limit predicted by the theory.

Fig. 6.6 shows that the actual strength of the structure usually exceeds the full plastic moment, $M_p$, if the shear force, $V$, is less than $V_p$ (the value which assumes full yielding of the web). The exception is Beam No. 13, which was deficient by only 4%. The influence of shear force may thus be neglected when this condition exists. Even when the shear force is greater than $V_p$, the test results show a moment-carrying capacity greater than that predicted by Eq. 6.11. It is evident, however, that the latter is a reasonable limit.

Although it might appear from these results that a more than ample load factor exists with regard to shear force when $V \leq V_p$, this fact cannot be utilized because of practical limitations. A beam with pure moment, for example, usually buckles when strain hardening commences, and therefore cannot be counted on to support a moment greater than $M_p$.

The test results on the effect of both shear and axial forces (6.10) show a tendency similar to that of the bar graph in Fig. 6.6. The observed values of $M_{pm}/M_p$ are in good agreement with the theoretical predictions in Fig. 6.4.

### Design Approximation.

The effect of shear on the full plastic moment will usually be negligible for frames. High shear and moment occur in localized zones, so that strain hardening will set in quickly and, in most cases, permit the moment to reach the full plastic value. Therefore no reduction in the plastic moment, $M_p$, is required for the effect of shear if at the ultimate load $V < V_p$ as given by Eq. 6.12.

---

**COMBINED MOMENT AND SHEAR FORCE**

The design is satisfactory as regards shear force, $V$, if its magnitude at the maximum load does not exceed

$$V_p = \frac{\sigma_y}{\sqrt{3}} \, wd_w \quad \dots \dots \dots \dots \dots (6.12)$$

in which $V_p$ is in kips and $w$ and $d_w$ in inches. No modification of the plastic moment is required.

---

## 6.2  LOCAL BUCKLING

### Statement of the Problem.

In plastic analysis it is tacitly assumed that the moment capacity of the member will remain at the level of the plastic moment until enough hinges have developed to form a mechanism. It is, therefore, necessary that the moment capacity not be impaired by local or lateral-torsional buckling until the required rotation has been achieved. The resistance to local buckling of the compression flange is dependent on its width-to-thickness ratio and the web restraint. A similar situation also exists in web buckling. The resistance to lateral-torsional buckling depends on the slenderness ratio of the unbraced segment of the member. The problem is thus to find geometrical properties, in the form of ratios, which will permit the member to perform its function so that the structure can reach the computed maximum load.

Local and lateral-torsional buckling are not always independent phenomena. In Fig. 6.7 two experimental moment-rotation curves are shown,

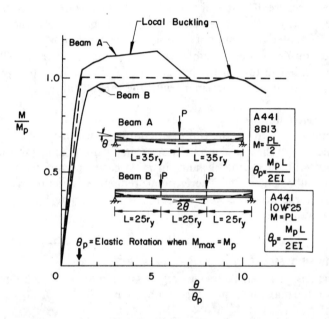

FIG. 6.7.—EXPERIMENTAL MOMENT-ROTATION CURVES FOR STEEL WIDE-FLANGE BEAMS

one for a beam with a two-point load (uniform moment in the central segment), and one for a beam with a single load (beam under moment gradient). The corresponding typical failure patterns are shown in Fig. 6.8. The compression flange of the beam under uniform moment begins to deflect noticeably in the lateral direction as soon as $M_p$ is attained (near a rotation of about $2\theta_p$) (6.17), but the capacity to support moment is not reduced until local buckles begin to develop in the compressed half of the compression flange [Fig. 6.8(b)]. Eventually the beam under moment gradient either will develop local buckles in the flanges near the load point [Fig. 6.8(a)] or it will buckle in the lateral-torsional mode. It is evident, therefore, that these two phenomena tend to exert a mutual influence on each other. In certain cases the dominant mode will be local buckling. In others it will be lateral buckling. For example, for closely braced beams,

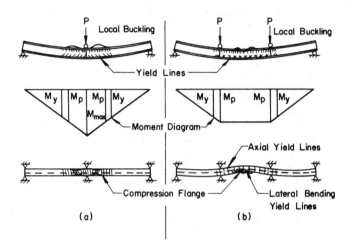

FIG. 6.8.—LOCAL AND LATERAL-TORSIONAL BUCKLING OF STEEL WIDE-FLANGE BEAMS

local buckling will have the dominant effect and the strength of these beams will not be significantly affected by lateral buckling.

**Previous Research.**

Even though local and lateral-torsional buckling in the inelastic range are manifestations of the same phenomenon, namely, the development of large cross-sectional distortions at large strains (about one order of magnitude larger than the yield strains), they have been treated as independent problems in the literature dealing with these subjects. This is mainly due to the complexity of the combined problem.

The problems of elastic and inelastic buckling of plate elements are discussed in Ref. 6.18. Ref. 6.19 gives the first application of the deformation theory (finite stress-strain relations) to the plastic plate buckling problem, and this theory was further developed in Ref. 6.20 and modified in Ref. 6.21. The problem of local flange buckling was discussed in an approximate manner in Ref. 6.22, and possible limitations on width-to-thickness ratios were proposed. The flow theory (incremental stress-strain relations) has been applied to perfectly flat plates in Refs. 6.23 and 6.24.

Studies of the stability of plates in the strain-hardening range have been presented in Refs. 6.25 through 6.29. This research was performed to study the problem of local buckling in plastically designed steel structures, and the following discussion is a review of this work.

**Theoretical Analysis.**

**Flanges.**—The physical model in the local buckling analyses consists of a flange plate element which is subjected to a uniform stress, $\sigma_y$, across the flange area $bt$, and which is restrained at the web-to-flange intersection by the web (Fig. 6.9). It is treated as a problem in classical buckling with

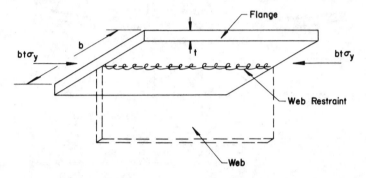

FIG. 6.9.—COMPRESSION FLANGE LOCAL BUCKLING MODEL

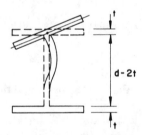

FIG. 6.10.—SHAPE OF THE DEFORMED CROSS SECTION AFTER LOCAL BUCKLING

bifurcation of the equilibrium position. The cross-sectional shape before and after buckling that is assumed in the solution is shown in Fig. 6.10. The distorted shape shows only the effect of local buckling, and for clarity the distortion produced by possible lateral buckling is not shown (see Fig. 6.8 for a diagrammatic picture of the combined effect).

There are two possible ways in which the problem of flange buckling can be treated: (1) by solving the problem of the buckling of an orthotropic plate (6.25, 6.26), or (2) by solving the problem of the torsional buckling of a restrained rectangular plate (6.28). In both solutions, it is assumed that the flange is strained uniformly to a strain equal to $\epsilon_{st}$. It is also assumed that the material will strain harden at this strain with a strain-hardening modulus $E_{st}$. In the case of a long plate with zero restraint from the web, the two solutions give identical results

$$\sigma_{cr} = \left(\frac{t}{\dfrac{b}{2}}\right)^2 G_{st} \quad \ldots \ldots \ldots \ldots \quad (6.15)$$

in which $\sigma_{cr}$ = the critical buckling stress; $t$ = thickness of flange; $b$ = width of flange; and $G_{st}$ = the strain-hardening modulus in shear. In the derivation of Eq. 6.15 it was assumed that the flange plate is uniformly strained into the strain-hardening range. At the onset of strain hardening $\sigma_{cr} = \sigma_y$, and therefore the plate width-thickness ratio at which local buckling of a perfect plate will start is

$$\frac{b}{t} = 2\sqrt{\frac{G_{st}}{\sigma_y}}. \quad \ldots \ldots \ldots \ldots \ldots \quad (6.16)$$

If web restraint is included, the form of the solution is different for the two types of approach, even though the difference in the numerical results is not significant. The orthotropic plate solution (6.25, 6.26) involves the determination of several material constants for which values have been determined only for ASTM A7-type steel. On the other hand, the solution according to the torsional buckling (restrained plate) theory involves fewer mechanical properties, and it can be extended to steels other than ASTM A7. Therefore this theory will be considered here.

In the torsional-buckling theory (6.29), local buckling occurs when (1) the average strains in the plate are at the strain-hardening strain, $\epsilon_{st}$, and (2) a long enough portion of the plate has yielded so that at least one full wave length of the buckle can develop. This buckle-wave is illustrated in Fig. 6.11 for the case of a beam under uniform moment and that of a beam under moment gradient. In Ref. 6.28, it was found that the critical flange force can be given in the form

$$bt\,\sigma_{cr} = \frac{12}{b^2}\left[G_{st}K_T + \left(\frac{n\pi}{L}\right)^2 E_{st}I_w + K\left(\frac{L}{n\pi}\right)^2\right]. \quad \ldots \ldots \quad (6.17)$$

in which             $K_T$ = St. Venant torsion constant of the flange

$$= \frac{bt^3}{3}. \quad \ldots \ldots \ldots \ldots \ldots \ldots \ldots \quad (6.18)$$

$$I_w = \text{warping constant} = \frac{7b^3 t^3}{2{,}304} \quad \ldots \ldots \quad (6.19)$$

$$K = \text{spring constant of the web}$$

$$= \frac{G_{st}w^3}{3\,(d - 2t)} \quad \ldots \ldots \ldots \ldots \ldots \quad (6.20)$$

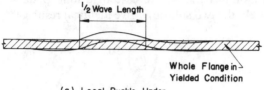

(a) Local Buckle Under
Uniform Moment

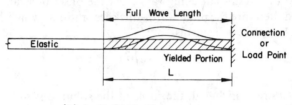

(b) Local Buckle Under
Moment Gradient

FIG. 6.11.—LOCAL BUCKLING CONDITIONS

and $w$ = web thickness, $d$ = beam depth, and $E_{st}$ = the strain-hardening modulus of the material; $L/n$ is the half-wave length of the local buckle. The lowest critical value for the stress is obtained by differentiating Eq. 6.17 and solving for the half-wave length. After substitution and simplification, the expressions for the half-wave length and the required width-thickness ratio when $\sigma_{cr} = \sigma_y$ become, respectively (6.28)

$$\frac{L}{n} = \frac{\alpha L}{2} = 0.713b \left( \frac{t}{w} \right) \left( \frac{bt}{w\,d_w} \right)^{1/4} \quad \ldots \ldots \ldots (6.21)$$

$$\frac{b}{t} = 2 \sqrt{\frac{G_{st}}{\sigma_y} + 0.381 \left( \frac{E_{st}}{\sigma_y} \right) \left( \frac{w}{t} \right)^2 \left( \frac{bt}{w\,d_w} \right)}. \quad \ldots \ldots (6.22)$$

The first term in Eq. 6.22 is identical with Eq. 6.16, and the second term represents the contribution of the restraint offered by the web.

According to the conditions assumed in this theory, local buckling will commence at the onset of strain hardening when the $b/t$ ratio is equal to the limiting ratio from Eq. 6.22, and if a length of flange equal to a full wave length has become yielded.

In Eq. 6.22 the material properties are the yield stress, $\sigma_y$, the strain-hardening modulus, $E_{st}$, and the strain-hardening modulus in shear, $G_{st}$. Of these, $\sigma_y$ and $E_{st}$ are determined from a tensile or compression test, but $G_{st}$ must be obtained indirectly. Several possible approaches to obtain $G_{st}$ values have been proposed (6.19, 6.25, 6.28). The torsional-buckling theory presented in Ref. 6.29 uses a $G_{st}$ value developed from the discontinuous yield process shown in Ref. 6.28. This is

$$G_{st} = \frac{2G}{1 + \dfrac{E}{4E_{st}(1 + \nu)}} \qquad \ldots \ldots \ldots \ldots (6.23)$$

in which $\nu$ = Poisson's ratio. According to Eq. 6.23, $G_{st}$ = 2,800 ksi for $E_{st}$ = 800 ksi (the approximate compressive value of $E_{st2}$ given in Fig. 5.2), and $\nu = 0.3$.

In Eq. 6.22 the effect of web restraint was found to be, on the average, about 3% of the first term under the radical. If this modification to Eq. 6.22 is made, and if $\nu$ is taken to be 0.3 and $E/G$ to be 2.6, then the equation for the limiting $b/t$ ratio becomes

$$\frac{b}{t} = \frac{1.78}{\sqrt{\dfrac{\sigma_y}{E}}} \sqrt{\frac{1}{1 + \dfrac{E}{5.2\,E_{st}}}} \qquad \ldots \ldots \ldots \ldots (6.24)$$

Using $E_{st}$ = 800 ksi, the width-to-thickness ratios, $b/t$, calculated from Eq. 6.24 are

for A36 steel                 $\dfrac{b}{t} = 17.9$

for A441(50) steel        $\dfrac{b}{t} = 15.2$          $\ldots \ldots \ldots \ldots (6.25)$

and for A572(65) steel    $\dfrac{b}{t} = 13.4$

In the case of beams under moment gradient, strain hardening tends to occur very early, and it has been found that buckling normally occurs at a stress level higher than the yield stress (6.28). It has been suggested that a possible empirical stress level at which local buckling is likely to occur is

$$\sigma_{ym} = \frac{1}{4}\left(3 + \frac{\sigma_f}{\sigma_y}\right)\sigma_y \qquad \ldots \ldots \ldots \ldots (6.26)$$

in which $\sigma_f$ = the tensile strength. If this modification is made to Eq. 6.24, a possible limiting $b/t$ ratio is given by

$$\frac{b}{t} = \frac{3.56}{\sqrt{\dfrac{\sigma_y}{E}}} \sqrt{\frac{1}{\left(3 + \dfrac{\sigma_f}{\sigma_y}\right)\left(1 + \dfrac{E}{5.2\,E_{st}}\right)}} \qquad \ldots \ldots \ldots (6.27)$$

Using $E_{st}$ = 800 ksi and the minimum tensile stresses from the ASTM Specifications, the $b/t$ ratios for A36 steel, $\sigma_u = 58,$ $\dfrac{b}{t} = 16.7$

for A441(50) steel, $\sigma_u = 70,$ $\dfrac{b}{t} = 14.5$  . . . . . . . . (6.28)

and for A572(65) steel, $\sigma_u = 80,$ $\dfrac{b}{t} = 13.0$

are obtained.

**Webs.**—The problem of the buckling of the web of a wide-flange beam subjected to both axial load and bending moment has been studied in Ref. 6.26, and a diagram has been presented for the allowable $d_f/w$ ratio of the web of a wide-flange section. In Fig. 6.12 the curves are plotted for differ-

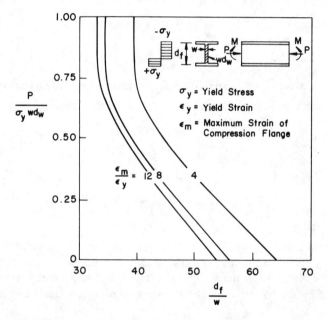

FIG. 6.12.—ALLOWABLE $d_f/w$ RATIO OF WEB OF FULLY PLASTIFIED WIDE-FLANGE SECTIONS

ent ratios of maximum strain to yield strain, $\epsilon_m/\epsilon_y$. As the maximum strain of the compression flange increases, the critical $d_f/w$ ratio decreases. The critical value of the axial force, $P$, also decreases as the ratio of the depth to the thickness of the web increases. The curves in Fig. 6.12 apply only to steel having the mechanical properties specified in ASTM A36.

**Experimental Correlation.**

A wide variety of tests on beams, beam-columns, and frames indicates that the local buckling criteria described above result in satisfactory per-

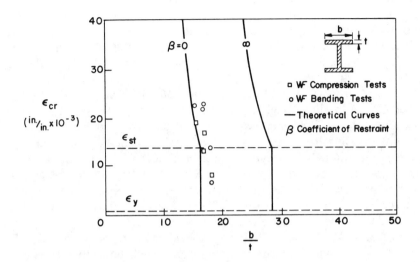

FIG. 6.13.—RESULTS OF TESTS ON WIDE-FLANGE SHAPES SHOWING COR-RELATION WITH PREDICTED STRAIN AT BUCKLING OF FLANGES

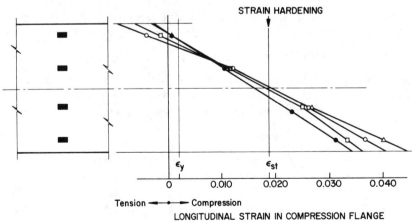

FIG. 6.14.—STRAIN DISTRIBUTIONS AT LOCAL BUCKLING FOR BEAMS UNDER UNIFORM MOMENT

formance. The test points in Fig. 6.13 were taken from tests reported in Ref. 6.26, and they represent axial compression tests and beam tests. The term $\beta$ in Fig. 6.13 represents the degree of restraint offered by the web, with $\beta = 0$ corresponding to no web restraint and $\beta = \infty$ corresponding to full restraint. The solid lines refer to theoretical solutions of the orthotropic plate equation. The test points fall close to, but to the right of, the curve for $\beta = 0$.

Fig. 6.14 provides another confirmation of the local buckling theory based on the torsional-buckling model. Shown in Fig. 6.14 is the strain distribution across the compression flange at the first observed occurrence of local buckling for a beam under uniform moment [loaded as in Fig. 6.8(b)]. Even though the large lateral deflection [see Fig. 6.8(b)] causes a strain gradient across the flanges, local buckling first started when the average strain was equal to $\epsilon_{st}$. The information in Fig. 6.14 is from four tests which are reported in Ref. 4.8. The flange width-thickness ratio was 13.4 and the value of $\sigma_y$ was 52 ksi for these tests.

Another series of tests on flange local buckling is reported in Ref. 5.7. Beams under a single concentrated load were tested. The unbraced length of the beams was 35 $r_y$ and the flange slenderness was the variable. Plotted in Fig. 6.15 is the experimentally observed rotation capacity, $R$, versus the quantity $\dfrac{b}{t} \sqrt{\dfrac{\sigma_y}{E}} \left( 3 + \dfrac{\sigma_f}{\sigma_y} \right)$. The rotation capacity is defined as

$$R = \frac{\theta_u}{\theta_p} - 1 \quad \ldots \ldots \ldots \ldots \quad (6.29)$$

in which $\theta_u$ = the rotation when the moment capacity reaches $M_p$ on the unloading branch of an $M$-$\theta$ curve such as that shown in Fig. 6.7, and $\theta_p = M_p L/2EI$. Also shown in Fig. 6.15 is the limiting $\dfrac{b}{t} \sqrt{\dfrac{\sigma_y}{E}} \left( 3 + \dfrac{\sigma_f}{\sigma_y} \right)$ ratio from Eq. 6.27 for $E_{st} = 800$ ksi. From Fig. 6.15 it can be seen that in the vicinity of the limiting ratios the rotation capacities are quite high, but that the rotation capacities decrease rapidly as the quantity $\dfrac{b}{t} \sqrt{\dfrac{\sigma_y}{E}} \left( 3 + \dfrac{\sigma_f}{\sigma_y} \right)$ increases.

Local buckling of the compression flange does not appear to terminate rotation capacity in itself, but rather because the cross section becomes unsymmetrical, the rate of lateral deformations is increased. It is this action which accompanies unloading. The tests described in Ref. 5.7 closely simulate the situation in the hinge areas of a structure. Thus relatively large rotation capacities were obtained. In addition, the rotation capacities obtained from these tests can be compared directly with the hinge-rotation requirements for a given structure.

Fig. 6.16 shows the limited amount of information that is available on

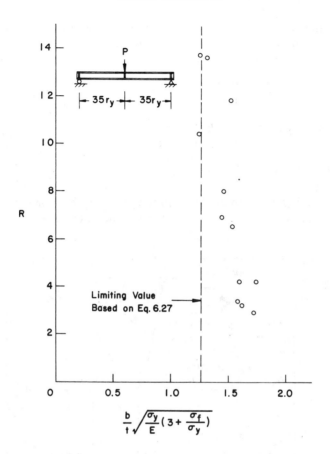

FIG. 6.15.—RELATIONSHIPS BETWEEN ROTATION CAPACITY $R$ AND $\dfrac{b}{t}\sqrt{\dfrac{\sigma_y}{E}}\left(3 + \dfrac{\sigma_f}{\sigma_y}\right)$ RATIO (5.7)

web buckling (6.26). Partial correlation for the case of web buckling under combined compression and bending is obtained from connection tests (6.30), if one accepts the fact that the conditions of these tests were somewhat different from those on which the theory is based. This comparison is shown in Fig. 6.17, in which the rotation of a selected length of member is plotted versus the $d_f/w$ ratio for $P/P_y = 0.10$. Test results do not check the predictions precisely, but they do indicate a large rotation capacity.

### Design Approximations.

**Flanges and Outstanding Plate Elements.**—The critical flange slenderness ratios have been given as Eqs. 6.24 and 6.27. The two sets of limiting width-to-thickness ratios given by Eqs. 6.25 and 6.28 demonstrate that the $b/t$ ratios for the moment-gradient case are more critical than those for the uniform-moment case. Taking into account the current state of research, the following $b/t$ ratios

for A36 steel, $\qquad \dfrac{b}{t} = 17$

for A441(50) steel, $\qquad \dfrac{b}{t} = 14$ $\qquad$ . . . . . . . . . . . . . . . . . . . (6.30)

and for A572(65) steel, $\dfrac{b}{t} = 12$

are recommended for both the uniform-moment and the moment-gradient case. The value $b/t = 12$ for A572(65) steel is more conservative than the

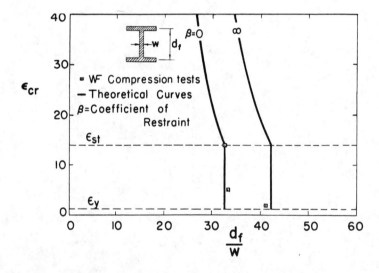

FIG. 6.16.—RESULTS OF TESTS ON WIDE-FLANGE SHAPES SHOWING STRAIN AT WHICH WEB BUCKLING OCCURRED

value given in Eqs. 6.25 and 6.28. This is on the basis of stub column tests with $b/t = 12.0$ and beam tests with $b/t = 11.5$. In the theory, some approximations have been made and the data on some of the mechanical properties in the inelastic region are limited. Further research is currently under way, and the results of that work may well permit liberalization of some of the limiting values given above.

For outstanding flanges and plate stiffeners, it is satisfactory to use one-half the recommended value.

**Webs.**—The limiting $d/w$ values recommended in Ref. 6.26 are strictly applicable only for A36 steel. Until information from additional research becomes available, and in view of the satisfactory performance of the webs in beam and frame tests, it has been suggested (6.29) that those ratios

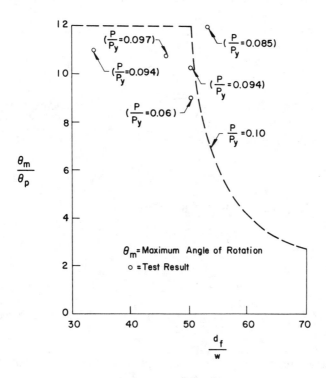

FIG. 6.17.—RESULTS OF TESTS ON WIDE-FLANGE SHAPES IN WHICH BOTH AXIAL FORCE AND BENDING WERE PRESENT

should be multiplied by the ratio $\sqrt{36/\sigma_y}$ for steels with yield stresses other than 36 ksi. The limiting ratios are

$$\frac{d}{w} = 43 \sqrt{\frac{36}{\sigma_y}} \text{ for } \frac{P}{P_y} > 0.27 \ldots \ldots \ldots (6.31)$$

and

$$\frac{d}{w} = \left(70 - 100\frac{P}{P_y}\right)\sqrt{\frac{36}{\sigma_y}} \text{ for } \frac{P}{P_y} \leq 0.27 \ldots (6.32)$$

**LOCAL BUCKLING OF STRUCTURAL SHAPES**

For I-section, wide-flange beams or welded H-shapes:

1. Flanges—compression due to bending or axial force, or both:

for A36 steel, $\quad\quad\quad\quad\quad \dfrac{b}{t} = 17$

for A441(50) steel, $\quad\quad\quad \dfrac{b}{t} = 14$ $\quad$ . . . . . . . . . . . . (6.30)

and for A572(65) steel, $\quad \dfrac{b}{t} = 12$

2. Web—under compression:

$$\frac{d}{w} \leq 43 \sqrt{\frac{36}{\sigma_y}} \quad \text{. . . . . . . . . . . (6.31)}$$

3. Web—bending and compression:

$$\frac{d}{w} = 43 \sqrt{\frac{36}{\sigma_y}} \quad\quad\quad \text{for } \frac{P}{P_y} > 0.27 \text{. . . . . (6.31)}$$

$$\frac{d}{w} = \left(70\text{–}100\frac{P}{P_y}\right) \sqrt{\frac{36}{\sigma_y}} \quad \text{for } \frac{P}{P_y} \leq 0.27 \text{. . . . . (6.32)}$$

in which $b$ = width of flange, $t$ = thickness of flange, $d$ = section depth, and $w$ = web thickness.

For other outstanding flanges and plate stiffeners intended to be stable in the plastic region, it is satisfactory to use one-half the recommended value given by Eq. 6.30.

## 6.3 LATERAL BRACING SPACING FOR BEAMS

*Statement of the Problem.*

In order to realize the necessary inelastic rotations at plastic-hinge locations a member must have sufficient lateral support to assure that the plastic moment at these hinge locations is not reduced by lateral-torsional buckling before a mechanism has formed. Local buckling is controlled by limiting the width-thickness ratios of the flanges and the web, and lateral-torsional buckling is controlled by limiting the unbraced length of the member.

The schematic relationship between the unbraced length and the moment capacity is illustrated in the upper part of Fig. 6.18. When the unbraced length is very large, the member will fail by elastic lateral-torsional buckling. When the length is relatively short, the full plastic moment will be attained or exceeded. Between these two extremes there is a transition range in which part of the member has yielded, but buckling occurs before $M_p$ is reached.

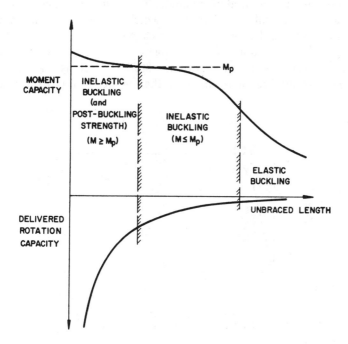

FIG. 6.18.—SCHEMATIC VARIATION OF MOMENT AND ROTATION CAPACITY WITH UNBRACED SLENDERNESS RATIO

The lower part of Fig. 6.18 shows diagrammatically the variation of rotation capacity with the unbraced length. In the region of elastic buckling, the delivered rotation capacity is small. When the unbraced length is small, the delivered rotation capacity is much larger. In the inelastic buckling region, the moment-carrying capacity will be less than $M_p$, and the rotation capacity begins to increase. In certain cases the load could reach $M_p$, but the rotation capacity may be insufficient. For satisfactory performance, the delivered rotation capacity should be equal to or greater than the required hinge angle (see Chapter 9 for methods of calculating the required hinge angles in a structure).

The rotation capacity of a beam depends largely upon its unbraced length on either side of a plastic hinge. Fig. 6.19 shows, qualitatively, for different $L/r_y$ ratios, the moment-rotation relationship of a beam under uniform moment. As $L/r_y$ decreases, the rotation capacity increases. In order to maintain the plastic moment and provide adequate rotation capacity for wide-flange beams, the $L/r_y$ ratio must be controlled. The ideal condition would be a limiting $L/r_y$ that would permit the beam to deliver precisely the required hinge angle. The problem in plastic design is to find this limiting unbraced length at which $M_p$ can be maintained for the required rotation. Unfortunately, the calculation of the required hinge angle can be involved, and therefore most design provisions are based on an approximation given in terms of the strain-hardening strain, $\epsilon_{st}$ (5.8, 6.28, 6.31). An additional problem is that of determining the required

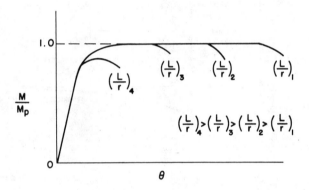

FIG. 6.19.—SCHEMATIC MOMENT-ROTATION RELATIONSHIP OF BEAMS WITH DIFFERENT $L/r_y$ RATIO UNDER UNIFORM MOMENT

strength and stiffness of the lateral bracing system and of the connecting details.

**Previous Research.**

The study of elastic lateral-torsional buckling is part of the discipline of Elastic Stability, and this topic is reviewed in (for example) Refs. 2.12, 5.2, 6.18, 6.32, 6.33, 6.34, and 6.35. The lateral-torsional buckling behavior in the transition region has also received considerable attention, and this work is described in Refs. 6.36 through 6.43. Elastic buckling and inelastic buckling in the transition region are, however, of only peripheral interest in plastic design.

The work on the problem of lateral-torsional buckling in the vicinity of plastic hinges falls into the following categories:

1. Experimental studies (Refs. 4.8, 5.7, 6.17, and 6.44 through 6.49).

2. Studies of the behavior of beams under uniform moment (Refs. 6.31 and 6.50).
3. Studies of the behavior of beams under moment gradient (Refs. 5.8 and 6.51).
4. Studies of the required strength and stiffness of the lateral bracing (Ref. 6.52).

**Theoretical Analysis.**

**Beams Under Uniform Moment.**—The beam model of Figs. 6.20(a), (b), and (c) was used to develop design equations for the critical spacing of the

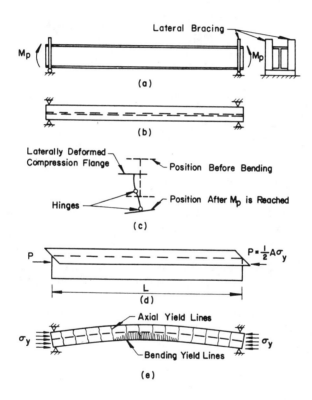

FIG. 6.20.—BUCKLING OF A BEAM UNDER UNIFORM MOMENT

lateral bracing for beams under uniform moment $M_p$ (6.31). That analysis is based on the experimentally observed behavior of a segment of a beam under uniform moment [Fig. 6.7 (curve B), Fig. 6.8(b), and Fig. 6.21]. The available test results indicate that the compression flange starts to deflect laterally as soon as $M_p$ is reached (6.17). This lateral deflection increases, while at the same time $M_p$ is maintained and rotation in the plane of bending continues until local buckling occurs in the most compressed portion of the compression flange [Figs. 6.8(b) and 6.21].

Local buckling does not commence until the average strain is equal to $\epsilon_{st}$ (Fig. 6.13) at the center of the segment if $b/t$ of the compression flange is equal to or less than the critical ratio given by Eq. 6.22. The tension flange moves only a small amount in the lateral direction (Fig. 6.21). As can be seen there and in Fig. 6.20(c), the relatively large lateral deformations of the compression flange with respect to the tension flange result in gross distortion of the web.

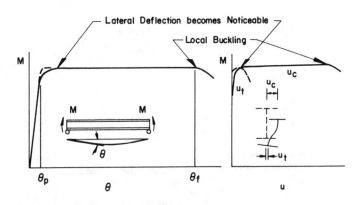

FIG. 6.21.—ROTATIONS AND LATERAL DEFLECTIONS OF A BEAM UNDER UNIFORM MOMENT

In the analysis it is assumed that the compression flange and one-half of the web act as a column under an axial load $P = (1/2)A\sigma_y$ [Fig. 6.20(d)]. The compressed portion of the beam is, therefore, assumed to act independently from the portion which is in tension, that is, two hinges are assumed in the web [Fig. 6.20(c)]. The resulting compression tee is assumed pin-ended. The buckling load of this column is [Fig. 6.20(e)]

$$P_{cr} = \frac{A\sigma_y}{2} = \frac{\pi^2 \tau EI}{L^2} \quad \ldots \ldots \ldots \ldots (6.33)$$

in which $\tau$ represents a reduction factor by which the elastic stiffness is multiplied to account for yielding. Eq. 6.33 can be solved for the critical slenderness ratio, $L/r_y$, if it is noted that $I = I_y/2$ and $r_y^2 = I_y/A$. Thus

$$\frac{L_{cr}}{r_y} = \pi \sqrt{\tau} \sqrt{\frac{E}{\sigma_y}} \quad \ldots \ldots \ldots \ldots (6.34)$$

The derivation of the stiffness reduction coefficient is based on a model of the compression flange which is yielded as shown in Fig. 6.20(e) (6.31,

6.50). The analysis is based on a discontinuous yield concept in which $\epsilon = \epsilon_{st}$ in the yield lines, and elsewhere $\epsilon = \epsilon_y$. The "axial yield lines" are those introduced by the force $P$ [Fig. 6.20(e)]. They reach across the whole width of the flange. The "bending yield lines" in the more severely compressed half of the flange are the result of lateral deformation. The analysis takes into account the reduction in stiffness due to both of these effects. According to Art. 6.2, local buckling will be imminent when the average strain at the center of the columns is equal to $\epsilon_{st}$ (Fig. 6.14). It is assumed that unloading takes place as soon as local buckling occurs.

From Ref. 6.31 the value of $\tau$ is obtained as

$$\tau = \cfrac{1}{1 + 0.7\,R\left(\cfrac{E}{E_{st}}\right)\left(\cfrac{1}{\cfrac{\epsilon_{st}}{\epsilon_y} - 1}\right)} \qquad \ldots \ldots \ldots (6.35)$$

In Eq. 6.35, $R$ is the rotation capacity defined as

$$R = \frac{\theta_f}{\theta_p} - 1 \ldots \ldots \ldots \ldots \ldots (6.36)$$

in which $\theta_f =$ the end slope of the uniformly bent segment at the start of local buckling and $\theta_p =$ the idealized slope corresponding to elastic theory applied to the case where $M = M_p$ (Fig. 6.21). The derivation of Eq. 6.35 is quite lengthy (6.31, 6.50), but in concept $\tau$ is simply a measure of the resistance of a yielded member to an increase of the lateral bending moment.

The critical unbraced length of a uniformly bent simply-supported beam is obtained by substituting Eq. 6.35 into Eq. 6.34. Thus

$$\frac{L}{r_y} = \frac{\pi}{\sqrt{\epsilon_y}} \sqrt{\cfrac{1}{1 + 0.7\,R\left(\cfrac{E}{E_{st}}\right)\left(\cfrac{1}{\cfrac{\epsilon_{st}}{\epsilon_y} - 1}\right)}} \qquad \ldots \ldots (6.37)$$

Eq. 6.37 is valid for a simply-supported beam and for the maximum allowable $b/t$ ratio of the flanges. A beam segment under uniform moment is flanked either by elastic segments or, when the region of uniform moment is larger than the critical unbraced length, by inelastic segments. The restraint offered by these adjacent segments has been evaluated both experimentally (6.17, 6.45) and theoretically (6.31). The effect of the restraint can be included by the use of an "effective length factor," $K$, and thus Eq. 6.37 can be written in more general form

$$\frac{KL}{r_y} = \frac{\pi}{\sqrt{\epsilon_y}} \frac{1}{\sqrt{1 + 0.7\ R\ \left(\dfrac{E}{E_{st}}\right)\ \left(\dfrac{1}{\dfrac{\epsilon_{st}}{\epsilon_y} - 1}\right)}} \quad \dots \dots (6.38)$$

in which $K = 0.54$ if the adjacent segments are elastic and $K = 0.8$ if the adjacent segments are fully yielded.

Eq. 6.38 provides a relationship between the effective critical slenderness ratio, material constants, and the rotation capacity of beam segments under uniform moment at the instant when failure due to local buckling in the compressed half of a laterally distorted compression flange is imminent.

**Beams Under Moment Gradient.**—Several approaches based on different models have been developed for the lateral-torsional buckling of a beam under moment gradient (5.8, 6.43, 6.51). Two of these approaches will be discussed in detail.

**Approach A.**—The first approach assumes a beam model which is partly elastic and partly strain hardened (Fig. 6.22) (6.43). The differential equations of lateral-torsional buckling are solved, with the elastic moduli $E$ and $G$ in the elastic portion, and with $E_{st}$ and $G_{st}$ in the yielded portions, by the finite difference procedure. According to this model the critical unbraced slenderness ratio is

$$\frac{L_{cr}}{r_y} = (\nu_\rho \nu_\alpha \nu_s \nu_\gamma)\ \sqrt{\frac{\pi^2 E_{st}}{M_o}\ \sqrt{I_y I_w}} \quad \dots \dots \dots (6.39)$$

in which $M_o$ = the maximum moment at the hinge and $I_w$ = the warping moment of inertia. The entire term under the square root sign is the critical length of a fully strain hardened, simply-supported beam under uniform moment. Correction factors $\nu$ in Eq. 6.39 are defined as follows:

$\nu_\rho$ = correction factor for moment gradient;

$\nu_\alpha$ = correction factor for partial yielding;

$\nu_s$ = correction factor for St. Venant torsion; and

$\nu_\gamma$ = correction factor for end restraint.

The square root term of Eq. 6.39 can be simplified by noting that for wide-flange shapes the warping moment of inertia, $I_w$, is equal to $(I_y/4)(d - t)^2$, by using the relationships $Z/S = f;\ M_p = Z\sigma_y;\ I_y = Ar_y^2;\ I_x = Ar_x^2;\ S = 2\ I_x/d;$ and by assuming the approximate values $f = 1.14;$ $d/r_x \approx 2.4;$ and $1 - (t/d) \approx 0.95$. Thus Eq. 6.39 can also be written

$$\frac{L_{cr}}{r_y} = \frac{100}{\sqrt{\dfrac{E}{E_{st}}}\ \sqrt{\dfrac{M_o}{M_p}}}\ \sqrt{\frac{36}{\sigma_y}}\ (\nu_\rho \nu_\alpha \nu_s \nu_\gamma) \quad \dots \dots (6.40)$$

In applying Eq. 6.40, the maximum moment, $M_o$, at the plastic hinge is likely to be greater than $M_p$ because of strain hardening (see discussion in Art. 2.3). The correction factors used in Eq. 6.40 can be obtained from charts in Refs. 6.43 and 6.44, where there is more detailed discussion on its application.

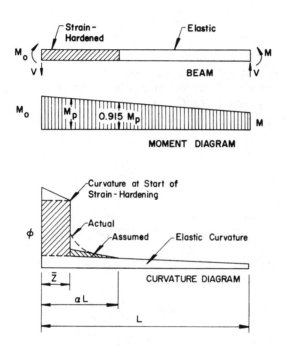

FIG. 6.22.—MOMENT-CURVATURE DIAGRAM FOR A PARTLY YIELDED BEAM UNDER MOMENT GRADIENT

Very approximate values of the correction factors are given in Ref. 6.44. These are

$$\nu_p = 1.34 + 0.34 \frac{M}{M_o} \quad \ldots \ldots \ldots \ldots \ldots (6.41)$$

$$\nu_\alpha = 0.875 + \frac{0.125}{\alpha^{1.4}} \quad \ldots \ldots \ldots \ldots \ldots (6.42)$$

$$\nu_s = 1.08 + 0.04 \frac{M}{M_o} \quad \ldots \ldots \ldots \ldots (6.43)$$

and

$$\nu_\gamma = 1.18 \quad \ldots \ldots \ldots \ldots \ldots (6.44)$$

in which $M$ and $M_o$ are the moments as defined in Fig. 6.22 (positive in the clockwise direction), and $\alpha L$ = the yielded length. The value of $\alpha$ is also dependent on the moment ratio, that is

$$\alpha = \frac{1 - \dfrac{M_p}{M_o}}{1 + \dfrac{M}{M_o}} \ldots \ldots \ldots \ldots \ldots \ldots (6.45)$$

(see Fig. 6.22). The application of Eqs. 6.40 and 6.45 is made difficult by the fact that, in a usual plastic analysis, the exact moment distribution, including the effect of strain hardening, is not known. Studies on fixed-end and on three-span beams have shown, however, that $M_o/M_p$ seldom exceeds the value of 1.2 (2.9). Using this value, a rough approximation of $\alpha$ is given by

$$\alpha = \frac{0.167}{1 + \dfrac{M}{M_o}} \ldots \ldots \ldots \ldots \ldots \ldots (6.46)$$

It should be realized, however, that the dominant correction factor is $\nu_\alpha$, and errors in estimating $\alpha$ can have significant effects. Nevertheless, with the approximation introduced in the above for the four correction factors, and assuming that $E = 29.6 \times 10^3$ ksi and $E_{st} = 800$ ksi, Eq. 6.40 can be replaced by the straight-line formula

$$\frac{L_{cr}}{r_y} = \left(60 + 40\, \frac{M}{M_p}\right) \sqrt{\frac{36}{\sigma_y}} \ldots \ldots \ldots \ldots (6.47)$$

In Eq. 6.47, the critical slenderness ratio is expressed in terms of $M/M_p$ instead of $M/M_o$ so as to make it applicable to design.

Because some conservative assumptions and approximations have been made in reducing Eq. 6.40 to the simplified form of Eq. 6.47, it was recommended in Ref. 6.44 that Eq. 6.47 be used only for $M/M_p > -0.625$. For the case of $M/M_p < -0.625$, it was recommended that the limiting $L/r_y$ be

$$\frac{L_{cr}}{r_y} = 35 \sqrt{\frac{36}{\sigma_y}} \ldots \ldots \ldots \ldots \ldots (6.48)$$

The discussion in Refs. 6.43 and 6.44 gives a much more thorough description of this approach, as did Art. 6.3 in the first edition of this Manual. The discussion here simply outlines the procedure to show how the design formula was developed.

**Approach B.**—The second approach assumes as a model an axially loaded column with an area of one flange and half the web, as shown in Figs. 6.23 and 6.24 (5.8). For simplicity it is assumed that the yield strength of the column will not be affected by the presence of shear stress.

Therefore the axial stress $= \sigma_y$, and the total force in the column $= A\sigma_y/2$. No rotational restraint is assumed at the end where a plastic hinge has developed, and at the other end the restraint from an adjacent span is represented by an elastic spring. This restraint is expressed as $kEI_y/L$, in which $EI_y/L$ pertains to the beam span under consideration. The buckling equation for the column in Fig. 6.24 may be written

$$\frac{\tan \dfrac{\lambda\pi\alpha}{\sqrt{\omega}}}{\tan [\lambda\pi (1 - \alpha)]} + \frac{1}{\sqrt{\omega}} \left[ \frac{\lambda\pi + k \left\{ \dfrac{1}{\lambda\pi} - \cot [\lambda\pi (1 - \alpha)] \right\}}{\lambda\pi + k \left\{ \dfrac{1}{\lambda\pi} + \tan [\lambda\pi (1 - \alpha)] \right\}} \right] = 0. \ . \ . \ (6.49)$$

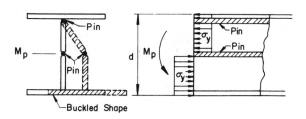

FIG. 6.23.—LATERAL BUCKLING MODEL OF THE CROSS SECTION

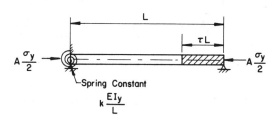

FIG. 6.24.—LATERAL BUCKLING MODEL OF THE BEAM

in which $\omega =$ the ratio of the lateral bending stiffness in the yielded region to its elastic value, $EI$, and is equal to

$$\omega = \frac{2}{\dfrac{E}{E_{st}} + \sqrt{\dfrac{E}{E_{st}}}} \ . \ . \ . \ . \ . \ . \ . \ . \ . \ . \ . \ . \ (6.50)$$

The yielded length ratio, $\alpha$, may be found directly from the bending moment diagram or from Eq. 6.45. The quantity $\lambda$ is the beam slenderness factor defined by

$$\lambda = \frac{L}{r_y}\left(\frac{\sqrt{\epsilon_y}}{\pi}\right) \quad \dots \dots \dots \dots \quad (6.51)$$

The graphical solution of Eq. 6.49 is given in Fig. 6.25 for four values of the end-restraint term $k$ ($k = 0, 3, 6, \infty$). The value of $E_{st} = 800$ ksi is used in evaluating $\omega$. For a given value of $k$, therefore, Fig. 6.25 gives the proportion $\alpha$ of a beam of slenderness factor $\lambda$ which will need to be yielded to cause lateral buckling. The predictions of Fig. 6.25 with respect to lateral buckling will be conservative.

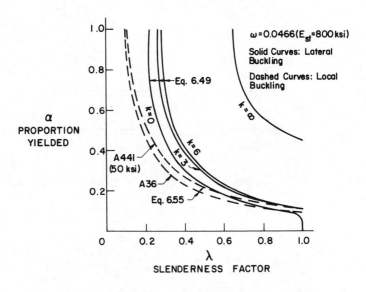

FIG. 6.25.—BUCKLING CURVES FOR A PARTLY YIELDED BEAM

The problem of lateral-torsional buckling is complicated by the fact that local buckling also will occur (5.8). In Art. 6.2 it was stated that local buckling will occur as soon as a sufficient length of the beam flange has yielded to enable a local buckle to form. In a beam under moment gradient there is a stiffener at the point of the plastic hinge, and at the other end of the yielded flange the elastic portion acts essentially as a fixed end [Fig. 6.11(b)]. Therefore a local buckle will develop as soon as $\alpha L$ is long enough for a full wave, or using Eq. 6.21

$$\alpha L = 1.42\left(\frac{t}{w}\right)\left(\frac{w\,d_w}{bt}\right)^{1/4}b \quad \dots \dots \dots \quad (6.52)$$

Eq. 6.52 and Eq. 6.51 can be combined to yield, for the product of $\alpha$ and $\lambda$

$$\alpha\lambda = 1.42 \ \frac{\sqrt{\epsilon_y}}{\pi} \ \frac{b}{r_y} \ \frac{t}{w} \ \left(\frac{wd_w}{bt}\right)^{1/4} \quad \ldots \ldots \ (6.53)$$

With average ratios of $b/r_y$, $t/w$, and $A_w/A_f$ for all available compact sections, the section property term in Eq. 6.53 reduces to approximately

$$\frac{1.42}{\pi} \ \frac{b}{r_y} \ \frac{t}{w} \ \left(\frac{wd_w}{bt}\right)^{1/4} \approx 2.65 \quad \ldots \ldots \ldots \ (6.54)$$

and so a typical evaluation of Eq. 6.54 is

$$\alpha\lambda = 2.65 \ \sqrt{\epsilon_y} \quad \ldots \ldots \ldots \ldots \ldots \ (6.55)$$

which is plotted in Fig. 6.25 for A36 steel ($\epsilon_y = 0.00122$) and A441 steel ($\epsilon_y = 0.00169$).

The curves in Fig. 6.25 illustrate that, for practical cases of inelastic beams under moment gradient, failure will be initiated by local buckling rather than by lateral buckling. It can be seen that, for all cases, a smaller value of $\alpha$ is required to cause local buckling than to cause lateral buckling. This conclusion is reinforced by the fact that a more accurate and less conservative lateral buckling derivation would give even larger $\alpha$ values than those plotted in Fig. 6.25. In many experiments unloading did not follow immediately after local buckling, and some postbuckling rotation capacity can be assumed to exist.

The theoretical prediction of local buckling can also be compared with that of lateral buckling based on the model of Fig. 6.22. Eq. 6.52 can be rearranged as

$$\frac{L}{r_y} = \frac{1.42}{\alpha} \ K_B \quad \ldots \ldots \ldots \ldots \ldots \ (6.56)$$

in which

$$K_B = \frac{b}{r_y} \ \frac{t}{w} \ \left(\frac{wd_w}{bt}\right)^{1/4} \quad \ldots \ldots \ldots \ldots \ (6.57)$$

Therefore, when the unbraced length determined from Eq. 6.40 exceeds $L/r_y$ from Eq. 6.56, local buckling will occur first. A rough estimate of the local buckling length can be obtained by noting that for rolled beam-type wide-flange beam shapes, $K_B$ varies from about 5.1 to 7.6. Using $\alpha$ from Eq. 6.45, and $M_o/M_p = 1.2$, the local buckling length will vary as

$$43 \left(1 + \frac{M}{M_p}\right) < \frac{L}{r_y} < 65 \left(1 + \frac{M}{M_p}\right) \quad \ldots \ldots \ldots \ (6.58)$$

Eq. 6.58 is, however, applicable only to A36 steel. It has been suggested in Ref. 6.29 that the local buckling length for high-strength steels can be obtained by multiplying Eq. 6.58 by a factor of $\sqrt{\sigma_y/36}$, thus

$$43 \left( 1 + \frac{M}{M_p} \right) < \frac{L}{r_y} \sqrt{\frac{\sigma_y}{36}} < 65 \left( 1 + \frac{M}{M_p} \right) \ldots \ldots (6.59)$$

The curves of $\frac{L}{r_y} \sqrt{\frac{\sigma_y}{36}} = 43 \left( 1 + \frac{M}{M_p} \right)$ and $\frac{L}{r_y} \sqrt{\frac{\sigma_y}{36}} = 65 \left( 1 + \frac{M}{M_p} \right)$ are compared in Fig. 6.26 with the lateral-torsional buckling solution of Eq. 6.40 for $M_o/M_p = 1.2$. The two limiting curves for local buckling (Eq. 6.59) overlap the lateral-torsional buckling solution for $E_{st} = 800$ ksi, thus indicating that in some cases local buckling and in other cases lateral-torsional buckling may govern, depending on the cross-section properties. The two events, therefore, seem closely related.

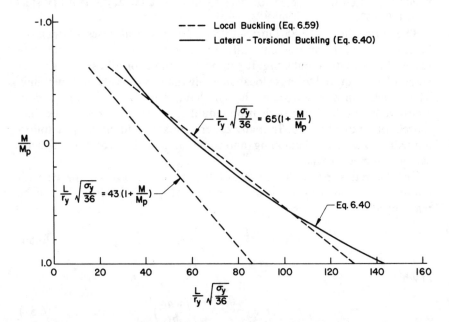

FIG. 6.26.—CRITICAL LENGTHS FOR LOCAL AND LATERAL-TORSIONAL BUCKLING

It should be emphasized that the curves in Fig. 6.26 are extreme simplifications presented to achieve a simple solution. The main assumption is that the moment at the plastic hinge $= 1.2 M_p$. This moment may be more but often will be less than this value. Realizing this, it was assumed in Ref. 5.8 that local buckling will always occur first and, therefore, the spacing of lateral bracing does not enter into consideration. This is certainly true for many cases, because the local buckling solutions form a band overlapping the lateral-torsional buckling solution (Fig. 6.26). Because of the greater likelihood of local buckling, it was suggested in Ref. 5.8 that the lateral bracing spacing should be determined by considering the beam to be under uniform moment. This moment $= M_p$, and is maintained for a rotation capacity of $R = 1$ (see Eq. 6.38). Accordingly, it was recommended that the bracing spacing for any moment ratio $-0.5 \le M/M_p \le 1.0$ should be

$$\frac{L}{r_y} = 70 \text{ for } \sigma_y = 36 \text{ ksi}$$

$$\frac{L}{r_y} = 55 \text{ for } \sigma_y = 50 \text{ ksi} \quad \Big\} \quad \dots\dots\dots (6.60)$$

and
$$\frac{L}{r_y} = 45 \text{ for } \sigma_y = 65 \text{ ksi}$$

For moment ratios less than $-0.5$ it was recommended that the bracing spacing for the case of uniform moment (Eq. 6.38) be used.

**Experimental Verification.**

**Beams Under Uniform Moment.**—The relationship in Eq. 6.38 connects the geometrical and material properties of a beam under uniform moment

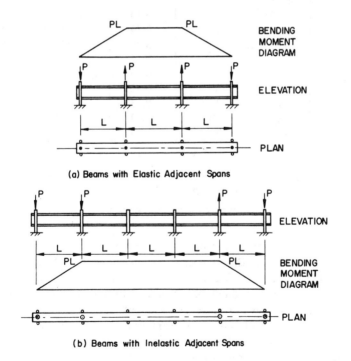

(a) Beams with Elastic Adjacent Spans

(b) Beams with Inelastic Adjacent Spans

FIG. 6.27.—TESTING ARRANGEMENT FOR BEAMS UNDER UNIFORM MOMENT

with the rotation capacity, $R$. Several test series were carried out to study beams under uniform moment with elastic adjacent beams (4.8, 6.17) [see Fig. 6.27(a)] and with inelastic adjacent beams (6.45) [see Fig. 6.27(b)]. The beams tested in Refs. 6.17 and 6.45 were A36 steel, and those in Ref. 4.8 were A441 steel. The experimental data for these tests are given in Table 6.1, and the comparisons between the experimental rotation capac-

TABLE 6.1—EXPERIMENTAL ROTATION CAPACITIES:
BEAMS UNDER UNIFORM MOMENT

| Test number (1) | Reference (2) | $\dfrac{L}{r_y}$ (3) | $K$ (4) | $\dfrac{KL}{r_y}\left(\dfrac{\sqrt{\epsilon_y}}{\pi}\right)$ (5) | Experimental rotation capacity (6) |
|---|---|---|---|---|---|
| LB 11[a] | 6.17 | 35 | 0.52 | 0.20 | 12.8 |
| LB 15 | 6.17 | 40 | 0.52 | 0.23 | 11 |
| LB 10 | 6.17 | 45 | 0.53 | 0.26 | 7 |
| LB 16 | 6.17 | 50 | 0.54 | 0.30 | 5 |
| G12[b] | 6.45 | 30 | 0.80 | 0.30 | 4.6 |
| G10 | 6.45 | 35 | 0.80 | 0.34 | 3.8 |
| G9 | 6.45 | 40 | 0.79 | 0.39 | 2.6 |
| G11 | 6.45 | 45 | 0.78 | 0.44 | 1.5 |
| HT41[c] | 4.8 | 25 | 0.52 | 0.18 | 10.4 |
| HT31 | 4.8 | 30 | 0.52 | 0.22 | 6.9 |
| HT29 | 4.8 | 35 | 0.52 | 0.25 | 4.4 |
| HT37 | 4.8 | 37.5 | 0.53 | 0.27 | 3.4 |
| HT30 | 4.8 | 40 | 0.54 | 0.30 | 2.9 |
| HT36 | 4.8 | 45 | 0.54 | 0.34 | 1.5 |

[a]Tests with the prefix LB were for 10 **WF** 25, with $\sigma_y = 35$ ksi, $\epsilon_{st} = 11.5\ \epsilon_y$, and $E_{st} = 900$ ksi.
[b]Tests with the prefix G were for 10B15, with $\sigma_y = 43$ ksi, $\epsilon_{st} = 11.5\ \epsilon_y$, and $E_{st} = 900$ ksi.
[c]Tests with the prefix HT were for 10 **WF** 25, with $\sigma_y = 54$ ksi, $\epsilon_{st} = 10.5\ \epsilon_y$, and $E_{st} = 660$ ksi.

ities and the corresponding theoretical curves are shown in Figs. 6.28 and 6.29. The comparison of theory with experiment is quite satisfactory.

**Beams Under Moment Gradient.**—A fairly large number of tests on beams under moment gradient has been performed on simply-supported wide-flange beams. Some of these tests are described in Refs. 4.8, 5.5, 5.7, 5.9, 6.44, 6.46, and 6.49. The significant parameters and test results are summarized in Table 6.2. The principal purpose of these tests was to study the moment-rotation characteristics of wide-flange beams and to evaluate their inelastic rotation capacities, rather than to check the theories for bracing spacing previously developed. No definite conclusion can be

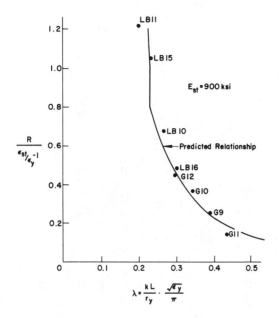

FIG. 6.28.—RESULTS OF LB AND G TESTS (6.17, 6.45)

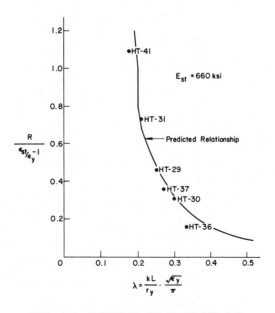

FIG. 6.29.—RESULTS OF HT TESTS (4.8)

TABLE 6.2—RESULTS OF TESTS ON BEAMS
UNDER MOMENT GRADIENT

| Reference (1) | Test number (2) | $\dfrac{L}{r_y}$ (3) | $\dfrac{b}{t}$ (4) | $\dfrac{d}{w}$ (5) | $\sigma_y$, in kips per square inch (6) | $\dfrac{M}{M_p}$ (7) | Experi-mental rotation capacity (8) |
|---|---|---|---|---|---|---|---|
| 6.44 | LB5 | 48 | 16.9 | 41.3 | 38 | −0.39 | 5 |
| 6.44 | LB6 | 38 | 16.9 | 41.3 | 38 | −0.71 | 6.4 |
| 6.46 | 5 | 25 | 13.2 | 34 | 41 | 0 | 13 |
| 6.46 | 6 | 35 | 13.4 | 34 | 41 | 0 | 10 |
| 6.46 | 7 | 17 | 14.0 | 21 | 42 | 0 | 27 |
| 6.46 | 8 | 23 | 14.0 | 21 | 42 | 0 | 16 |
| 6.46 | 9 | 32 | 14.0 | 21 | 42 | 0 | 14 |
| 6.46 | 10 | 20 | 10.7 | 40 | 38 | 0 | 21 |
| 6.46 | 11 | 27 | 10.8 | 41 | 38 | 0 | 19 |
| 6.46 | 12 | 38 | 10.7 | 41 | 38 | 0 | 11 |
| 6.46 | 13 | 19 | 14.5 | 42 | 39 | 0 | 12 |
| 6.46 | 14 | 26 | 14.6 | 42 | 39 | 0 | 8 |
| 6.46 | 15 | 36 | 14.4 | 43 | 39 | 0 | 9 |
| 6.46 | 16 | 23 | 17.3 | 55 | 44 | 0 | 8 |
| 6.46 | 17 | 31 | 17.6 | 56 | 44 | 0 | 1 |
| 6.46 | 18 | 43 | 18.0 | 58 | 44 | 0 | 2 |
| 6.46 | 19 | 17 | 18.6 | 28 | 41 | 0 | 8 |
| 6.46 | 20 | 23 | 18.7 | 28 | 41 | 0 | 7 |
| 6.46 | 21 | 32 | 18.6 | 28 | 41 | 0 | 7 |
| — | G1 | 47 | 14.9 | 43.5 | 42 | −0.5 | 5 |
| — | G2 | 56 | 14.9 | 43.5 | 42 | −0.5 | 4 |
| — | G3 | 56 | 14.9 | 43.5 | 42 | 0 | 3 |
| 5.5 | T5 | 60 | 13.2 | 45.1 | 36 | 0 | 4 |
| 5.9 | 1 | 32 | 9.2 | 23.8 | 36 | 0 | 8 |
| 4.8 | HT28 | 15 | 15.8 | 34.8 | 54 | 0 | 11 |
| 4.8 | HT43 | 10 | 15.8 | 34.8 | 54 | 0 | 8 |
| 4.8 | HT52 | 70 | 15.8 | 34.8 | 54 | 0 | 3 |
| 5.7 | A-1 | 35 | 18.8 | 32.7 | 41 | 0 | 5 |
| 5.7 | A-2 | 35 | 16.3 | 32.7 | 41 | 0 | 6.5 |
| 5.7 | B-1 | 35 | 19.4 | 45.0 | 54 | 0 | 1.5 |
| 5.7 | B-2 | 35 | 14.0 | 45.0 | 54 | 0 | 4.5 |
| 5.7 | B-3 | 35 | 16.3 | 45.0 | 54 | 0 | 4 |
| 5.7 | B-4 | 35 | 17.8 | 45.0 | 54 | 0 | 2 |
| 5.7 | B-5 | 35 | 18.3 | 45.0 | 54 | 0 | 2 |
| 5.7 | C-1 | 35 | 19.4 | 54.5 | 53 | 0 | 2 |
| 5.7 | C-2 | 35 | 14.0 | 54.5 | 53 | 0 | 6 |
| 5.7 | C-3 | 35 | 16.3 | 54.5 | 53 | 0 | 3 |
| 5.7 | C-4 | 35 | 17.8 | 54.5 | 53 | 0 | 2 |
| 5.7 | C-5 | 35 | 17.1 | 54.5 | 53 | 0 | 3 |
| 6.49 | D-1 | 70 | 14.0 | 43.6 | 42 | 0 | 2.0 |
| 6.49 | D-2 | 38 | 14.1 | 43.6 | 42 | −0.63 | 1.0 |
| 6.49 | D-3 | 104 | 13.9 | 43.6 | 44 | 0 | 0.5 |
| 6.49 | D-4 | 85 | 13.8 | 42.9 | 41 | −0.42 | 0.8 |
| 6.49 | D-5 | 89 | 13.8 | 42.9 | 41 | 0 | 1.2 |
| 6.49 | D-6 | 35 | 14.0 | 43.3 | 44 | 0 | 7.2 |
| 6.49 | E-1 | 70 | 18.0 | 42.0 | 44 | 0 | 2.3 |
| 6.49 | E-2 | 40 | 18.3 | 43.6 | 42 | −0.62 | 1.0 |
| 6.49 | E-3 | 105 | 18.3 | 43.6 | 41 | 0 | 0.7 |
| 6.49 | E-4 | 86 | 18.4 | 43.6 | 41 | −0.41 | 0.4 |
| 6.49 | E-5 | 90 | 18.4 | 43.6 | 42 | 0 | 0.7 |
| 6.49 | E-6 | 35 | 18.3 | 43.4 | 44 | 0 | 3.1 |

drawn as to which theory is correct. Nevertheless, the test results are given in Table 6.2 for possible use in future studies.

Perhaps the most direct tests to check the aforementioned theories of lateral buckling of beams are those described in Ref. 6.48. A total of 17 tests was performed on beams fabricated from A52 steel made in Belgium. This steel has $\sigma$-$\epsilon$ characteristics quite similar to A441 steel, and has a yield stress of about 55 ksi. The purpose of the tests was to establish a simple bracing rule for high-strength beams designed plastically. The beams were tested with $M/M_p$ ratios of $-1$, $-0.42$, 0, and $+1$. Two wide-flange shapes were used in this study. One shape had a $b/t$ ratio of 11, which is less than the limiting value recommended in Art. 6.2. The other shape had

TABLE 6.3—SUMMARY OF TEST RESULTS (6.48)

| Type of section (1) | | Type of loading (2) | $L$, in centimeters (3) | $\dfrac{L}{r_y}$ (4) | $\theta_e$, in radians $\times 10^{-2}$ (5) | $\theta_{max}$, in radians $\times 10^{-2}$ (6) | $\dfrac{\theta_{max}}{\theta_e}$ (7) | $M_{max}$, in ton-meters (8) | $\dfrac{M_{max}}{M_p \text{ (calculated)}}$ (9) | Failure mode[a] (10) |
|---|---|---|---|---|---|---|---|---|---|---|
| IPE 200 | 1 | $M/M_p = -1$ | 78.4 | 35.70 | 1.60 | 10.38 | 6.49 | 9.29 | 0.995 | A |
| | 2 | | 67.2 | 30.60 | 1.52 | 13.67 | 9.00 | 10.13 | 1.087 | A |
| | 3 | | 56.0 | 25.55 | 1.40 | 16.09 | 11.46 | 10.29 | 1.110 | A |
| | 4 | | 44.8 | 20.40 | 0.69 | 9.30 | 13.47 | 10.70 | 1.142 | B |
| | 5 | $M/M_p = 0$ | 78.4 | 35.70 | 4.07 | 44.20 | 10.87 | 11.35 | 1.215 | A |
| | 6 | | 67.2 | 30.60 | 3.65 | 40.30 | 11.10 | 12.88 | 1.380 | B |
| | 7 | | 56.0 | 25.55 | 4.20 | 51.80 | 12.10 | 12.62 | 1.352 | B |
| | 8 | | 44.8 | 20.40 | 4.50 | 53.30 | 11.85 | 12.10 | 1.295 | B |
| | 9 | $M/M_p = +1$ | 175.0 | 79.80 | 1.01 | 9.62 | 9.43 | 12.25 | 1.315 | A |
| | 10 | $M/M_p = -0.42$ | 76.0 | 34.50 | 1.33 | 12.75 | 9.60 | 10.80 | 1.160 | A |
| HEA 200 | 11 | $M/M_p = -1$ | 150.0 | 29.90 | 3.15 | 28.33 | 9.00 | 16.72 | 0.965 | A |
| | 12 | | 125.0 | 24.95 | 2.30 | 23.90 | 10.40 | 15.20 | 0.875 | A |
| | 13 | | 100.0 | 19.96 | 2.00 | 23.00 | 11.50 | 18.30 | 1.065 | B |
| | 14 | $M/M_p = 0$ | 250 | 49.90 | 2.40 | 23.00 | 9.75 | 22.50 | 1.325 | A |
| | 14 | | 200 | 39.90 | — | — | — | — | — | C |
| | 15 | | 150 | 29.90 | 1.90 | 20.30 | 10.80 | 19.50 | 1.125 | B |
| | 16 | | 100 | 19.95 | 1.70 | 19.30 | 11.35 | 23.00 | 1.325 | B |
| | 17 | $M/M_p = -0.42$ | 175 | 35.00 | 2.25 | 23.10 | 10.27 | 19.15 | 1.103 | A |

[a] A = lateral buckling; B = local buckling followed by lateral buckling; C = rupture.

a $b/t$ ratio of 19.8, which is considerably higher than the limiting $b/t$ ratio. Thus, it is possible to study the influence of local buckling on the choice of bracing spacing. A summary of the test results is given in Table 6.3.

The maximum elastic rotation, $\theta_e$, in Column 5 of Table 6.3, was found from the intersection on a measured moment-rotation curve of the extension from the elastic portion of the curve and the extension of the flat plateau in the inelastic region. The maximum plastic rotation, $\theta_{max}$, in Column 6, was the maximum rotation a beam could sustain before instability occurred due to lateral or local buckling.

Using $\theta_{max}/\theta_e = 10$ as the basis of adequate rotation capacity for the steel beams, the test results for every $M/M_p$ ratio were analyzed individually. A computed $L/r_y$ ratio, corresponding to $\theta_{max}/\theta_e = 10$, was obtained by interpolation or extrapolation from a $\theta_{max}/\theta_e$ versus $L/r_y$ plot for each $M/M_p$ ratio. The $L/r_y$ ratios so obtained were then plotted in Fig. 6.30 as abscissa and the corresponding $M/M_p$ ratios as ordinates. These adjusted

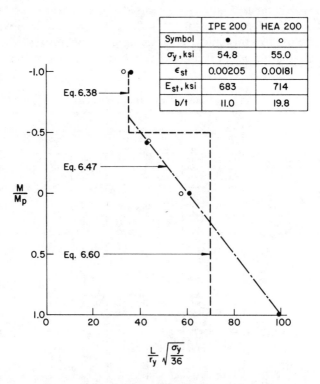

|  | | IPE 200 | HEA 200 |
|---|---|---|---|
| Symbol | | ● | ○ |
| $\sigma_y$, ksi | | 54.8 | 55.0 |
| $\epsilon_{st}$ | | 0.00205 | 0.00181 |
| $E_{st}$, ksi | | 683 | 714 |
| b/t | | 11.0 | 19.8 |

FIG. 6.30.—BUCKLING TEST RESULTS (6.48)

test data were compared with the bracing rules for beams under uniform moment and under moment gradient as given by Eqs. 6.38, 6.47, and 6.60. In the uniform moment case, the value for $K$ in Eq. 6.38 was taken as 0.52. The adjusted test points agree well with the theoretical prediction of Eq. 6.38 for the uniform-moment case. In the moment-gradient case, if a rotation capacity of 10 is assumed adequate, it is evident that the adjusted test data agree somewhat better with the linear variation rule of Eq. 6.47.

This series of tests is by no means conclusive, since no data are available for beams with large $b/t$ ratios in the region of $M/M_p > 0$. It is in this region that the local buckling criterion of the second approach becomes significant. Tests performed on beams under moment gradient with $(L/r_y)\sqrt{\sigma_y}/36$ between 120 and 200 confirm the noncritical nature of lateral buckling as postulated by the second theory using the model of Fig. 6.23 (6.5).

A significant point which emerges from a study of Fig. 6.30 is that in a design that satisfies Eq. 6.47 for the moment-gradient case, a rotation capacity of 10 could be expected. However, it has not been demonstrated that a smaller rotation capacity would significantly reduce the strength of redundant structures.

By comparing the IPE and HEA tests shown in Fig. 6.30, it is seen that local buckling did not significantly change the rotation capacity of the test beams when the same bracing was used. This points to a need for further study on the interaction between compression flange $b/t$ ratios and bracing spacing, and their influence on the strength of redundant structures.

**Design Approximation.**

The design of the lateral bracing and the determination of its spacing is usually a routine secondary check, performed after the primary design problems have been completed. Often the problem of bracing design does not even appear. An example is the case of continuous lateral support due to a concrete slab which is either acting with the steel beam or into which the top flange is embedded. In case lateral bracing is required, simple formulas depending on two or three variables are preferred. The following simplified formulas serve this purpose, and it has already been demonstrated that they are conservative.

**Beams Under Uniform Moment.**—The critical slenderness ratio for this case is given by Eq. 6.38. In Ref. 6.31 it was shown that the optimum rotation capacity is

$$R_o = 0.8 \left( \frac{\epsilon_{st}}{\epsilon_y} - 1 \right) \quad \dots \dots \dots \dots (6.61)$$

in which "optimum" relates to the maximum which can be delivered.

Substitution of Eq. 6.61 into Eq. 6.38 gives

$$\frac{KL}{r_y} = \frac{\pi}{\sqrt{\epsilon_y}} \left( \frac{1}{\sqrt{1 + \dfrac{0.56E}{E_{st}}}} \right) \dots \dots \dots \dots (6.62)$$

For the usual case of elastic adjacent spans with $K = 0.54$ and $E = 29{,}500$ ksi, and using specified values for $\sigma_y$ (36, 50, and 65 ksi) and $E_{st} = 800$ ksi, Eq. 6.62 gives

$$\left( \frac{L}{r_y} \right)_{cr} = \frac{214}{\sqrt{\sigma_y}} \quad \dots \dots \dots \dots \dots (6.63)$$

A limited number of tests has been conducted on 65 grade steel. They do not confirm Eq. 6.63, but indicate that a more conservative value is needed for the higher-strength material. The expression

$$\left(\frac{L}{r_y}\right)_{cr} = \frac{1,375}{\sigma_y} \quad \ldots \ldots \ldots \ldots \ldots (6.64)$$

provides such an approximation and yet approximates Eq. 6.63 in the lower yield point region. This formula appears in the 1969 AISC Specification. A comparison of Eqs. 6.63 and 6.64 is given in Fig. 6.31.

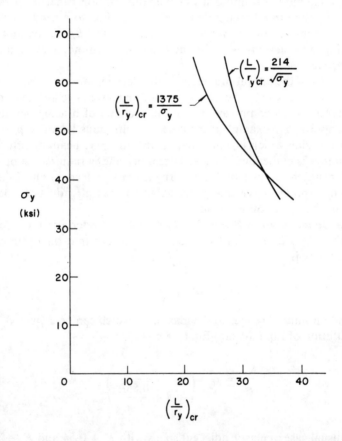

FIG. 6.31.—LATERAL BRACING PROVISIONS FOR BEAMS UNDER UNIFORM MOMENT

**Beams Under Moment Gradient.**—In view of the lack of complete experimental verification, there is no clear guide as to which approach (Eq.

6.47 or Eq. 6.60) is more appropriate for design. Until such time as the needed data become available, both approaches are summarized here. The first is more liberal in the region of $-0.5 < M/M_p < 0$. The second is more liberal in the region of $M/M_p > 0$. The ratio $(L/r_y)_{cr}$ for beams under moment gradient may, therefore, be calculated from either

$$\left(\frac{L}{r_y}\right)_{cr} = \left(60. + 40 \frac{M}{M_p}\right)\sqrt{\frac{36}{\sigma_y}} \quad \left(-0.625 < \frac{M}{M_p} \leq 1.0\right) \ldots (6.47)$$

or alternatively

$$\left(\frac{L}{r_y}\right)_{cr} = 70 \qquad (\sigma_y = 36 \text{ ksi})$$

$$\left(\frac{L}{r_y}\right)_{cr} = 55 \qquad (\sigma_y = 50 \text{ ksi}) \quad \Bigg\} \ldots \ldots (6.60)$$

$$\left(\frac{L}{r_y}\right)_{cr} = 45 \qquad (\sigma_y = 65 \text{ ksi})$$

For the second approach, a good approximation is given by

$$\left(\frac{L}{r_y}\right)_{cr} = \frac{1,375}{\sigma_y} + 25 \quad \left(-0.5 < \frac{M}{M_p} \leq 1.0\right) \ldots (6.65)$$

---

**LATERAL BRACING**

Lateral bracing shall be provided at each hinge location and at distances no greater than $L_{cr}$ to either side of the hinge.

*Uniform Moment (M/M$_p$ ≤ −0.5):*

$$\left(\frac{L}{r_y}\right)_{cr} = \frac{1,375}{\sigma_y} \ldots \ldots \ldots \ldots (6.60)$$

*Moment Gradient:*
Either

$$\left(\frac{L}{r_y}\right)_{cr} = \left(60 + 40 \frac{M}{M_p}\right)\sqrt{\frac{36}{\sigma_y}} \quad \left(-0.625 < \frac{M}{M_p} \leq 1.0\right) \ldots (6.47)$$

or alternatively

$$\left(\frac{L}{r_y}\right)_{cr} = \frac{1,375}{\sigma_y} + 25 \quad \left(-0.5 < \frac{M}{M_p} \leq 1.0\right) \ldots (6.65)$$

*Bracing Requirements.*

Lateral bracing is usually provided by floor beams or purlins which frame into the beam to be braced. These bracing members must have adequate axial strength and axial stiffness to resist the tendency to lateral deflection. These requirements are usually quite small (1.2, 5.11). Although it has been derived theoretically that lateral braces must possess some bending stiffness about their own major axis (6.52), there are insufficient experimental results to indicate the magnitude required.

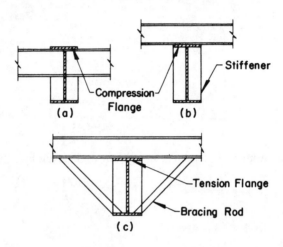

FIG. 6.32.—BRACING DETAILS

It is desirable that lateral braces be welded or bolted to the compression flange [Figs. 6.32(a), (b), and (c)] and, in addition, a vertical stiffener be provided at the braced point. Concrete slab into which the compression flange is embedded or to which the compression flange is mechanically connected, as in composite construction, or metal decks tacked to the top flange of the beam in the positive moment region, would provide sufficient restraint to lateral and torsional displacements.

## 6.4  VARIABLE REPEATED LOADING

*Statement of the Problems.*

In the previous discussions it has been assumed that the structures under consideration were subjected to all of the applied loads acting simultaneously. It has been further assumed that the applied loads increase in their magnitude until the plastic limit load is reached. During this process none of the applied loads are permitted to change their directions, and the ratio of load magnitudes to one another remains fixed. Such loading is termed proportional loading.

In reality the separate loads on a structure may not satisfy the condition of proportionality. Instead, the separate loads may change independently of each other. In general, loads can act on a structure in a random manner and vary in magnitude, sense, and direction. Since such loads are usually repetitive or cyclic in their nature, they are termed "variable repeated loads."

The two classes of problem encountered in variable repeated loading on a structure must be clearly differentiated. In one class, after one or at most a few cycles of load applications, residual stresses or moment develop such that the structural response for the subsequent loadings becomes completely elastic. The determination of the maximum loads causing this condition will assure that no fatigue failure is likely to occur under a great many cycles of lesser loading. Likewise, the possibility of progressively increasing deflections for reapplied cyclic loading is precluded. The determination of such loads is of importance in the design of bridges, crane girders, and buildings exposed to frequent and unusually severe wind or other types of lateral loadings. These two modes of failure will be discussed in this section under the heading "Alternating Plasticity and Deflection Stability."

In the second class of problem encountered in connection with variable repeated loading, a member behaves inelastically during every load application. In contrast with the first case, energy dissipation or, conversely, energy absorption capacity of members per cycle of load application of members in the inelastic range is basic for earthquake and blast-resistant design. Some of the available experimental data on this behavior of steel structures are given in the section on "Repeating Inelastic Strains."

***Alternating Plasticity and Deflection Stability.***

    ***(a) Definitions.***

    ***Fatigue and Alternating Plasticity.***—Fatigue is failure of the material by fracture as a result of repeated loading on the structure. In particular, failure will occur at a relatively low number of cycles when the repeated loading is such that yielding of the material occurs alternately in tension and compression at a given cross section. This phenomenon is known as "alternating plasticity." During each cycle of load application plastic flow will take place and eventually will lead to fracture.

Fatigue within the nominally elastic range is of little concern in usual building frames.

    ***Deflection Stability.***—Failure is characterized by an increase in deflection during each cycle of loading, the increments of deflection being in the same direction. This mode of failure is termed "incremental collapse." The problem is to determine the limits on the loads for which these increments cease after a few cycles of load application and the deflection "stabilizes." When a structure reaches this state of stabilized deflection it is said to have "shaken down" and the corresponding set of loads is referred to as the "stabilizing load" or the "shakedown load." The structure henceforth responds to the load in a purely elastic manner.

*(b) Previous Investigations.*

Ref. 6.54 was the first to recognize that under variable repeated loads, a structure may fail due to a lack of deflection stability. Further extensive studies in this field were reported in Refs. 6.55, 6.56, and 6.57. In recent years, the basic shakedown theorems were developed and checked by experiments (6.58–6.67). Studies have also been made on the behavior of beams subjected to moving loads (6.68, 6.69). A complete survey of the available literature can be found in Ref. 6.70.

*(c) Theoretical Analysis.*

***Alternating Plasticity.***—A condition of alternating plasticity is illustrated by the example of a cantilever beam with a concentrated load acting at the free end (Fig. 6.33). The load $P$ is assumed at first as being applied in

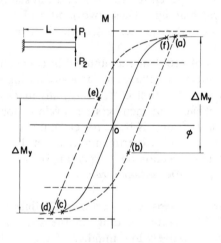

FIG. 6.33.—MOMENT-CURVATURE RELATIONSHIP AT THE BUILT-IN END OF A CANTILEVER BEAM UNDER ALTERNATING PLASTICITY

a downward direction and the resulting moment-curvature relationship at the built-in section is shown from (o) to (a) in Fig. 6.33. If instead, the load were applied in the opposite direction, the corresponding $M$-$\phi$ curve would be that shown in Fig. 6.33 from (o) to (c). If at point (a) the load $P$ is gradually released and finally applied in the opposite direction, the $M$-$\phi$ relationship is linear for a range of moment designated as $\Delta M_y$. The magnitude of $\Delta M_y$ is less than or at most equal to $2\,M_y$, the precise value being a function of the residual stress and the Bauschinger effect. At point (b), yielding starts in the opposite direction. Finally a point (d) corresponding to $-P_{max}$ is reached. To complete the cycle, as loads are released and then reversed, the resulting behavior would be as shown by the dashed line d-e-f-a.

Failure due to alternating plasticity will not occur when ranges of moment values exist for which a section behaves elastically regardless of its previous loading history. As a first approximation the Bauschinger effect may be ignored and this range of moment ($\Delta M_y$ in Fig. 6.33) may be taken as

$$\Delta M_y = 2 \, M_y = 2 \, \frac{M_p}{f} \ldots \ldots \ldots \ldots (6.66)$$

The necessary condition for eliminating the possibility of alternating plasticity is

$$(M_i)_{\max} - (M_i)_{\min} \leq \Delta M_y = 2\frac{M_p}{f} \ldots \ldots \ldots (6.67)$$

in which $M_i$ denotes the elastic moment values at any section $i$ being investigated. Procedures for calculating the limit for alternating plasticity in the case of indeterminate structures may be found in Ref. 1.6.

**Deflection Stability.**—As noted previously, under repeated application of a certain sequence of loads an increment of plastic deformation in the

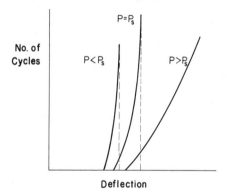

FIG. 6.34.—DIAGRAMMATIC REPRESENTATION OF DEFLECTION STABILITY (SHAKEDOWN)

same sense may occur during each cycle. The maximum load for which these increments cease after a few cycles is called the stabilizing (or shakedown) load. In Fig. 6.34 is plotted diagrammatically the number of loading cycles versus the deflection under the load at the end of each cycle. When $P$ is equal to or less than a certain critical value $P_s$, a set of residual moments will be set up in the structure after a few cycles during which the deflection approaches a limit value. All further repetitions of load are carried elastically. If $P$ is greater than $P_s$, the deflection does not stabilize but continues to grow for each cycle of load application. A description of this phenomenon may be found in Refs. 1.5 and 1.8.

It is possible to determine mathematically the maximum load $P_s$ for which the deflection of the structure will finally stabilize. The condition to be fulfilled is that at points of maximum moment the absolute value of the sum of the residual moment, $M_r$, and the elastic moment, $M$, produced by the loads does not exceed the full plastic moment value, $M_p$. In general terms

$$\left| (M_i)_r + (M_i)_{max} \right| = M_p \quad \ldots \ldots \ldots \ldots (6.68)$$

Eq. 6.68 may be applied to the problem shown in Fig. 6.35(a), a continuous beam of two equal spans, the supports of which can take upward and

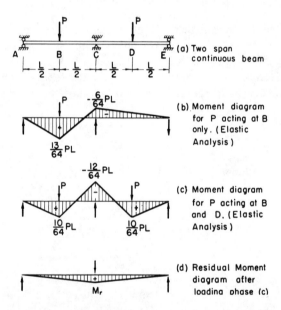

FIG. 6.35.—TWO-SPAN CONTINUOUS BEAM UNDER VARIABLE REPEATED LOADING (DEFLECTION STABILITY)

downward reactions. Suppose the load $P$ is first applied at B. An elastic analysis would produce the moment diagram shown in Fig. 6.35(b) with $M_B = (13/64) P L$. As a second phase of the loading, two equal loads applied at B and D would give the elastic moment diagram shown in Fig. 6.35(c). Due to any inelastic deformation that may occur under load, the only possible shape of the residual moment diagram is that shown in Fig. 6.35(d).

Applying Eq. 6.68, and defining the residual moment diagram positive as shown in Fig. 6.35(d), the conditions to be satisfied are

At section B: $\qquad \left| \dfrac{13}{64} P L + (M_r)_B \right| = M_p$ . . . . . . . . . (6.69)

At section C: $\qquad \left| -\dfrac{12}{64} P L + (M_r)_C \right| = M_p$ . . . . . . . . . (6.70)

However, the residual moments can have only a linear variation across the span with the maximum value at C [Fig. 6.35(d)], so that

$$(M_r)_B = \frac{1}{2}(M_r)_C \qquad \ldots \ldots \ldots \ldots (6.71)$$

Expressions for the stabilizing load $P_s$ are obtained from Eqs. 6.69, 6.70, and 6.71. Thus

$$\frac{13}{64} P_s L + \frac{1}{2}(M_r)_C = M_p$$

and

$$\frac{12}{64} P_s L - (M_r)_C = M_p$$

From these two conditions the stabilizing load, $P_s$, and the residual moment, $(M_r)_C$, are determined. Hence

$$P_s = \frac{96}{19}\frac{M_p}{L} = 5.06\frac{M_p}{L} \qquad \ldots \ldots \ldots \ldots (6.72)$$

and

$$(M_r)_C = -\frac{1}{19} M_p \qquad \ldots \ldots \ldots \ldots (6.73)$$

The results of this calculation are shown in Fig. 6.36. The elastic moment diagram due to $P_s$ acting at B is shown in Fig. 6.36(a). The moment diagram with loads at B and D is shown in Fig. 6.36(b). Fig. 6.36(c) is the residual moment diagram after stabilization at load $P_s$. Combining Fig. 6.36(c), in turn, with Figs. 6.36(a) and 6.36(b), one obtains the final moment diagram for $P_s$ acting at B only [Fig. 6.36(c)] and at B and D simultaneously [Fig. 6.36(e)]. It is evident that Eq. 6.68 is satisfied.

According to the simple plastic theory

$$P_p = \frac{6 M_p}{L} \qquad \ldots \ldots \ldots \ldots \ldots (6.74)$$

Thus, from Eqs. 6.72 and 6.74

$$\frac{P_s}{P_p} = 84.4\% \quad \ldots \ldots \ldots \ldots \ldots \quad (6.75)$$

Eq. 6.75 indicates that the stabilizing load is theoretically about 16% lower than the ultimate load $P_p$ in this example.

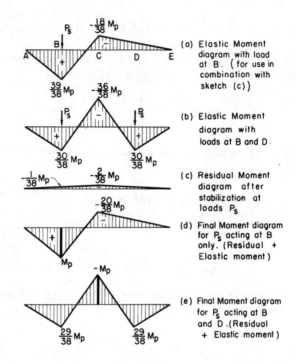

FIG. 6.36.—TWO-SPAN CONTINUOUS BEAM OF FIG. 6.35 UNDER STABILIZING LOAD $P_s$

As a check on alternating plasticity, the condition

$$(M_i)_{max} - (M_i)_{min} \leq 2\,\frac{M_p}{f} = 2\,M_y$$

must be satisfied. In the previous example at section $B$

$$(M_B)_{max} = \frac{13}{64}\left(\frac{96}{19}\,M_p\right) = \frac{39}{38}\,M_p$$

$$(M_B)_{min} = -\frac{3}{64}\left(\frac{96}{19}\,M_p\right) = -\frac{9}{38}\,M_p$$

$$(M_B)_{max} - (M_B)_{min} = \frac{48}{38}\,M_p < 2\,M_y$$

Actually, the increase in deflection for a load $P < P_s$ will cease as strain hardening sets in. A discussion of the effect of strain hardening can be found in either Ref. 6.62 or 6.65.

***(d)  Experimental Correlation.***

Experimental studies have been performed using continuous beams and rectangular frames. An investigation of two-span continuous beams was reported in Ref. 6.71. Later, tests of the same structure were made using loads applied at the center of each span (6.64) and using off-center loads to simulate the worst possible condition (6.65).

Deflection stability has been investigated (6.59) by testing small-scale rectangular portal frames with symmetrical vertical load and horizontal load. Test results indicated that the observed stabilizing loads were about 10% higher than those given by theory. Experiments on a series of frames subjected to variable repeated loading have been made (6.66) investigating both alternating plasticity and deflection stability phenomena. Test results show that the theoretical analysis (based on no strain hardening) gives conservative predictions, and that strain hardening may increase the stabilizing load (6.62, 6.65).

All results indicated that the experimental values were higher than those given by theory. Tables 6.4 (6.64), 6.5 (6.65), 6.6 (6.66), and 6.7 (6.59) contain a summary of each of the previous important observations. In these tables is indicated the loading sequence used in a given cyclic load test. The terms $\alpha$ and $\beta$ denote the proportion of a particular load applied during one phase of a cyclic loading sequence.

***(e)  Relationship to Design.***

Practically every recent investigator of the subject has concluded that the problem of variable repeated loading may be disregarded for building frames designed for the usual conditions of static loading. The probability of failure by a single overload appears to be much greater than the probability of failure by alternating plasticity or by loss of deflection stability. Analytical studies of a number of typical one-story bents show that neither the deflection instability nor the alternating plasticity phenomenon is likely to prove important in the prediction of failure of typical bents (6.72).

Of particular significance is the fact that the ratio of live load to dead load must be very large before the load-carrying capacity is reduced because of load repetitions. In nearly all of the tests described in this section, extreme examples were chosen in which all of the load was considered to be live load. It is unusual to find such extreme load variations in building structures. The live load is seldom more than two-thirds of the total load and usually it is of the order of one-third of the total.

It must be remembered that the load factor $F$ does not provide for possible overloads alone. It also accounts for such additional factors as variation in material properties, dimensions, workmanship, fabrication, meth-

TABLE 6.4.—TEST RESULTS OF DEFLECTION STABILITY OF TWO-SPAN
CONTINUOUS BEAMS

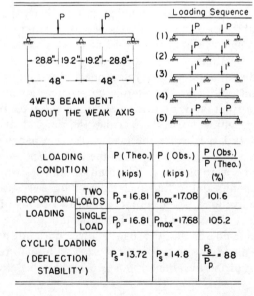

| LOADING CONDITION | $\alpha$ | THEORETICAL RELATIONSHIP $\frac{P_s}{P_p}$ (%) | OBSERVED RELATIONSHIP | $\frac{P_s(\text{obs.})}{P_s(\text{theo})}$ (%) |
|---|---|---|---|---|
| CYCLIC LOADING (DEFLECTION STABILITY) | 0 | 84.2 | 85.7 | 100 |
| | 1/4 | 87.6 | 86.7 | 99 |
| | 1/2 | 91.5 | 96.2 | 105 |
| | 3/4 | 95.6 | 95.6 | 100 |
| PROPORTIONAL LOADING | 1 | $\frac{P_{max.}}{P_p} = 100$ | $\frac{P_{max.}}{P_p} = 105$ | |

$P_s$  = Stabilizing Load
$P_p$  = Theoretical failure load by simple plastic theory
$P_{max}$ = Observed plastic failure load

TABLE 6.5.—TEST RESULTS OF DEFLECTION STABILITY OF TWO-SPAN
CONTINUOUS BEAMS

| LOADING CONDITION | | P (Theo.) (kips) | P (Obs.) (kips) | $\frac{P(\text{Obs.})}{P(\text{Theo.})}$ (%) |
|---|---|---|---|---|
| PROPORTIONAL LOADING | TWO LOADS | $P_p = 16.81$ | $P_{max} = 17.08$ | 101.6 |
| | SINGLE LOAD | $P_p = 16.81$ | $P_{max} = 17.68$ | 105.2 |
| CYCLIC LOADING (DEFLECTION STABILITY) | | $P_s = 13.72$ | $P_s = 14.8$ | $\frac{P_s}{P_p} = 88$ |

TABLE 6.6.—TEST RESULTS OF RIGID FRAMES UNDER VARIABLE
REPEATED LOADING

| LOADING CONDITION | STRUCTURES | $P_s$ or $P_a$ (theo.) kips | $P_s$ or $P_a$ (obser.) kips | $\dfrac{P(obs.)}{P(theo.)}$ (%) | $P_p$ (theo.) kips | $\dfrac{P_s}{P_p}$ or $\dfrac{P_a}{P_p}$ (%) |
|---|---|---|---|---|---|---|
| ALTERNATING PLASTICITY | | 5.68 | 6.00 | 106 | 5.76 | 104.0 |
| DEFLECTION STABILITY | Loading sequence $\{\begin{array}{l}\alpha=1\\\alpha=0\end{array}$ | 5.81 | 6.80 | 117 | 7.76 | 87.7 |

TABLE 6.7.—TEST RESULTS OF RIGID FRAMES UNDER VARIABLE
REPEATED LOADING

| LOADING CONDITION | STRUCTURES* | $P_p$ (Theo) lbs. | $P$ (Obs) lbs. | $\dfrac{P(obs.)}{P(theo)}$ (%) | $\dfrac{P(obs)}{P_p(theo)}$ (%) |
|---|---|---|---|---|---|
| Proportional Loading | | 92.5 | 101 | 109.2 | 109.2 |
| | ( 2 Tests) | 92.4 | 101 | 109.2 | 109.2 |
| Cyclic Loading | | 87.9 | 93.5 | 106.5 | 101.0 |
| | ( 3 Tests ) | 87.2 | 95.5 | 109.5 | 103.0 |
| | Loading sequence $\{\begin{array}{ll}\alpha=1&\beta=1\\\alpha=0&\beta=0\\\alpha=0&\beta=1\\\alpha=0&\beta=0\end{array}$ | 88.9 | 93.0 | 104.8 | 101.5 |
| | (2 Tests) | 78.0 | 89.5 | 114.8 | 96.8 |
| | Loading sequence $\{\begin{array}{ll}\alpha=1&\beta=1\\\alpha=0&\beta=0\\\alpha=-1&\beta=1\\\alpha=0&\beta=0\end{array}$ | 79.3 | 90.5 | 114.1 | 97.9 |

* All members were 1/4" sq. sections

ods of analysis, etc. Therefore, variation in live load alone could not properly be assumed to account for the full value of the factor of safety.

The fact has been emphasized (6.62) that failure due to increase of deflection is a gradual process so that ample warning of danger is available. This implies that a lower load factor is acceptable for $P_S$ than that provided for $P_p$.

Finally, the results of the most recent tests using rolled shapes have shown that the observed stabilizing load was always greater than the theoretically predicted value. Since the theoretical values of $P_S$ are seldom more than 20% below $P_p$, the practicality of this problem loses much of its significance. Although account could be taken of variable repeated loading by using a higher load factor, such a procedure is neither reasonable nor necessary for ordinary building frames.

---

**VARIABLE REPEATED LOADING**
Deflection stability need not be investigated in the design of statically loaded building frames.

---

### Repeating Inelastic Strains.

*(a) Previous Studies.*—In some applications, steel members or frames may be subjected to variable repeated loading of such a large magnitude that inelastic strains occur during each loading process. This condition can arise, for example, in the joints of a building frame during a severe earthquake. Due to the vibration of a building caused by the ground motion, several excursions into the inelastic range can occur.

Analytical treatment of the structural response of members for such a condition is being rapidly developed. However, a considerable number of tests has been performed in recent years on structures and structural components under repeated and reversed loads. These studies have resulted in a better understanding of the response of structures during an earthquake. In one series of tests, cantilever beams were tested to study the behavior of these beams under reversed loads (6.73). Further studies in this series subjected various types of building connections to similar loadings (6.73–6.77). Additional reversed bending tests on different types of beams have also been performed (6.78, 6.79, 6.80). Beam-columns bent in double and single curvature have been tested under constant axial loads and alternating end moments (6.81, 6.82). More comprehensive experiments, including interaction of beams subjected to repeated and reversed loading with axially loaded columns, have been carried out (6.83, 6.84), and several reversed load tests of model frames and small frames with W cross sections have been reported (6.85–6.88). In addition, as an adjunct to recent tests of multistory frames designed to study the static behavior under a monotonic load application, four frames were tested under reversed loading after large inelastic deformations had occurred due to the initial loading (6.89, 6.90, 6.91). Several full-scale frames have been designed and tested to study in particular their behavior under constant gravity loads and cyclic lateral displacements of the top of the frame (6.92, 6.93). Preliminary experimental load-versus-deflection hysteresis loops obtained from static and dynamic tests on one specimen show that the loops have similar shapes (6.94). Although the shapes were similar, further studies are needed to show the relationship between static and dynamic energy absorption.

*(b) Cantilever Beams Subjected to Repeated Loading.*—A typical experimental arrangement for applying repeated loading to beams is shown diagrammatically in Fig. 6.37(a) (6.95). By applying a load $P$ first in one

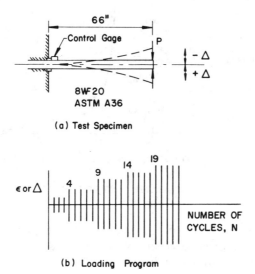

(a) Test Specimen

(b) Loading Program

FIG. 6.37.—REPEATED LOADING TEST ON CANTILEVER BEAM

direction and then in the opposite direction, various amounts of deformation can be induced in the cantilever beam. Either the end deflection $\Delta$ or the longitudinal strain $\epsilon$ in the bottom flange of a beam may be used to control the experiment. Besides the "step ladder" loading program shown in Fig. 6.37(b), others have been used.

The behavior of steel members depends on the induced intensity of the maximum alternating strain. The number of cycles required to cause complete failure by fracture of several different beams as a function of the controlling strain is shown in Fig. 6.38. These results were obtained on small steel beams in the as-rolled condition with clamping blocks shaped to conform to the cross section of the members. Based on these results it appears that the number of cycles a member can withstand when severely strained is adequate for conceivable practical application. Since fabricated beams have unavoidable stress concentrations at beam-to-column connections, the curve shown in Fig. 6.38 must be considered an upper bound for such members, because it was obtained for smooth (clamped) specimens. Similar information on the behavior of various types of beam-to-column connections between a cantilever beam and a stub column is available (6.75, 6.76, 6.77). The hysteresis loops for the various fabricated members remain stable, although the shape of the loops is different for the different

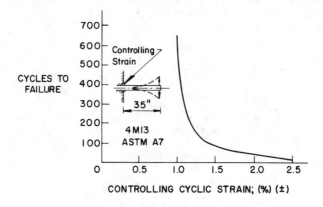

FIG. 6.38.—SAMPLE TEST RESULTS

types of connections described. However, the limited number of samples of each different type of connection tested precluded any statistical significance to allow preparation of a diagram similar to Fig. 6.38.

It is well established that as a material experiences inelastic strains a hysteresis loop develops during each cycle (6.96, 6.97). The area enclosed by such a loop is a measure of the energy dissipated. Essentially a similar type of hysteresis loop is generated for a rolled steel member in bending as for a short coupon subjected alternately to tensile and compressive axial loading (6.98, 6.99, 6.100). A series of typical consecutive hysteresis loops for a cantilever beam is shown in Fig. 6.39. The remarkable reproducibility of hysteresis loops during the consecutive cycles of load application can be noted. These loops continued to remain stable during severe buckling of the flanges in tests conducted on sections having compact flanges and using relatively close bracing spacing.

Until failure occurred, the areas enclosed by the hysteresis loops in-

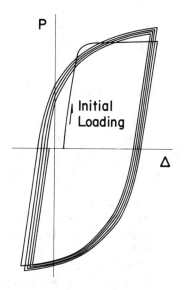

FIG. 6.39.—STABILITY OF CONSECUTIVE HYSTERESIS LOOPS

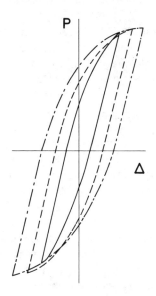

FIG. 6.40.—SELECTED (NONCONSECUTIVE) LOAD-DEFLECTION CURVES FOR CANTILEVER BEAM

creased with increasing load magnitudes, as shown in Fig. 6.40. During the large displacements (corresponding to the larger loops shown in Fig. 6.40) the flanges were severely buckled. The characteristic mode of flange buckling in such an advanced stage is shown in Fig. 6.41.

The number of cycles a specimen can resist before failure occurs depends on the selected loading program [Fig. 6.37(b)]. Some detailed results are reported in Refs. 6.98, 6.100, and 6.101.

---

**CANTILEVER BEAMS SUBJECTED TO REPEATED LOADING**

From the results of the cantilever beam tests (on plain beams), the following conclusions may be drawn when closely braced compact members are used:

1. Both the moment-curvature and the load-deflection hysteresis loops have remarkably stable shapes. This implies that a practically constant amount of energy absorption can be depended upon per cycle at each level of strain.
2. The onset of flange buckling did not signal an immediate loss of moment capacity. Instead, the load continued to increase independently of the buckling action. Neither did the severe buckling of flanges and web signal a failure of the system, but the buckles appeared and then disappeared cyclically until failure for equal amplitude cycling.
3. Both the A36 and A441 rolled steel specimens are able to withstand severe reverse loadings. Failure occurs only after a large number of complete reversals of extremely high strains (where the number of cycles is considerably greater than what is probably encountered in ordinary design).

---

*(c) Frames Subjected to Repeated Load.*—Most of the research on frames is concerned with analysis and design for maximum strength of the frame subjected to monotonic static loading. However, the results from previously mentioned test programs on steel frames give quantitative comparisons between monotonic and reversed loading on steel members and frames.

Three full-scale frames of practical proportions of A36 steel showed significant increases in the maximum lateral load capacity over the maximum monotonically applied lateral load predicted by second-order elastic-plastic analysis (6.102). An increase of about 40% is shown in Fig. 6.42 for a single-story single-bay frame. Similar behavior was also observed on tests of four frames subjected to reversed loads after sustaining

FIG. 6.41.—CHARACTERISTIC FLANGE BUCKLING

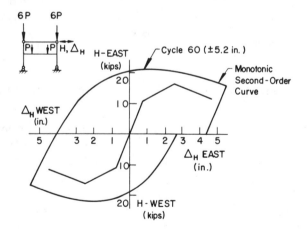

FIG. 6.42.—MAXIMUM LATERAL LOADS ON A FRAME SUBJECTED TO MONO-
TONIC AND TO REPEATED LOADING

large initial deformations (6.89, 6.90, 6.91). Since the analyses of the latter frames indicated that the maximum lateral load capacity would be reached before the formation of a mechanism, the second-order effects on frames should not be ignored in design or analysis.

When a frame is loaded by constant vertical loads and an increasing horizontal load into the inelastic range and then unloaded to zero horizontal load, a residual deflection remains in the frame. The residual $P\Delta$ moments existing in the frame when the horizontal loading begins in the opposite direction have a significant effect on the behavior of the frame

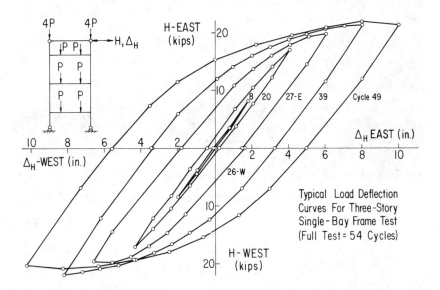

FIG. 6.43.—LOAD-DEFLECTION CURVES FOR 3-STORY SINGLE-BAY FRAME

(6.93). Particularly for frames subjected to reversed loading where energy absorption is measured in terms of plastic hinge rotation, the second-order analysis would give more realistic hinge rotations than a first-order analysis (6.103).

In recent tests on steel frames, the frames were subjected initially to constant gravity loads (at the working value), and then sets of lateral displacements of increasing amplitudes were applied at the top of the frames. These were 1-story or 3-story frames at 10 ft per story, and with a single-bay width of 15 ft. The member sizes selected by the design were 10 **WF** 29 beams and 8 **WF** 40 columns oriented for major-axis bending. The hysteresis loops for selected displacement amplitudes for the 3-story frame are shown in Fig. 6.43 (6.92).

Except for cycles in the elastic range, the number of repetitions at each amplitude was set equal to five to observe the stability of the hysteresis loops at the various amplitudes of deflection and inelastic conditions of the frame. As in the case of the hysteresis loops generated for the canti-lever beam tests, the repetitions of the cycles at all amplitudes indicated stable hysteresis loops. However, for the frame, the downward sloping portion of the curves between the deflection at the maximum load and the maximum deflection shown in Fig. 6.44 is important. In this portion of

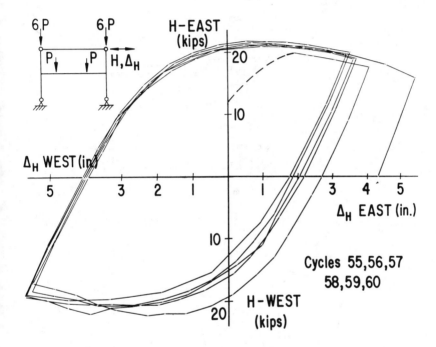

FIG. 6.44.—STABILITY OF LOAD-DEFLECTION CURVES FOR FRAME

the curves, the instability effect governs the over-all behavior of the frame, yet Fig. 6.44 shows that during this instability of the 1-story frame, the five large amplitude hysteresis loops remain stable (6.92). The tests show the significant influence of strain hardening when the frames were sub-jected to large lateral displacements. On each of the large amplitude cycles of these frames, once the deflection at the maximum lateral load had been exceeded, the lateral load-carrying capacity dropped off much more slow-ly, compared with the theoretical predictions that ignored strain harden-ing. This effect of strain hardening occurring at the plastic hinge locations is demonstrated experimentally and analytically in Fig. 6.45 for the mono-tonically loaded fixed-base portal frame shown (6.90).

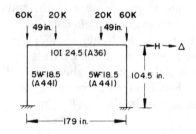

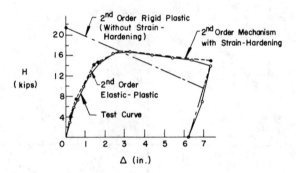

FIG. 6.45.—LOAD-DEFORMATION CURVES FOR PORTAL FRAME FOR INITIAL LOADING

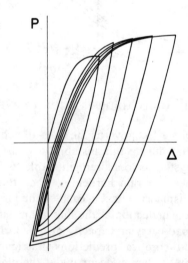

FIG. 6.46.—EFFECT OF HORIZONTAL SHIFT OF HYSTERESIS LOOPS FOR CANTILEVER BEAM

The curved shape of the hysteresis loops for frames subjected to reversed loading is caused not only by the Bauschinger effect in the material, but also by the reduction in frame stiffness due to the spread of yielding at the plastic hinge locations.

Dynamic analyses of frames subjected to reversed loading attempt to give an estimate of the response or energy absorption of the frame when subjected to a given earthquake. Analytical treatments of damped vibrations which normally assume an elasto-plastic or empirical representation for the moment-curvature relationship of a member are available (6.104–6.107). After the system has been yielded by deflection in one direction and then unloaded, the next dynamic loadings are considered from the deflected (residual) position of the system (6.108). Experimental justifications permitting a moderate horizontal shift of hysteresis loops as necessitated by the inelastic structural response are indicated in Fig. 6.46. The "reserve energy" technique to determine empirically the energy absorption capacity of a frame is also available (6.109).

The effects of the gravity loads acting through sway displacements ($P\Delta$) on the dynamic behavior of frames is an area of current investigation (6.110). In addition, the deformations in the connection panel zones of beam-to-column joints have an influence on the behavior of frames, and efforts have been reported on existing studies (6.111, 6.112, 6.113).

---

**FRAMES SUBJECTED TO REPEATED LOADING**

1. Hysteresis loops of horizontal load versus deflection appear to be stable for the deformations selected in the studies.
2. Lateral load capacity is larger for reversed loading than for monotonic lateral loading.
3. For large amplitude cycles of the steel frames tested, once the deflection at the maximum load had been exceeded, the load dropped off at a slower rate than predicted by the monotonic analysis which neglects strain hardening at the plastic hinge locations.
4. The presence of significant residual $P\text{-}\Delta$ moments must be included in analytical methods.
5. The shape of the hysteresis loops under repeated and reversed loading is influenced by:
   a. The spread of yielding in the plastic hinge locations;
   b. The Bauschinger effect in the material;
   c. Strain hardening; and
   d. The residual $P\text{-}\Delta$ moments.

# CHAPTER 7.—COMPRESSION MEMBERS

## 7.1 INTRODUCTION

Simple plastic theory assumes that a member subjected to bending moments will sustain a certain limiting bending moment (the plastic moment, $M_p$) that is dependent only on the geometrical properties of the cross section and the yield stress of the steel. When this maximum moment is approached, curvature increases indefinitely and a hinge type of action occurs. The presence of axial force tends to alter this situation. The various effects of axial force on the behavior of individual members and on the frames as a whole will be described in the following.

For an individual member which is subjected to bending moments and an axial force (a beam-column), and which is sufficiently braced in the lateral direction, or for a member which is bent about its weak axis, the mode of failure will be instability due to secondary bending moment in the plane of the applied moment.

If a member bent about the strong axis has insufficient lateral bracing, and if a large difference exists between the bending stiffnesses about each of the principal axes of the cross section, the member may bend out of the plane of the applied moments and twist at the same time. This type of failure is called "lateral-torsional buckling."

As loads are applied to a rigid frame, the individual members which comprise the structure are subjected to various combinations of axial thrust, end moments, and end restraints. In many cases in plastically designed structures, the stiffnesses of the end restraints do not influence the behavior of the column because of the formation of plastic hinges. In many other practical cases, however, the beams framing into the ends of the beam-columns act as elastic restraints, and this "subassemblage" of several members can accept more load even after the individual unrestrained beam-column would have failed.

An additional type of failure, which is different from those described previously, involves the structure as a whole, and may occur when sidesway of the structure is not prevented. This condition is characterized by a shift of the total structural deformation pattern from one that is symmetrical to one that is antisymmetrical and is accompanied by an over-all lateral displacement of the frame. This situation will occur in a symmetrical structure that is symmetrically loaded when, at a critical magnitude of the loading, the total resistance of the structure to lateral movement becomes zero. The possibility of this "sway" or "frame" type of instability places a restriction on the ranges of applicability of the individual member-strength and individual subassemblage-strength solutions.

A further situation may develop when the structure deforms horizontally from the first load application. For these cases the horizontal displacement of the column top with respect to the base may alter the carrying capacity of the frame itself. This type of action would be similar in nature to that limiting the maximum carrying capacity of beam-columns. As in that case, a certain loading would be reached for which the structure would continue to deform in the direction of initial movement. This effect is called the $P\Delta$ effect, and it must be considered in the design of tall multi-story frames. The problem of frame instability is discussed in detail in Chapter 10.

As pointed out in previous sections of this Manual (Art. 6.3), the problem of rotation capacity may also influence the design. It may be necessary in certain situations to assure a relatively large rotation at near-maximum loads.

In the following articles, the effects of axial force will be discussed, and methods will be outlined for their consideration in the design of individual members in rigid frames.

## 7.2 REDUCTION OF THE PLASTIC MOMENT DUE TO AXIAL THRUST

### Statement of the Problem.

If a member is subjected to the combined action of bending moment and axial force, the available plastic moment capacity is reduced from the full value of $M_p$ to a lesser value that will be designated as $M_{pc}$. The analysis or design procedure, of course, can easily be modified to take this reduction into account. The value $M_{pc}$ is a property of the cross section. It is independent of the slenderness ratio, and it is immaterial whether the axial force is in compression or tension. Even though instability effects are excluded, the methods developed here give a good approximation of the actual behavior of very short compression members and of certain other columns of practical proportions, as will be shown in Art. 7.3.

### Previous Research.

Ref. 7.1 is the first published work on the influence of axial thrust on the moment capacity of a short column. Methods of determining $M_{pc}$ are given in Refs. 7.2 to 7.5, 3.1, and 1.6.

### Theoretical Analysis.

As an illustration of the influence of axial thrust on the plastic moment value, consider the rectangular section shown in Fig. 7.1. Assuming, for example, that the thrust is maintained constant and that the moment is progressively increased, the moment-curvature relationship will be that shown nondimensionally in Fig. 7.1. (The moment is nondimensionalized by dividing it by $M_p$, and the curvature is nondimensionalized by dividing it by $\phi_y$, the curvature at the inception of yielding.) It is assumed here that the axial force is in compression. For purposes of comparison, the curve for no axial force is shown as a dashed line in Fig. 7.1. Yielding starts first in the outer fiber of the compression side of the member (stress diagram A

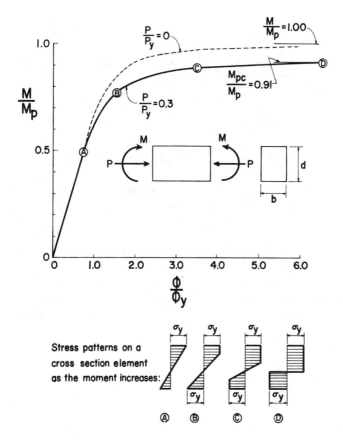

FIG. 7.1.—MOMENT-CURVATURE RELATIONSHIP FOR RECTANGULAR SECTION

in Fig. 7.1). Only after a portion of this side has yielded will the tension side begin to yield (stress diagram B).

As was the case when axial force was not present, the hinge condition corresponds to that situation in which the cross section is fully yielded (stress diagram D in Fig. 7.1, or as redrawn in Fig. 7.2). However, there will no longer be equal areas yielded in tension and compression as in the case of bending without axial load. Thus the neutral axis no longer coincides with the centroidal axis. The hinge rotations for the computation of the virtual work performed by the mechanism may still be assumed about the centroid of the section; the error for the structures considered in this Manual is negligible. For very deep built-up sections, however, the effect of the shift of the neutral axis may not be neglected (7.6).

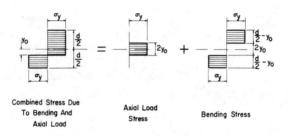

Combined Stress Due
To Bending And
Axial Load

Axial Load
Stress

Bending Stress

FIG. 7.2.—STRESS PATTERN AT $M = M_{pc}$

The value of $M_{pc}$ for any cross section can be obtained from the equations of equilibrium of the internal and external forces, that is

$$P = \int_A \sigma \, dA \quad \dots \dots \dots \dots \dots (7.1a)$$

$$M = \int_A \sigma \, y \, dA \quad \dots \dots \dots \dots \dots (7.1b)$$

In Eq. 7.1, $\sigma$ = the stress at a given fiber, $y$ = the distance of that fiber from the centroidal axis, $dA$ = the differential area element, and the integration is performed over the entire cross section. For the rectangular section (see Fig. 7.2), Eq. 7.1a results in

$$y_o = \frac{P}{2\,\sigma_y\,b} \quad \dots \dots \dots \dots \dots (7.2)$$

Eq. 7.1b gives

$$M_{pc} = \frac{\sigma_y\,b}{4}\,(d^2 - 4\,y_o^2) \quad \dots \dots \dots \dots (7.3)$$

Substituting Eq. 7.2 into Eq. 7.3, and noting that $\sigma_y\,b\,d = \sigma_y\,A = P_y$ and that for no axial force present $M_{pc} = M_p = \sigma_y\,b\,d^2/4$, the nondimensional expression for the reduced plastic moment for a rectangular section is

$$\frac{M_{pc}}{M_p} = 1 - \left(\frac{P}{P_y}\right)^2 \dots \dots \dots \dots \dots (7.4)$$

By a similar process the values of $M_{pc}$ can be computed for any section. Equations follow for wide-flange sections subjected to bending about the strong and weak axes. The nomenclature is shown on the inset in Fig. 7.3.

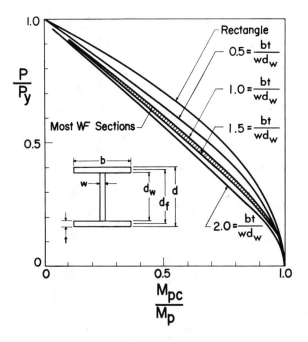

FIG. 7.3.—INTERACTION CURVE FOR STRONG-AXIS BENDING OF WIDE-FLANGE SECTION (MOMENTS ABOUT x-x ONLY; $L = 0$)

***Strong Axis Bending of Wide-Flange Sections.***—Neutral axis in web (3.1)

$$\left.\begin{array}{c} \dfrac{M_{pc}}{M_p} = 1 - \dfrac{\left[\dfrac{P}{P_y}\left(1 + \dfrac{2\,bt}{wd_w}\right)\right]^2}{\left(1 + \dfrac{4\,btd_f}{wd_w^2}\right)} \\[4ex] 0 \le \dfrac{P}{P_y} \le \dfrac{1}{1 + \dfrac{2\,bt}{wd_w}} \end{array}\right\} \quad \cdots \cdots \cdots \; (7.5)$$

***Strong Axis Bending of Wide-Flange Sections.***—Neutral axis in flange (3.1)

$$\left.\begin{array}{c} \dfrac{M_{pc}}{M_p} = \dfrac{2\left(\dfrac{d}{d_w}\right)\left(1 - \dfrac{P}{P_y}\right)\left(1 + \dfrac{2\,bt}{wd_w}\right)}{1 + \left(1 + \dfrac{d}{d_w}\right)\dfrac{2\,bt}{wd_w}} \\[4ex] \dfrac{1}{1 + \dfrac{2\,bt}{wd_w}} \le \dfrac{P}{P_y} \le 1.0 \end{array}\right\} \quad \cdots \cdots \cdots \; (7.6)$$

**Weak Axis Bending of Wide-Flange Sections.**—Neutral axis in web

$$
\left.
\begin{array}{c}
\dfrac{M_{pc}}{M_p} = 1.00 - \left(\dfrac{w}{b}\right)\left(\dfrac{d_w}{d}\right)\left[\dfrac{1 + \left(\dfrac{2\,bt}{wd_w}\right)^2}{\dfrac{2\,bt}{wd_w} + \dfrac{w}{b}}\right]\left(\dfrac{P}{P_y}\right)^2 \\[6ex]
0 \le \dfrac{P}{P_y} \le \dfrac{d}{d_w}\left(\dfrac{1}{1 + \dfrac{2\,bt}{wd_w}}\right)
\end{array}
\right\} \quad \dots (7.7)
$$

**Weak Axis Bending of Wide-Flange Sections.**—Neutral axis in flange

$$
\left.
\begin{array}{c}
\dfrac{M_{pc}}{M_p} = \left(1 - \dfrac{P}{P_y}\right)\left[\dfrac{\left(1 + \dfrac{2\,bt}{wd_w}\right)^2}{\left(\dfrac{2\,bt}{wd_w}\right)\left(\dfrac{2\,bt}{wd_w} + \dfrac{w}{b}\right)}\right] \\[6ex]
\times \left[\dfrac{2}{\left(1 + \dfrac{wd_w}{2\,bt}\right)} - \left(1 - \dfrac{P}{P_y}\right)\right] \\[6ex]
\left(\dfrac{d}{d_w}\right)\left(\dfrac{1}{1 + \dfrac{2\,bt}{wd_w}}\right) \le \dfrac{P}{P_y} \le 1.00
\end{array}
\right\} \quad \dots (7.8)
$$

Eqs. 7.5 through 7.8 contain the simplifications that for wide-flange shapes $d/d_w$ and $d_f/d_w$ are about the same for all shapes used as columns, and are approximately equal to 1.10 and 1.05, respectively (3.1). The non-dimensional plot of these equations for various $bt/wd_w$ ratios is shown in Fig. 7.3 for strong-axis bending. Assuming such typical values as $w/b = 0.04$ and $d/d_w = 1.10$, the curves shown in Fig. 7.4 are obtained for weak-axis bending.

From Figs. 7.3 and 7.4 it is evident that the range of the equations for most wide-flange sections falls in a very narrow band. This fact simplifies the problem of formulating design rules (see subsequent section on design recommendations).

The strength of wide-flange shapes subjected to biaxial bending (that is, where the applied bending moment is not about one of the principal axes) is discussed in Refs. 7.7 and 7.8.

**Experimental Correlation.**

Fig. 7.5 shows the correlation between a set of experimental data and theory (5.4). Each of the three tests was carried out on 12 **WF** 36 members which were so short that instability was no problem ($L/r_x = 7.0$). Furthermore, flexure about the weak axis was prevented by the arrangement of the knife edges at the column ends. This permitted rotation in the strong direction only. The results are plotted as nondimensional moment-versus-

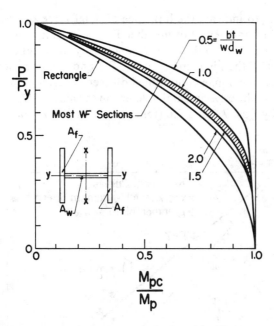

FIG. 7.4.—INTERACTION CURVE FOR WEAK-AXIS BENDING OF WIDE-FLANGE SECTION (MOMENTS ABOUT y-y ONLY; $L = 0$)

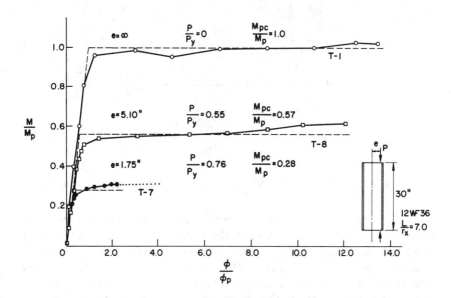

FIG. 7.5.—TESTS OF ECCENTRICALLY LOADED SHORT COLUMNS

curvature curves to indicate the influence of axial force on the reduction of the plastic hinge moment. For member T-1 the axial load was zero (pure bending). Members T-7 and T-8 were loaded by an eccentric force. As would be expected, the hinge moment for T-7 and T-8 does not reach the full value of $M_p$. The hinge condition, however, was realized in all cases (see Fig. 7.5), and the experimentally determined value of $M_{pc}$ was close to that predicted by Eqs. 7.5 and 7.6 (represented by horizontal dashed lines in Fig. 7.5).

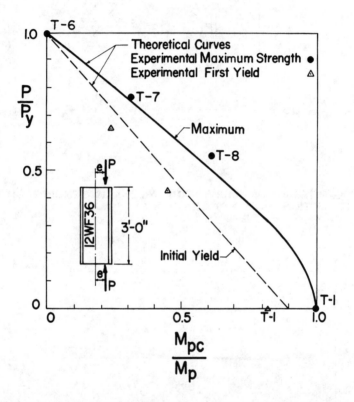

FIG. 7.6.—TESTS OF ECCENTRICALLY LOADED SHORT COLUMNS

To afford a clearer indication of the correlation between this set of test data and predictions, Fig. 7.6 gives the experimentally determined initial yield and maximum strength values plotted on an interaction diagram similar to that described earlier. [The interaction diagram for the theoretical ultimate strength was constructed using Eqs. 7.5 and 7.6; the initial yield curve represents the elastic limit computed from the equation $\sigma_y = (P/A) + (M/S)$.] Included in this comparison is the result of a pure axial load test (T-6) of the same cross section. Due to the presence of residual stress, the elastic interaction curve slightly overestimates initial yielding. The maximum load curve, on the other hand, slightly underestimates the capacity; this is because of strain hardening. Further experiments on high-strength steel eccentrically loaded steel columns show similarly good correlation with the predicted value of $M_{pc}$ (7.9).

Results of a series of tests (7.4) on short 3-in. standard British I-beams are shown in Fig. 7.7; excellent agreement with the theory is indicated. A constant moment was first applied to the member and axial force was subsequently increased until the member had fully plastified.

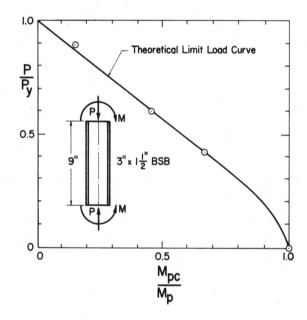

FIG. 7.7.—SHORT COLUMNS LOADED IN BENDING AND COMPRESSION

The experimental evidence shows that for mild steel the reduction in moment capacity due to the presence of axial force can be closely predicted by the theories outlined.

**Design Recommendations.**

To account for the influence of axial force in design, any of the appropriate equations or curves of this section could be used. However, since the curves for wide-flange shapes fall within a relatively narrow band (see Figs. 7.3 and 7.4), it is possible to obtain simple approximate expressions for these cross sections.

For strong-axis bending the influence of axial force may be neglected if $P$ is less than 15% of $P_y$, in which $P_y = \sigma_y A$. If the axial force is larger,

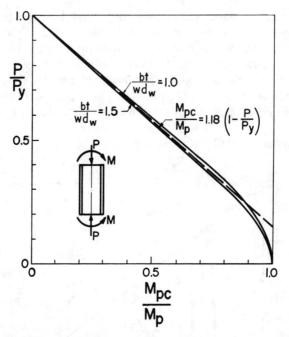

FIG. 7.8.—APPROXIMATE INTERACTION EQUATION FOR WIDE-FLANGE
SHAPE (STRONG-AXIS BENDING, SHORT COLUMN)

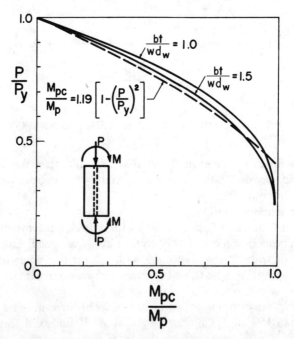

FIG. 7.9.—APPROXIMATE INTERACTION EQUATION FOR WIDE-FLANGE
SHAPE (WEAK-AXIS BENDING, SHORT COLUMN)

the interaction between moment and force may be expressed as

$$\frac{M_{pc}}{M_p} = 1.18 \left( 1 - \frac{P}{P_y} \right) \quad \dots \dots \dots \dots \quad (7.9)$$

The corresponding equation for weak-axis bending is

$$\frac{M_{pc}}{M_p} = 1.19 \left[ 1 - \left( \frac{P}{P_y} \right)^2 \right] \quad \dots \dots \dots \dots \quad (7.10)$$

Eq. 7.10 need only be used when $P$ is more than 40% of $P_y$. These equations give $M_{pc}$ values within 5% of the exact values (Figs. 7.8 and 7.9).

One way of using these interaction equations is to find a trial section based on bending considerations alone, and then to adjust this section by successive corrections until the conditions of the interaction equations are fulfilled.

Thus a design guide may be formulated in order to account for the influence of axial thrust. It must be kept in mind that instability effects are disregarded, and so these equations apply in the strictest sense only to short columns. Calculations including the effects of instability have shown that the strong axis interaction equation (Eq. 7.9) is also valid for columns subjected to certain loading conditions (see Art. 7.3).

In summary, the following equations are suitable for determining the reduction of plastic moment due to axial force:

---

**REDUCTION OF PLASTIC MOMENT CAPACITY**
*Strong Axis Bending, Wide-Flange Sections:*
For $0 \le P \le 0.15 \, P_y$ use

$$M_{pc} = M_p$$

For $0.15 \, P_y \le P \le P_y$

$$M_{pc} = 1.18 \left( 1 - \frac{P}{P_y} \right) M_p \quad \dots \dots \dots \dots \quad (7.9)$$

*Weak Axis Bending, Wide-Flange Sections:*
For $0 \le P \le 0.4 \, P_y$ use

$$M_{pc} = M_p$$

For $0.4 \, P_y \le P \le P_y$

$$M_{pc} = 1.19 \left[ 1 - \left( \frac{P}{P_y} \right)^2 \right] M_p \quad \dots \dots \dots \quad (7.10)$$

*Rectangular Section:*

$$M_{pc} = \left[ 1 - \left( \frac{P}{P_y} \right)^2 \right] M_p \quad \dots \dots \dots \dots \quad (7.4)$$

---

## 7.3 MOMENT-CARRYING CAPACITY OF COLUMNS
### Statement of the Problem.

Although the solutions that were obtained in the preceding section represent a basic characteristic of the cross section and are adequate for short columns, they do not always correspond to the loading that a longer column can sustain.

As an illustration of the problem, consider the eccentrically loaded column of Fig. 7.10. As the load is increased beyond initial yielding at

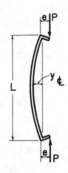

FIG. 7.10.—ECCENTRICALLY LOADED COLUMN

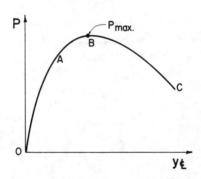

FIG. 7.11.—LOAD-DEFLECTION CURVE FOR ECCENTRICALLY LOADED COLUMN

mid-length, plastification progresses along and across the column, thereby reducing its resistance to further loading. Fig. 7.11 shows a typical load-versus-center-deflection curve for an eccentrically loaded column. The portion of the curve from O to A represents the column behavior when the stresses are still elastic. The portion A-B represents the range of partial yielding. Finally, when the curve reaches point B, a further increase in load becomes impossible because the internal stiffness of the column is just enough to resist $P$ and the moment $P(e + y_{\ell})$. It is with the determination of this maximum value of $P$ that this section is concerned. This type of instability is due to secondary bending moment in the plane of the applied moments.

A column will not fail in the manner just discussed if the cross section under consideration has markedly different values of bending stiffness in the two principal directions (a characteristic of wide-flange sections). If the member is subjected to bending about the stronger of the two axes, and if no torsional restraint at its ends or intermediate lateral restraint is provided, the column will twist and bend out of the plane of loading; in general its strength will be reduced. This phenomenon is known as "lateral-torsional buckling" and is the subject of Art. 7.5.

If lateral-torsional buckling is prevented, the eccentrically loaded column (or the column with end bending moments plus an axial thrust) can "fail" only after a certain amount of yielding has taken place. The problem is therefore not one of stress but one of stability. The maximum load is reached when the internal stiffness is just enough to resist the external moments. Thus for certain columns the condition of full plasticity (defined by stress diagram D in Fig. 7.1) will not be reached.

**Previous Research.**

An extensive survey of the early work on eccentrically loaded columns is contained in sections 9 through 12 of Ref. 6.18.

Recent work has extended the investigations of the early researchers in this field. Solutions to the problem of eccentrically loaded, end-restrained rectangular columns were presented in Refs. 1.1 and 7.10. Other investigations have been made of the problem of hinged-end, as-rolled, wide-flange steel columns bent about their major axes (7.11–7.16).

Parallel to the efforts to determine the strength of eccentrically loaded columns by rational means, attempts to define empirical interaction equations for predicting column strength have been made. Among these, the most recent and most extensive work is reported in Refs. 6.36, 7.17, and 7.18, which propose the interaction equation

$$\frac{P}{P_{cr}} + \frac{M_{eq}}{M_p \left(1 - \frac{P}{P_e}\right)} \leq 1.0 \quad \ldots \ldots \ldots \ldots (7.11)$$

in which $P$ = axial load on the column; $P_{cr}$ = maximum axial force the column can carry if no bending moment is present—this value includes the influence of the effective length (in the plane of bending), residual stress, and yielding; and $M_{eq}$ = equivalent end bending moment, which may be expressed as

$$M_{eq} = \sqrt{0.3 \, (M_1^2 + M_2^2) + 0.4 \, M_1 \, M_2} \quad \ldots \ldots (7.12)$$

or by

$$M_{eq} = 0.6\, M_2 - 0.4\, M_1 \quad \ldots \ldots \ldots \quad (7.13)$$

in which $M_{eq}$ may not be less than $0.4\, M_2$. Also in these equations,

$M_2$ = larger of the two end moments;

$M_1$ = smaller of the two end moments ($M_2$ is positive in Eqs. 7.12 and 7.13 if it acts in the same sense as $M_1$);

$P_e$ = the elastic ("Euler") buckling load of the column in the plane of the moments; and

$M_p$ = full plastic moment of the cross section.

In case the maximum moment occurs at the end of the column, the following equation holds for the interaction between $P$ and $M$

$$\frac{P}{P_y} + \frac{0.85\, M_2}{M_p} = 1.00 \quad \ldots \ldots \ldots \ldots \quad (7.14)$$

This is identical with Eq. 7.9 and it represents the case of full yielding at the end of the member. In design, both Eq. 7.11 and Eq. 7.14 must be checked. The governing equation is the one that furnishes the smaller values of $M$ or $P$. (Eq. 7.14 is a rearrangement of Eq. 7.9.)

Eq. 7.11 is valid for the case in which no relative translation occurs between the ends of the columns. Thus, in applying this equation, the maximum axial load, $P_{cr}$, is computed for the actual length (or slenderness ratio) of the column, that is, the effective length factor, $K$, is assumed to be equal to unity. For columns with relative translation such as those occurring in a laterally unbraced frame, it has been shown that Eq. 7.11 is still valid, but the terms $P_{cr}$ and $P_e$ must be determined differently (7.19). In this case, these two loads are computed on the basis of an effective column length which is often greater than the actual length. The effective column length is usually determined for the sidesway mode of over-all frame buckling. (See later discussion in Chapter 10.)

Besides the theoretical work on this topic, many experiments have been conducted, notably those reported in Refs. 7.10, 7.11, 7.20, 7.21, 7.22, and 6.36. These tests are summarized and compared to "exact" theoretical predictions and to maximum strength predicted by the empirical interaction equation (Eqs. 7.11 and 7.14) in Ref. 7.23.

It is impossible herein to do full justice to the immense effort that has been put forth in solving the various aspects of the eccentrically loaded column problem. Therefore, only a few have been mentioned; a more complete review of work done before 1950 has been listed in Ref. 6.18, and the most recent research has been summarized by the Column Research Council in Ref. 5.2.

**Theoretical Analysis.**

From the many available solutions, one has been selected which represents most nearly the conditions that exist in a plastically designed rigid frame of the type considered in this Manual. The results of Ref. 7.12 have been chosen because they represent a so-called "exact" solution (for including the influence of residual stress on column strength), and are directly applicable to columns fabricated from as-rolled wide-flange shapes which are subjected to bending about their strong axes. Another approach is based on the Column Deflection Curves discussed in Art. 7.4 (7.15).

In the development of the theory, the following assumptions are made:

1. The mode of failure will be that of excessive bending in the plane of the moments; furthermore, this plane is taken to be the strong plane of the section.
2. Lateral-torsional buckling is prevented.
3. The material is structural steel which is assumed to possess the idealized stress-strain curve of Fig. 2.1.
4. Members are originally straight, free from accidental end eccentricities, and are of uniform cross section along their length.
5. Plane sections before bending remain plane after bending.
6. The end slope of the deflected column is small.
7. End restraints are neglected. This means that the behavior of the column in the frame is the same as that of an isolated member loaded with axial force and end bending moments.

Interaction curves for strong-axis bending of a rolled wide-flange section are developed in Ref. 7.12 by an iterative procedure. The influence of residual stresses due to cooling after rolling is included in these calculations, thus giving solutions for as-delivered columns. The particular residual stress pattern which is used (see Fig. 7.12) is typical for rolled columns of A36 steel (7.11, 4.4). Welded columns or columns made of other grades of steels will have other patterns whose influence would have to be separately assessed. A maximum compressive residual stress of 0.3 $\sigma_y$ is assumed in the calculations.

Interaction curves for wide-flange sections are shown in Figs. 7.13 and 7.14 for two loading conditions. These curves have been computed numer-

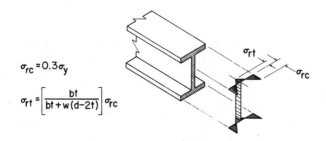

$$\sigma_{rc} = 0.3\sigma_y$$

$$\sigma_{rt} = \left[ \frac{bt}{bt + w(d - 2t)} \right] \sigma_{rc}$$

FIG. 7.12.—ASSUMED COOLING RESIDUAL STRESS PATTERN

ically for the 8 **W** 31 shape; however, they represent a good approximation for any other wide-flange section. The 8 **W** 31 section has been chosen because of its low shape factor ($f = 1.10$, as compared to the average value of 1.14). Hence the curves are conservative for other sections in the ratio of their shape factor to 1.10. The interaction curves show a nondimensional plot of the relationship between the axial force (abscissa) and end bending moment (ordinate) for constant values of the slenderness ratio in the direction of bending.

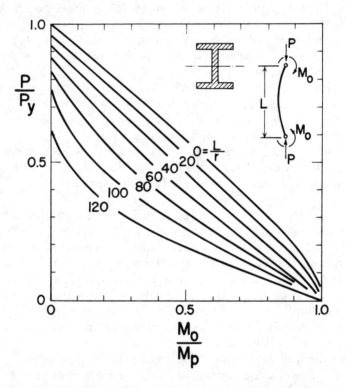

FIG. 7.13.—INTERACTION CURVES FOR STRONG-AXIS BENDING OF WIDE-FLANGE SECTIONS

Fig. 7.13 gives the curves for a loading condition in which two equal end moments cause the column to bend in single curvature; Fig. 7.14 shows the curves for the case where only one end moment is applied (moment ratios of 1.0 and 0, respectively).

A complete description of the calculations necessary to obtain these interaction curves is given in Ref. 7.12. Only a brief outline of the procedure is given here to show how one point on a curve is obtained. For a given section an axial force, length, and end bending moment value are assumed.

The end slope corresponding to this loading is computed by a numerical integration process; that is, curvatures obtained from the moment-curvature diagram of Fig. 7.15 are integrated to give the deflected shape and thus the end slope of the column. This process is repeated for several values of the end moment (length and axial force remaining constant) until an end moment versus end rotation curve can be constructed. The maximum point on this curve corresponds to the highest end moment which

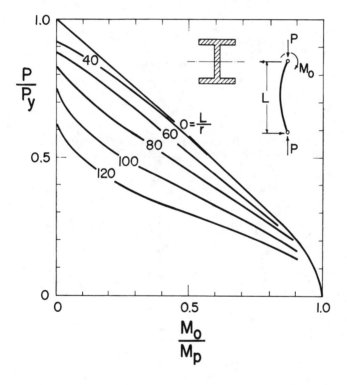

FIG. 7.14.—INTERACTION CURVES FOR STRONG-AXIS BENDING OF WIDE-FLANGE SHAPES

this column can support, thus giving one point on the interaction curves of Figs. 7.13 or 7.14.

The curves of Figs. 7.13 and 7.14 have been computed for steel with a yield stress of 33 ksi. The same curves can be used for wide-flange beam-columns with different yield stress levels by using an equivalent slenderness ratio equal to the actual slenderness ratio multiplied by the factor $\sqrt{\sigma_y/33}$, in which $\sigma_y$ = the yield stress of the particular steel (expressed in kips per square inch).

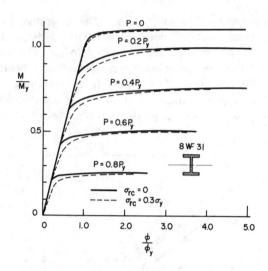

FIG. 7.15.—MOMENT-THRUST-CURVATURE RELATIONSHIPS FOR AN 8WF 31 SHAPE, WITH AND WITHOUT RESIDUAL STRESS

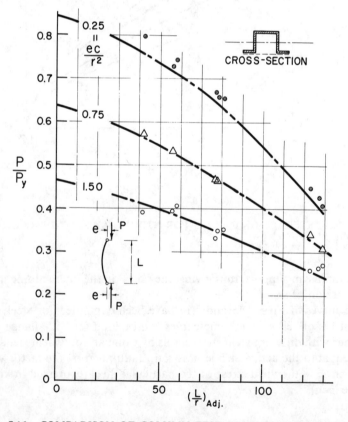

FIG. 7.16.—COMPARISON OF COLUMN TEST RESULTS WITH THEORY

**Experimental Correlation.**
Figs. 7.16 through 7.20 show the experimental correlation of various tests with the interaction curves of Figs. 7.13 and 7.14.

Fig. 7.16 correlates the theory with tests performed on hat-shaped sections (7.20). This cross section conforms most nearly to the assumptions

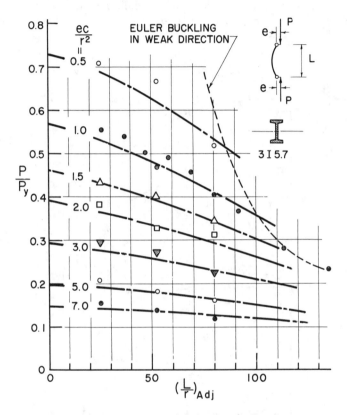

FIG. 7.17.—COMPARISON OF COLUMN TEST RESULTS WITH THEORY

made in the derivation of the interaction curves (namely, that lateral buckling cannot take place since bending is about the weak axis, and yet the action of a wide-flange shape bent about its strong axis is simulated). The correlation shown in Fig. 7.16 is good. [These tests also give good correlation with the interaction equation (Eq. 7.11) as shown in Fig. 6 of Ref. 7.20.] In Fig. 7.16, as well as in the following figures, the continuous line refers to the theoretical curves for the given eccentricities; the points represented by circles, squares, or triangles are the experimental points. These have been corrected to include the influence of specimen yield stress other than 33 ksi. In Fig. 7.16 the experimental points fall slightly above the theoretical curves; this is as would be expected, since the shape factors of the hat sections are slightly above those of wide-flange sections, and the residual stress is somewhat below that assumed in the theory outlined here ($f$ = 1.17, 1.18, and 1.25 for the three sections that were tested; $\sigma_{rc}$ (max) = 0.23 $\sigma_y$ by measurement, as compared to 0.3 $\sigma_y$ of the theory).

The correlation with tests reported in Ref. 7.21 is shown in Fig. 7.17. The test arrangement was such that the columns were essentially pin-ended with respect to bending in the strong direction, and fixed-ended in

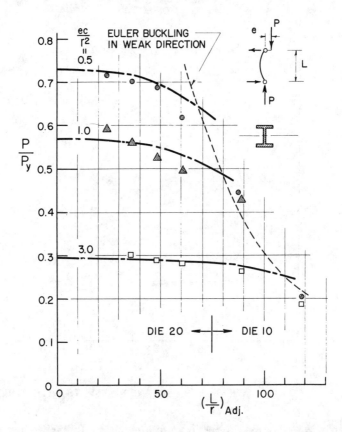

FIG. 7.18.—COMPARISON OF COLUMN TEST RESULTS WITH THEORY

the weak direction. This was done by the use of knife edges placed perpendicular to the web. The test columns usually failed by lateral-torsional buckling. It is interesting to note, however, that except for the tests which fall close to the region where failure would have been due to "Euler buckling" in the weak direction (see dotted curve), the correlation with the theory which neglects lateral-torsional behavior is reasonably good. In constructing the dotted Euler buckling curve the effective column length with respect to the $y$-axis was taken as 0.6 times the column length; this effective length was determined experimentally.

The test results published in Ref. 6.36 are compared with theoretical predictions in Fig. 7.18. The DIE profiles, of which the test columns were made, are geometrically similar to American wide-flange profiles. The end conditions of the columns were essentially pin-ended in both principal directions, since the end fixtures consisted of almost frictionless, hydraulically-seated steel hemispheres. For such end conditions the lowest possible restraint is offered to lateral-torsional buckling. As shown in Fig. 7.18, most of the test points agree rather well with the theory which ne-

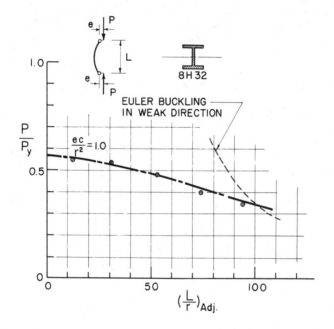

FIG. 7.19.—COMPARISON OF COLUMN TEST RESULTS WITH THEORY

glects this type of buckling, even though failure was by lateral-torsional instability. Comparison was made only for the loading case where moment was applied at one end of the column.

Fig. 7.19 shows the results of experiments reported in Ref. 7.22. The end conditions here were the same as for the tests in Ref. 7.21. The theoretical correlation is quite good.

Tests performed at Lehigh University also confirm the theoretical prediction (7.23). The test results are compared with theoretical curves in Fig. 7.20. The loading condition, slenderness ratio, and column size are indicated in this figure. Intermediate lateral braces were provided to prevent lateral-torsional buckling (except for tests T-13, T-23, and T-31). The location of these braces was determined in accordance with Eq. 6.25. These braces were adequate for the prevention of lateral-torsional buck-

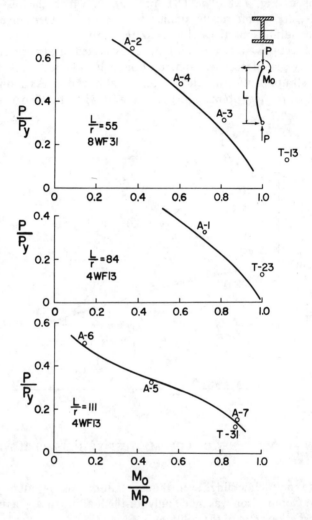

FIG. 7.20.—COMPARISON OF COLUMN TEST RESULTS WITH THEORY

ling. Good correlation is seen to exist between theory and experiment in Fig. 7.20, except for test T-13, which was considerably stronger than predicted. This was a relatively short column with a low axial force, and therefore its strength should reflect the influence of strain hardening.

The foregoing comparisons of theory with experimental results show that the interaction curves of Figs. 7.13 and 7.14 can be used to predict column behavior quite accurately, provided lateral-torsional buckling is prevented. The specimens used for the experiments in all but one of the test programs were rolled wide-flange shapes, probably containing a similar residual stress pattern to that present in the 8 **WF** 31 shape used in deriving these curves. The hat sections of Ref. 7.20 had quite a different residual stress pattern (see Fig. 3 of Ref. 7.20). However, correlation seems to be equally good for these tests also.

The comparison of the maximum moment of the Lehigh tests (7.23) with the empirical interaction equations (Eqs. 7.11 and 7.14) is shown in the

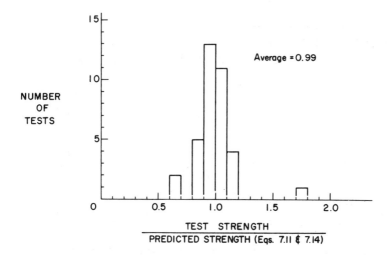

FIG. 7.21.—COMPARISON OF PREDICTED AND EXPERIMENTAL RESULTS

form of a bar diagram in Fig. 7.21. In this figure the ordinate is the number of tests and the abscissa is the ratio of the experimental moment to the empirically predicted moment. For the majority of the tests, the experimental strength is between the limits of ± 10% of the predicted strength.

**Design Recommendations.**

The interaction curves shown for two loading cases for the strong-axis bending of wide-flange shapes in Figs. 7.13 and 7.14 can be used directly in design. As a convenience in interpolating, the interaction curves have been reduced to approximate design equations by means of curve fitting (7.12). Curves for other moment ratios are published in Ref. 7.14, and the maximum moments are tabulated for a close spacing of the axial load ratios, the slenderness ratios, and the moment ratios in Ref. 7.24.

Whereas design recommendations could be based on these curves, it may be desirable to use the more general empirical interaction equations (Eqs. 7.11 and 7.14), because of their versatility and because of the direct way in which they can be adjusted to include the effects of lateral-torsional buckling (Art. 7.5) and, to some extent, frame stability (Chapter 10).

In order to apply the following design rules, the column must be adequately braced in the direction perpendicular to the applied moments so as to prevent lateral-torsional buckling. The ends are assumed torsionally restrained by the beams which frame into them, and they are assumed not to move laterally with respect to each other.

---

**WIDE-FLANGE COLUMNS**

To determine the maximum strength of beam-columns

$$\frac{P}{P_{cr}} + \frac{M_{eq}}{M_p \left(1 - \dfrac{P}{P_e}\right)} = 1.0 \quad \ldots \ldots \ldots (7.11)$$

and

$$\frac{P}{P_y} + \frac{0.85 \, M_2}{M_p} = 1.0 \quad \ldots \ldots \ldots \ldots (7.14)$$

can be used, in which

$$M_{eq} = 0.6 \, M_2 - 0.4 \, M_1 \geq 0.4 \, M_2 \quad \ldots \ldots (7.13)$$

These equations are applicable for any type of cross section where bending is in a plane of symmetry and where lateral-torsional buckling and sidesway are prevented. In the case when $M_1 = -M_2$ (single curvature bending), only Eq. 7.11 need be checked; in all other cases both Eqs. 7.11 and 7.14 must be considered, and the controlling case is that which gives the lower value of $P$ or $M$ from either of the two equations.

---

The above equations are useful in determining the maximum strength of individual columns. In some design situations, such as in designing columns in a multistory frame, it is necessary to know also the deformation capacity of the columns, particularly the end rotation characteristics. Design procedures that consider the deformation characteristics of the columns are described in Chapter 10.

## 7.4   COLUMN DEFLECTION CURVES

### Statement of the Problem.

In the design of many types of building frames it is often sufficient to know the maximum strength of beam-columns. Methods for determining this strength were discussed in Art. 7.3. However, in some instances of the design of columns in multistory frames, it will be necessary to know the whole end-moment versus end-rotation curve for a given member. A useful way of obtaining this curve is by employing the concept of the Column Deflection Curve (CDC). CDC's are possible equilibrium shapes of deformed beam-columns.

### Previous Research.

The idea of CDC's was introduced in 1934 by Chwalla (7.25), who generalized the double integration procedure used by von Kármán in 1909 for the analysis of initially curved axially loaded columns (7.26). In a series of papers in the 1930's, Chwalla established a rational basis for dealing with beam-columns. His ideas were taken up by others, including Ellis (7.27), Neal and Mansell (7.28), Horne (7.29), Bijlaard (7.30), and Lee and Hauck (7.31). An efficient use of CDC's was made possible by the development of $M$-$P$-$\phi$ curves for WF shapes with residual stress (Fig. 7.15), and by the advent of digital computers. The basis of the uses of CDC's as they are applied in this article is the work of Ojalvo (7.15). Levi applied CDC's in the analysis of multistory frames (7.32, 7.33). A thorough basic review of the CDC concept has been made by Lay (7.34).

### Basic Relationships of Column Deflection Curves.

**Equilibrium Equation.**—The equilibrium equation for beam-column AB (Fig. 7.22) is

$$M_E = M_I \quad \dots \dots \dots \dots \dots \quad (7.15)$$

in which $M_E$ = the external moment and $M_I$ = the internal moment at any cross section. Then

$$M_E = M_A \left[ 1 - \frac{z_c}{L} \left( 1 + \frac{M_B}{M_A} \right) \right] + P v_c \quad \dots \dots \quad (7.16)$$

$$M_I = f(\phi) = f(- v_c'') \quad \dots \dots \dots \dots \quad (7.17)$$

and

$$M_A \left[ 1 - \frac{z_c}{L} \left( 1 + \frac{M_B}{M_A} \right) \right] + P v_c = f(- v_c'') \quad \dots \dots \quad (7.18)$$

in which $\phi$ is the curvature and $v_c''$ is the second derivative of the deflection $v_c$ ($\phi = - v_c''$). The relationship $M = f(\phi)$ is defined by the $M$-$P$-$\phi$ curves of Fig. 7.15. In the elastic range Eq. 7.18 can be solved explicitly (6.32). In the inelastic range the integration of the $M$-$P$-$\phi$ curve is usually performed by a numerical procedure.

   A more general way of obtaining the equilibrium deflected shape of
beam-columns is possible if the end moments and axial force on member
AB in Fig. 7.22 are replaced by a single equivalent force, $F$. It can be

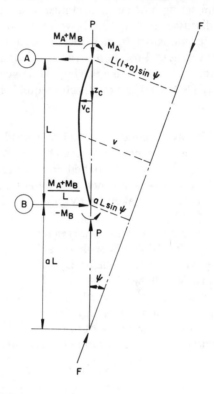

FIG. 7.22.—FORCES ON A BEAM-COLUMN

shown by summing vertical forces and moments about A and B, and by
noting the geometrical conditions given in Fig. 7.22, that

$$a = \frac{M_B}{M_A + M_B} \; ; \; F = \frac{P}{\cos \psi}; \tan \psi = \frac{M_A + M_B}{PL} \; \ldots \; (7.19)$$

and thus both the magnitude and line of action of $F$ are defined. The
equilibrium equation is now

$$Fv = f(-v'') \quad \ldots \ldots \ldots \ldots \ldots (7.20)$$

in which $v$ = the deflection of bar AB with respect to the line of action of $F$.
   **The Deflected Shape.**—Deflected shape AB of a beam-column (Fig.
7.22) can be obtained by integrating Eq. 7.20 over length AB. However,
there is no reason to limit the integration to this length only. Integration

can be extended beyond ends A and B until $v = 0$ (Fig. 7.23). The resulting deflected shape will be a symmetric curve of length $L_{CDC}$, and this curve is a half-wave length of a CDC (7.15).

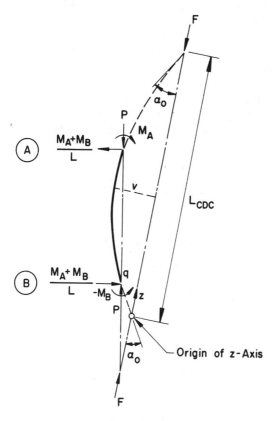

FIG. 7.23.—RELATIONSHIP BETWEEN CDC AND BEAM-COLUMN

Relative to Eq. 7.18 the formulation of the equilibrium as in Eq. 7.20 represents only a shift in coordinates, and thus it is no significant simplification. However, just as the portion AB of the CDC in Fig. 7.23 represents the equilibrium of a particular beam-column, so another portion of the CDC is the shape of another beam-column. Thus any one CDC can give information about an infinite combination of end moments, some of which are shown in Fig. 7.24.

Three half-wave lengths of a CDC, for a constant axial force, $F$, and a given value of the end slopes, $\alpha_o$, are shown in Fig. 7.24. Also shown in Fig. 7.24 are four particular beam-columns selected from the infinite number of end moment conditions which can be fitted to this one CDC: (1) A column with one end pinned, $M_B/M_A = 0$; (2) a column with equal end moments and double curvature, $M_B/M_A = +1.0$; (3) a column with one end fixed; and (4) a column with equal end moments and single curvature, $M_B/M_A = -1.0$. By changing the column lengths or the column end moment ratios $M_B/M_A$, or both, one can accommodate an infinite number of equilibrium deflected shapes from this one CDC.

The segments on the CDC and the corresponding beam-columns are not exactly identical. However, if small deflections are assumed such that $\tan \psi \approx \sin \psi \approx \psi$, and $\cos \psi \approx 1.0$, then $F \approx P$. This assumption is satisfactory in most cases (7.15). It has been shown that if a maximum error of 5% is accepted as tolerable, the assumption that $F \approx P$ applies as long as $P > 0.12 P_y$ for $\sigma_y = 36$ ksi, $P > 0.15 P_y$ for $\sigma_y = 50$ ksi, and $P > 0.22$

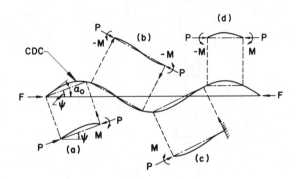

FIG. 7.24.—CDC AND RELATED BEAM-COLUMNS

$P_y$ for $\sigma_y = 100$ ksi (7.34). In most cases the error will be much less than 5%.

Within the limits of the assumption stated above, the CDC will represent an equilibrium deflected shape of the actual beam-column (Fig. 7.25). In addition, the CDC also represents the moment diagram of the beam-column. This moment diagram, as shown in Fig. 7.25, is composed of the moment due to the axial force times the column deflection (shaded area marked ①) and the moments due to the end moments (shaded area marked ②). Thus the CDC provides both the deflected shape and the moment diagram of actual beam-columns.

Elastic response is terminated at the center of the CDC column when the maximum stress reaches a value equal to the quantity $(\sigma_y - \sigma_{rc})$ under an axial force, $F$, and a moment, $Fv_o$, in which $v_o$ = the maximum deflection of the CDC at midheight of a half-wave, $S$ = the section modulus, $\sigma_{rc}$ = the maximum compressive residual stress, and $(F/A) + (Fv_o/S) = (\sigma_y - \sigma_{rc})$. For larger values of $v_o$ some regions in the center segment of the column become yielded. As a result, the curvature in the yielded region

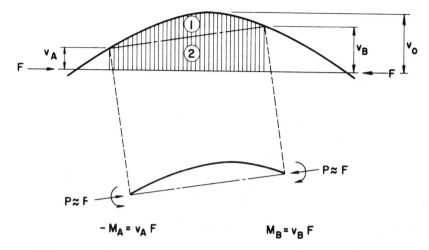

$-M_A = v_A F$            $M_B = v_B F$

FIG. 7.25.—MOMENT DIAGRAM OF A BEAM-COLUMN ON A CDC

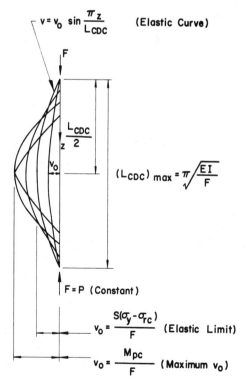

$v = v_0 \sin \dfrac{\pi z}{L_{CDC}}$    (Elastic Curve)

$(L_{CDC})_{max} = \pi \sqrt{\dfrac{EI}{F}}$

$F = P$ (Constant)

$v_0 = \dfrac{S(\sigma_y - \sigma_{rc})}{F}$ (Elastic Limit)

$v_0 = \dfrac{M_{pc}}{F}$ (Maximum $v_0$)

FIG. 7.26.—GEOMETRIC PROPERTIES OF CDC'S

FIG. 7.27.—FAMILY OF FULL CDC'S

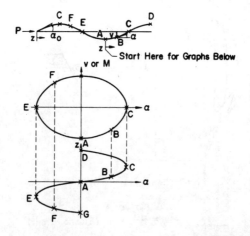

FIG. 7.28.—DEVELOPMENT OF A CDC NOMOGRAPH

becomes relatively larger than in the elastic regions, and therefore the length of the CDC wave decreases. The maximum possible deflection of the CDC occurs when a plastic hinge forms at the center under the moment $Fv_o = M_{pc}$. Higher deflections are impossible for $M = M_{pc}$, since equilibrium would require a reduction in $F$. However, equilibrium shapes having a maximum deflection $v_o = M_{pc}/F$ are possible with shorter lengths if an angular discontinuity is introduced at the center (corresponding to a plastic hinge rotation), as shown in Fig. 7.26.

For any given force, $F$, and a particular $M$-$P$-$\phi$ relationship, one can construct an infinite number of CDC's. They can be distinguished from each other by the slope at the ends, $\alpha_o$ (see Fig. 7.27, which shows an alternate representation of CDC curves to that shown in Fig. 7.26). In actual computations it is more convenient to work with nondimensional parameters. A useful way of presenting the CDC data in graphical form was suggested by Ojalvo, whose nomographic curves are described in Fig. 7.28 (7.15).

At the top of Fig. 7.28 a CDC is shown for a given value of $P$ and a given cross section and material. From the numerical integration the deflection $v$ (and thus $M$, since $M = Pv$) and the slope $\alpha$ at any point $z$ away from a half-wave end (or at any point $z$ away from a half-wave center) is known. Ojalvo suggested that the three pieces of information (i.e., $v$ or $M$, $z$ and $\alpha$) at each point along the CDC be arranged as shown in Fig. 7.28. One curve (the upper one) relates $v$ (or $M$) to $\alpha$. The other curve gives the relationship between $z$ and $\alpha$. Each full wave of a CDC can thus be represented by a closed $v$-$\alpha$ contour and a wavelike $z$-$\alpha$ curve. In Fig. 7.28 the corresponding points on each of the three curves are marked by capital letters.

In general it is not necessary to draw the nomographs for the full wave lengths. Nomographs in Ref. 7.29 show only the $+\alpha$ portions of the curves. One set of such curves (for $P = 0.2\, P_y$, $\sigma_y = 33$ ksi, $\sigma_{rc} = 0.3\,\sigma_y$ and an 8**WF**31 shape) is shown in Fig. 7.29. Each curve in each of the two portions of the nomographs is for one value of $\alpha_o$. These curves are strictly valid for the properties given above. Since the nondimensional $M$-$P$-$\phi$ curves show little variation due to cross-sectional size, the resulting CDC's will also be affected only very little, and thus the CDC's in Fig. 7.29 can be used as approximate solutions for any rolled wide-flange shape bent about its strong axis (7.15). (This approximation is probably too conservative for heavy shapes that are cold-straightened a significant amount. Also, research is under way to obtain corresponding solutions for welded shapes.) Adjustments for the variation in $\sigma_y$ can be made by multiplying $z/r$ by the factor $\sqrt{\sigma_y/33}$.

Also shown in Fig. 7.29 is an illustration of how the end-moment versus end-rotation curves can be constructed for a beam-column under equal end moments (see sketch of beam-column on the right side of Fig. 7.29). The particular member under consideration has a slenderness ratio of 80;

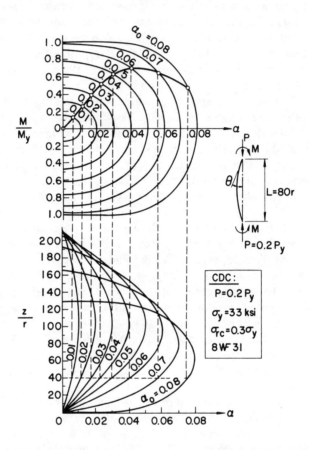

FIG. 7.29.—M-$\theta$ CURVE OF A BEAM-COLUMN FROM NOMOGRAPHS

the value of $z/r$ is thus 40, since the end of the member will be a distance $40r$ from the peak of the CDC. The construction proceeds as follows:

1. In the plot of $z/r$ versus $\alpha$, draw a horizontal line at $z/r = 40$.
2. Each intersection of the line $z/r = 40$ with a $z/r$ versus $\alpha$ curve corresponds to a point on the curve for the same $\alpha_o$ in the $M/M_y - \alpha$ system above it (Fig. 7.28). Draw vertical lines from one system of curves to the other to obtain the points in the $M/M_y - \alpha$ system.
3. Connect these points and obtain the desired M-$\theta$ curve for this problem (heavy solid curve).

The same nomographs can be used to obtain $M$-$\theta$ curves for other lengths. In fact, they can be used to obtain solutions for $M$-$\theta$ curves for any ratio of end moments and for any degree of elastic and inelastic end restraints. Such solutions are given and discussed in Ref. 7.35.

**Moment-Rotation Curves for Beam-Columns.**—Column Deflection Curves are the basic data from which moment-rotation curves for beam-columns are constructed. These curves, in turn, are used to solve for the maximum capacity of restrained columns—and such columns make up a great portion of the members in a multistory frame. In fact, the design of multistory frames consists of analyzing "subassemblages" of one or more columns with restraining beams (1.33). The basic information for solving these subassemblages is a set of $M$-$\theta$ curves; and a great variety of these, for various axial load ratios, slenderness ratios, and end moment ratios, is presented in Ref. 1.33.

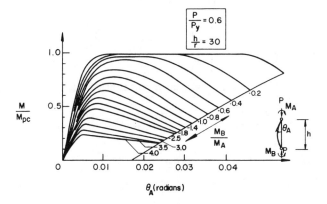

FIG. 7.30.—M-$\theta$ CHARTS FOR NONSWAY BEAM-COLUMNS

One such set of curves is shown in Fig. 7.30. These curves relate the moment at one end of a beam-column of length $h$ to the corresponding rotation, $\theta_o$, at that end for various values of the end moment ratio, $M_B/M_A$. This particular set of curves is for $P/P_y = 0.6$, $L/r = 30$, and negative values of the moment ratio (single curvature). The moment is nondimensionalized by $M_{pc}$, and $\theta$ is given in radians. These curves are valid for $\sigma_y = 33$ ksi. The use of these curves is as follows:

1. Given $M_A$ and $\theta_A$ at one end, find the moment ratio, $M_B/M_A$, from the chart. The moment at the other end, $M_B$, can thus be computed. From this moment and the ratio $M_A/M_B$ (the inverse of $M_B/M_A$), the rotation $\theta_B$ can be found from the charts. Thus the end rotation and the end moment at the other end have been determined.

2. Given $M_A$ and $M_B$, find the values of the two end rotations, $\theta_A$ and $\theta_B$, by computing the ratios of $M_A$ and $M_B$.

### Experimental Verification.

The theoretically obtained end-moment and end-rotation curves, determined from the CDC's, have been checked with test results in several

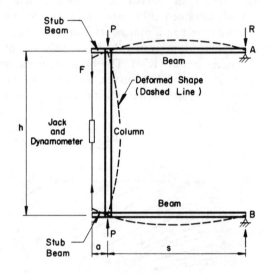

FIG. 7.31.—DIAGRAMMATIC VIEW OF TEST ARRANGEMENT

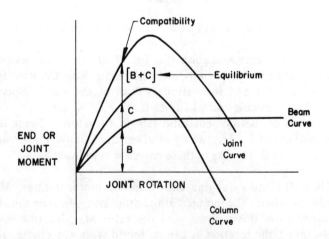

FIG. 7.32.—CONSTRUCTION OF JOINT CURVE FROM BEAM AND COLUMN CURVES

investigations. Single beam-column tests with end moments are reported in Refs. 7.36 and 7.37. Excellent correlation between the measured $M$-$\theta$ curves and the predicted behavior was observed in the tests where lateral-torsional buckling was prevented by lateral bracing.

Additional correlation was obtained in a series of restrained column tests (7.38). The end restraint was furnished by beams framing into the column ends (Fig. 7.31). The axial load was kept constant during the tests, and an exterior end moment was applied through end-stubs. The purpose of these tests was to show that the strength of such a system could be predicted from a knowledge of the $M$-$\theta$ curves of its component members, an example of which is given in Fig. 7.32. The "joint" curve represents the strength of the system. The results of one of the tests is shown in Fig. 7.33,

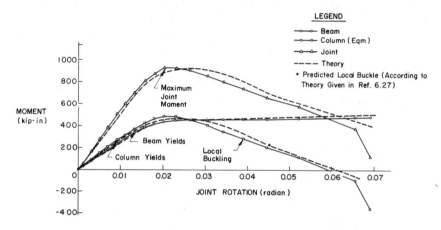

FIG. 7.33.—BASIC TEST RESULTS, TEST RC-3

where the theoretical and experimental $M$-$\theta$ curves for the column, the beam, and the whole system are compared. This test is test RC-3 of Ref. 7.38. The slenderness ratio of the column was 60, and the axial load was 0.42 $P_y$. The correlation between theory and experiment is seen to be excellent.

---

**BEAM-COLUMNS**

Through the use of Column Deflection Curves it is possible to obtain the complete moment-rotation relationship for beam-columns (Fig. 7.30). These curves, in turn, are used to solve for the capacity of beam-columns with end restraints (Fig. 7.32) and of subassemblages. The restrained beam-columns and subassemblages are the basic building blocks used in the design of multistory frames (Chapter 10).

## 7.5   THE INFLUENCE OF LATERAL-TORSIONAL BUCKLING

If a beam-column has sufficiently different bending stiffnesses in its two principal directions, and if the external bending moments are applied in the stronger direction, the beam-column may not reach the strength implied in Art. 7.3 unless adequate lateral bracing is provided. It will usually fail by lateral-torsional buckling before excessive bending in the plane of the moments is reached.

This type of buckling has been observed by investigators who have conducted eccentrically loaded column tests on wide-flange sections where the eccentricity caused bending about the strong axis (6.36, 7.21, 7.23, 7.39).

For beam-columns of intermediate slenderness ratio, lateral-torsional buckling does not take place until parts of the beam-column have yielded. Theoretical solutions for elastic lateral-torsional buckling are available for a wide range of loading and end conditions. For a summary of these, see Chapters 3 and 4 of Ref. 6.18 and Ref. 5.2; a most comprehensive treatment of the problem is given in Ref. 7.40. A complete solution to the inelastic problem, however, is still under development.

In a beam-column located in a plastically designed structure, lateral-torsional buckling leads to the following effects:

1. The maximum strength predicted by the theory of Art. 7.3 may not be fully realized.
2. The rotation capacity may be impaired.

The greatest reduction in strength is associated with beam-columns deflected in single curvature by equal end moments if the ends of the beam-columns are completely unrestrained against rotation in the weak direction (7.41). Tests of beam-columns under equal end moments causing single curvature, but in which almost full restraint about the weak axis was achieved (7.19), show that it is usually possible to reach the strength predicted by the theory of Art. 7.3 (see Figs. 7.17 and 7.19). The exception is where the axial load is close to the "Euler" buckling load. For other loading cases, such as the one shown in Fig. 7.18, the reduction of strength due to lateral-torsional buckling becomes even less.*

---

*If a calculation of the reduction in strength is desired, the methods of Ref. 7.40 may be used. An approximation of this strength may also be obtained by using the interaction equation (Eq. 7.11), in which $M_p$ is replaced by the critical lateral buckling moment and $P_{cr}$ is the weak axis buckling load.

Some theoretical solutions for the inelastic lateral-torsional buckling of wide-flange beam-columns bent about their major axis have been developed for the case of single curvature bending by equal end moments, and for the case in which one of the moments is zero (7.41, 7.42, 7.43, 7.44, 6.40, 6.42). These solutions apply to pinned-end beam-columns of specified cross-sectional shapes, and they provide only the critical moments corresponding to the initiation of lateral-torsional buckling. The behavior after this point has not yet been fully explored, and it is therefore not possible to evaluate the effect of this type of buckling on the rotation capacity. The limited available information seems to indicate that for members normally used for beam-columns and for relatively low slenderness ratios $(L/r_x \leq 40)$ the end moment and the rotation capacities may not be significantly affected (7.37, 7.43).

Because of the complexities of the mathematical analysis, not enough solutions of the inelastic lateral-torsional buckling problem have been performed to permit the development of interaction curves for all possible situations. It has been found that a satisfactory design approximation results by modifying Eq. 7.11 to

$$\frac{P}{(P_{cr})_y} + \frac{M_{eq}}{M_{cr}\left(1 - \dfrac{P}{P_e}\right)} \leq 1 \quad \ldots \ldots (7.21)$$

In Eq. 7.21 all terms are defined as for Eq. 7.11 except that:

$(P_{cr})_y$ = weak axis critical load of the beam-column in the absence of bending moment.

$M_{cr}$  = critical moment of the beam-column in the absence of axial load.

Methods for computing $M_{cr}$ are given in Ref. 6.40. Theoretical and experimental studies have shown that Eq. 7.21 is conservative (6.36, 6.42, 7.37, 7.41, 7.42, 7.44). It is therefore recommended that laterally unbraced beam-columns should be designed according to Eq. 7.21.

If it is desired to develop the maximum moment and maintain the deformation characteristics of beam-columns bent about their major axes (as discussed in Arts. 7.3 and 7.4), it will be necessary to provide adequate lateral bracing. For the case of beam-columns in single-curvature bending, the bracing spacing rules for beams under uniform moment should be applied (Art. 6.3). For beam-columns with moment at one end only, the bracing spacing rules for beams under moment gradient (Art. 6.3) apply if the axial load ratio, $P/P_y$, obeys the relationship (6.27)

$$\frac{P}{P_y} \leq \frac{1 - \dfrac{L}{r_x}\left(\dfrac{1}{\pi}\sqrt{\dfrac{\sigma_y}{E}}\right)}{1 + \dfrac{L}{r_x}\left(\dfrac{1}{\pi}\sqrt{\dfrac{\sigma_y}{E}}\right)} \quad \dots \dots \dots \dots (7.22)$$

If $P/P_y$ exceeds this limit, the bracing should be proportioned according to the rules for beams under uniform moment (Art. 6.3). In case of full double curvature $(M_A = M_B)$ the bracing spacing rules for beams under moment gradient apply (Art. 6.3).

The maximum loads computed by Eq. 7.21 are conservative. Studies have shown that for sections with large torsional stiffness, that is, $K/Ad^2 > 1.5 \times 10^{-3}$ (in which $K$ = the St. Venant torsion constant, $A$ = the cross-sectional area, and $d$ = the depth of the member), then the full in-plane strength as discussed in Art. 7.3 can be reached (6.42). Thus if only strength but not rotation capacity is a consideration, the in-plane capacity of such sections need not be reduced because of lateral-torsional buckling. A majority of the 8-in., 10-in., 12-in., and 14-in. column sections fall into this category (6.42). Furthermore, the solutions are for isolated and simply supported beam-columns. A beam-column in a real building will have restraints from adjacent members. The critical moment will be considerably increased because of these restraints. This problem is currently under study at Lehigh University.

It is also apparent that the beam rules for bracing spacing are conservative when applied to columns (7.45). This problem is also under present study. Thus the recommendations contained in this section should be considered as tentative.

**LATERALLY UNBRACED BEAM-COLUMNS**

The strength of a laterally unbraced beam-column may be predicted from

$$\frac{P}{(P_{cr})_y} + \frac{M_{eq}}{M_{cr}(1 - P/P_e)} \leq 1 \ldots \ldots \ldots (7.21)$$

**BRACING REQUIREMENTS FOR BEAM-COLUMNS**

If a beam-column is required to deliver its full moment and rotation capacities determined for the case of in-plane bending, adequate braces should be provided in accordance with the recommendations for beams as discussed in Art. 6.3.

For $\dfrac{M_B}{M_A} < 0$, use uniform moment rule.

For $\qquad M_B = 0$ and $\dfrac{P}{P_y} > \dfrac{1 - \dfrac{L}{r_x}\left(\dfrac{1}{\pi}\sqrt{\dfrac{\sigma_y}{E}}\right)}{1 + \dfrac{L}{r_x}\left(\dfrac{1}{\pi}\sqrt{\dfrac{\sigma_y}{E}}\right)}$

use uniform moment rule.

For $\qquad M_B = 0$ and $\dfrac{P}{P_y} \leq \dfrac{1 - \dfrac{L}{r_x}\left(\dfrac{1}{\pi}\sqrt{\dfrac{\sigma_y}{E}}\right)}{1 + \dfrac{L}{r_x}\left(\dfrac{1}{\pi}\sqrt{\dfrac{\sigma_y}{E}}\right)}$

use moment gradient rule.

For $\dfrac{M_B}{M_A} > 0$, use moment gradient rule.

## 7.6 COLUMNS SUBJECTED TO BIAXIAL BENDING

The information presented in Art. 7.4 and Art. 7.5 pertains only to the case for which the column is subjected to uniaxial bending. In building frames that employ rigid beam-to-column connections in two directions, the columns are often subjected to bending moments about both principal axes. In recent years, a considerable amount of work has been done on the ultimate strength of biaxially loaded beam-columns. Analytical studies on wide-flange columns have been reported in Refs. 7.46, 7.47, and 7.48, and experimental results have been presented in Refs. 7.49, 7.50, and 7.51. A survey of the present status is given in Ref. 7.52.

Based on the results of these studies, it has been observed that the following equation can be applied to estimate the strength of biaxially loaded columns (5.2)

$$\frac{P}{(P_{cr})_y} + \frac{(M_{eq})_x}{(M_{cr})_x \left[1 - \frac{P}{(P_e)_x}\right]} + \frac{(M_{eq})_y}{M_{py} \left[1 - \frac{P}{(P_e)_y}\right]} \leq 1.0 \ldots \ldots \ldots (7.23)$$

Eq. 7.23 is an extension of Eq. 7.21 to include the effect of bending moment applied about the $y$-axis. In the last term of the equation $M_{py}$ = the full plastic moment about the $y$-axis. The equation neglects the effect of torsional moments that are usually present in a biaxially loaded beam-column. Eq. 7.23 is not a simple extension of Eq. 7.11, because the latter is intended for the case of in-plane behavior which requires that the column be sufficiently braced about the weak axis.

# CHAPTER 8.—CONNECTIONS

## 8.1 INTRODUCTION

Connections play a key role in assuring that a structure can reach the design ultimate load. Since connections frequently are located at points of maximum shear and moment, the details must assure the performance that is assumed in design. The principal requirements for connections are:

1. Sufficient strength.
2. Adequate rotation capacity.
3. Over-all stiffness for maintaining the location of all structural units relative to each other.
4. Economical fabrication.

The various types of connections which will be discussed, and which are typical of those that might be encountered in steel framed structures, are

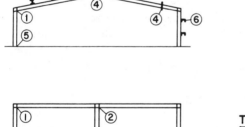

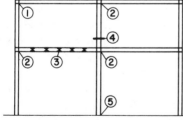

**Types**
① Corner
② Beam–Column
③ Beam–Beam
④ Splice
⑤ Column Anchorage
⑥ Miscellaneous

FIG. 8.1.—TYPES OF CONNECTIONS

designated in Fig. 8.1. These include corner connections (straight and haunched), beam-to-column connections, beam-to-beam connections, splices, column anchorages, and miscellaneous connections (purlins, girts, and bracing).

Primary attention is given herein to corner connections and beam-to-column connections. Methods of analysis are based on assumptions of stress distribution at the plastic limit load which satisfy equilibrium but do not violate the plasticity condition. Solutions thus constitute lower bounds to connection capacity. The same principles would be applicable, however, for the analysis of other types of connections.

Often connections may be placed at locations other than the points of maximum moment and shear. At those locations they should be proportioned for the maximum probable partial distribution of maximum moment and shear. Even where calculations show a lesser moment would be suitable, at least half the plastic limit capacity should be developed at these locations to provide for uncertainties in loading and distribution.

Numerous examples of the elastic and plastic design of welded structural connections are given in Refs. 8.1 and 8.2. A summary of the experimental behavior of several types of joints is given in Ref. 8.3.

## 8.2 STRAIGHT CORNER CONNECTIONS

Straight corner connections are formed by directly joining two members. Such connections in which the members are joined at right angles (as at ① in the 2-story frame of Fig. 8.1) are sometimes called square corner connections. Studies of the theory, design, and behavior of square corner connections may be found in Refs. 8.4, 8.5, 8.6, 8.7, 8.8, and 6.30.

The basic principles of the theory of connections will be illustrated by considering an unreinforced square corner connection. It is more critical than a connection in which the members do not join at right angles. Fig. 8.2(a) shows the moment diagram for a typical rectangular frame loaded with a uniformly distributed load. A typical unreinforced corner connection is sketched in Fig. 8.2(b). The moment, thrust, and shear acting on the connection are depicted in Fig. 8.2(c).

In arriving at a simple analysis of the forces in a knee it is assumed that normal stresses caused by bending moment and thrust are all carried in the flanges, and that shear stresses are all carried by the web—axial thrust is neglected. In Fig. 8.2(d), the action of the applied forces on the parts of the corner and of the parts on each other is represented by arrows. The tensile force in the outer flange of the beam is carried into the web in shear along line AB. In like manner, the tensile force in the outer flange of the column is carried through the end plate into the web as a shear along line AD. In each case, the tensile stress in the flange is assumed to be reduced from $\sigma_y$ at the edge of the corner (B or D) to zero at the external corner (A).

The prolongation of the inner flange of the beam carries two external forces: the shear of the column, and the normal force due to bending and thrust in the beam. The resultant of these two forces is carried into the corner as a shear along line DC. A similar pair of force components exerted on the vertical stiffener causes shear along line BC of the web.

In considering the effect of the forces on the equilibrium and behavior of the corner connection, it is rather obvious that an unsatisfactory condi-

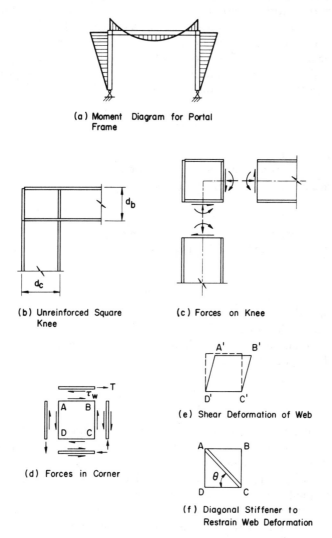

(a) Moment   Diagram   for Portal
     Frame

(b) Unreinforced   Square
     Knee

(c) Forces   on   Knee

(e) Shear   Deformation   of   Web

(d) Forces   in   Corner

(f) Diagonal   Stiffener   to
     Restrain   Web   Deformation

FIG. 8.2.—STRAIGHT CORNER CONNECTIONS

tion would exist if there were insufficient material to carry the forces without buckling or general yielding. Assuming that the horizontal beam continues through the knee, its flanges AB and CD of Fig. 8.2(d) are sufficient to resist any forces carried in the members outside the knee, and are selected to preclude local flange buckling. The end plate, AD, should have the same area as the flange of the column. The vertical stiffener, BC, must have sufficient area to carry the column compression flange force into the beam web. In all cases the welds must be sufficient to transmit the required shear or normal force. Study of the square web panel reveals that the shear forces would tend to deform the panel as shown in Fig. 8.2(e).

Consideration of the equilibrium of the horizontal forces on the portion of the outer flange between A and B in Fig. 8.2(d) will give an expression for the web thickness required to resist shear. According to the approximation stated earlier, the force in the flange is given by

$$T \cong \frac{M_p}{d_b}$$

in which $d_b$ = depth of beam.

The maximum web shear resisting force between A and B (neglecting the influence of axial stress and strain hardening) is

$$T_w = \tau_y \, w \, d_c$$

in which $w$ = thickness of web and $d_c$ = depth of column.
Equating the shear and flange forces gives

$$w_r = \frac{M_p}{\tau_y \, d_b \, d_c}$$

in which $w_r$ = the required web thickness.

According to the Mises yield criterion, the limiting shear yield stress, $\tau_y$, for the condition of pure shear is $\sigma_y/\sqrt{3}$. Using this criterion, the required web thickness becomes

$$w_r = \frac{\sqrt{3} \, M_p}{\sigma_y \, d_b \, d_c}. \quad \ldots \ldots \ldots \ldots \ldots \quad (8.1)$$

This resulting expression for $w_r$ is similar to that obtained in Ref. 8.4. It has been shown that the use of more exact analysis does not alter the results of calculations substantially (8.4).

For many wide-flange shapes the web thickness will be less than $w_r$, in which case reinforcement is required. This reinforcement may take the form of a doubler plate which increases the total thickness of the web to the required amount. However, it is sometimes more practical to provide a symmetrical pair of diagonal stiffeners. Diagonal stiffeners act somewhat like the diagonals of a truss panel in preventing shear deformation. Fig. 8.2(f) shows diagonal stiffeners between corners A and C of the web. The diagonal stiffeners are able to resist part of the normal stresses in the flanges.

By considering equilibrium of the forces on the top flange, the required area of the diagonal stiffeners may be obtained. The flange force, $T$, must be resisted by the web shear, $T_w$, and the horizontal component of the diagonal stiffener force, $T_s$. The magnitude of the latter component is given by

$$T_s = \sigma_y \, A_s \cos \theta$$

in which $A_s$ = area of a symmetrical pair of diagonal stiffeners and $\theta$ = angle of diagonal stiffeners with the horizontal (tan $\theta = d_b/d_c$).

Noting that $T$ must equal $T_w + T_s$ the stiffener area is found as

$$A_s = \frac{1}{\cos \theta} \left( \frac{M_p}{\sigma_y \, d_b} - \frac{w \, d_c}{\sqrt{3}} \right) \quad \ldots \ldots \ldots \quad (8.2)$$

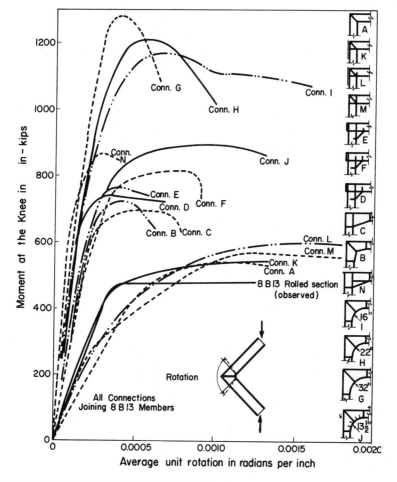

FIG. 8.3.—MOMENT-ROTATION CURVES OF CONNECTIONS (A7 STEEL)

The actual performance of straight corner connections has been studied in several tests. In Fig. 8.3 are shown the results of tests including a series on four straight connections, A, K, L, and M made from 8B13 members of A7 steel (8.4). The moment-rotation curves of the connections are compared with the moment-rotation curve for an 8B13 beam as shown by the heavy line. Of major interest are strength, stiffness, and rotation capacity. Each connection reached a maximum moment greater than that of an 8B13 beam. The rotation of each of the knees was great enough to be considered adequate to allow a structure to form a mechanism. The initial

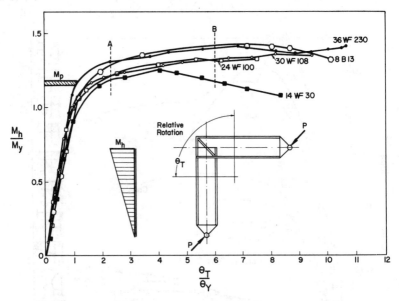

FIG. 8.4.—MOMENT-ROTATION CURVES FOR CONNECTIONS TESTED TO STUDY "SIZE-EFFECT"

stiffness of the knees was approximately the same as that of the rolled beam, but larger rotations occurred in the knees at a lower moment because of residual stresses. However, the larger rotations were not severe enough to impair the practical effectiveness of the connections.

Results of five additional tests on straight corner connections are given in Fig. 8.4. These tests were performed on knees joining several sizes of wide-flange beams (6.30). The shaded zone at $M_h/M_y = M_p$ is so marked to depict the range of spread in shape factor of the five wide-flange shapes that were tested. These tests confirm that these knees also satisfied the requirements for use in plastic design.

---

**STRAIGHT CORNER CONNECTIONS**
*Web Thickness Required:*

$$w_r = \frac{\sqrt{3}\,M_p}{\sigma_y\,d_b\,d_c} \quad \ldots \ldots \ldots \ldots \ldots \ldots \ldots \text{(8.1)}$$

*Web Stiffening:*

The web of a connection may be reinforced by doubler plates to meet the requirements of Eq. 8.1 or by diagonal stiffeners welded to the flanges and to the web. The area of a symmetrical pair of diagonal stiffeners should be

$$A_s = \frac{1}{\cos\theta}\left(\frac{M_p}{\sigma_y\,d_b} - \frac{w\,d_c}{\sqrt{3}}\right) \quad \ldots \ldots \ldots \ldots \text{(8.2)}$$

in which $\theta = \tan^{-1}(d_b/d_c)$.

---

## 8.3 HAUNCHES

Haunches of either the tapered or the curved type are sometimes used to achieve a pleasing appearance. Their use in allowable-stress design makes it possible to adapt the section of the haunch to follow more closely the shape of the moment diagram, furnishing approximately the resisting moment required at a number of given sections with resulting economies of material. Similarly, in plastic design the use of haunches also makes possible a reduction in size of the main member. Although the haunch will permit a reduction in main member size, it will be costly to fabricate, and thus may offset some of the savings that will be realized by using the smaller main member.

Tests of haunched connections designed by methods intended primarily for elastic structures revealed that the connections exhibited good strength, but that some lacked sufficient rotation capacity. The lack of rotation capacity was attributed to premature lateral buckling of the compression flanges (8.4). Recently developed methods of analysis, confirmed by tests, show that plastic hinges can function properly in the haunch if adequate provision is made to prevent such buckling (8.9).

The effect of haunches on the analysis of a frame is to increase the number of sections at which plastic hinges may form. However, the methods of analysis are unchanged. Fig. 8.5 gives the results of a mechanism analysis of a portal frame with haunches. The correct solution depends on the loading and geometry of the structure. For the given geometry and loading the correct solution would be Mechanism 4 [Fig. 8.5(e)], and the resulting moment diagram [Fig. 8.5(g)] shows that the plasticity condition is not violated. The required plastic hinge moment, $M_p$, of the main members is smaller as a result of using the haunches. At the same time, it is necessary that the haunch be able to carry a moment $M_h$ which is greater than this $M_p$ value. From the final moment diagram [Fig. 8.5(g)] the mo-

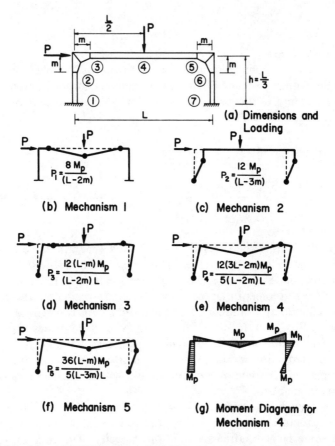

(a) Dimensions and Loading

(b) Mechanism 1

$$P_1 = \frac{8 M_p}{(L-2m)}$$

(c) Mechanism 2

$$P_2 = \frac{12 M_p}{(L-3m)}$$

(d) Mechanism 3

$$P_3 = \frac{12(L-m) M_p}{(L-2m) L}$$

(e) Mechanism 4

$$P_4 = \frac{12(3L-2m)M_p}{5(L-2m)L}$$

(f) Mechanism 5

$$P_5 = \frac{36(L-m)M_p}{5(L-3m)L}$$

(g) Moment Diagram for Mechanism 4

FIG. 8.5.—ANALYSIS OF A PORTAL FRAME WITH HAUNCHES

ment, thrust, and shear at any cross section of the frame may be determined for purposes of design.

## 8.4 TAPERED HAUNCHES

A sketch of a typical tapered haunch is given in Fig. 8.6. The forces to be considered in the design of the haunch are the moment, thrust, and shear at Section 1 where the beam is joined to the haunch. These forces would be determined from an analysis of the complete structure (Fig. 8.5).

Three main problems must be considered in the design of tapered haunches. These are: (1) resistance to bending in the tapered portion of the haunch, (2) resistance to local and lateral buckling, and (3) shear stresses in the web and flange forces in and around the corner panel BDFE (Fig. 8.6).

In analyzing the tapered portion of the haunch for resistance to bending, cross sections perpendicular to the layout line of the structure may be considered. The web thickness and flange width of the haunch are usually made equal to those of the adjoining member. This assures that the web is able to carry at least as much shear and axial force as the web of the beam. Changes in the resistance to bending moment of the haunch may be con-

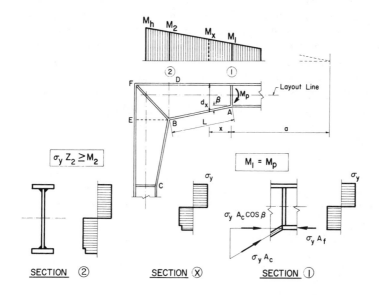

FIG. 8.6.—FORCES ON A TAPERED HAUNCH

trolled, therefore, by the thickness of the flanges and by the depth of the haunch. The outer flange is usually parallel to the layout line, and the inner flange makes an angle of taper $\beta$ with the layout line, thus defining the depth of the haunch at any point. At any distance $x$ along the haunch, the moment of resistance of the cross section perpendicular to the layout line must equal or exceed the applied moment at that section determined from the plastic analysis.

The plastic moment of resistance of any cross section is given by (8.9)

$$M_{px} = \sigma_y Z_x \quad \ldots \ldots \ldots \ldots \ldots \ldots (8.3)$$

in which $Z_x$ = the plastic modulus at the particular section. It has been shown that if the plastic moment of resistance is adequate at the beam connection (Section 1, Fig. 8.6) and at the re-entrant corner (Section 2, Fig.

8.6), there will be no need to check at other sections along the haunch (8.9).

In proportioning tapered haunches, it is sometimes desirable that the flanges have the same size as the nominal dimensions of the adjoining member. In this case, the flange area presented on a cross section perpendicular to the layout line would be different for a sloping flange at angle $\beta$ than for a flange parallel to the layout line. The effective cross section would be unsymmetrical with respect to its major axis, with resulting complexities in the calculation of the plastic modulus, $Z$.

In Ref. 8.9, a somewhat simplified analysis is suggested to reduce the complexities of computations. As shown in Fig. 8.6, the stress in the sloping compression flange is assumed to act in the direction of the flange. To calculate the moment in the desired direction, the component of flange force parallel to the layout line must be obtained by multiplying the flange force by cos $\beta$. By increasing the area of the sloping flange, the components of flange force in each flange may be made equal, thus providing effective symmetry to the cross section. The necessary area of the sloping flange is

$$A_c = \frac{A_t}{\cos \beta} \dots \dots \dots \dots \dots (8.4)$$

in which $A_c$ = area of sloping (compression) flange plate; $A_t$ = area of straight (tension) flange plate; and $\beta$ = angle between sloping flange and layout line.

The plastic modulus at any section will be

$$Z_x = b\, t_t\, (d_x - t_t) + \frac{w}{4}(d_x - 2\, t_t)^2 \dots \dots \dots (8.5)$$

in which $b$ = width of flange; $d_x$ = depth of haunch at any section $x$; $w$ = web thickness; and $t_t$ = thickness of the straight (tension) flange plate.

In cases where the angle $\beta$ is less than 20°, the required increase in area suggested in Eq. 8.4 would not exceed 6%. Most practical design procedures would neglect such a difference. For all practical purposes, both flanges should probably be made equal and still use the assumption that the cross section is symmetrical and that its centroid is at middepth.

The resistance to local buckling of the flanges of tapered haunches may be assured by adhering to the recommendations of Chapter 6.

Lateral buckling of tapered haunches depends on the slenderness of the compression flange and on the extent to which the flange is yielded and strain hardened. It is assumed that positive lateral support of the inner flange will be provided at points A, B, and C (Fig. 8.6). Since the web provides restraint against buckling of the flange about its weak axis, the flange must buckle in its strong direction between points of support.

A conservative approximate expression for the critical buckling length of the compression flange has been obtained (8.9) by using the tangent modulus buckling concept (6.18, 6.26). It is assumed that the compression flange is uniformly stressed to $\sigma_y$, that the strain in the flange just reaches $\epsilon_{st}$, and that the flange buckles as a pin-ended column between points of lateral bracing. These assumptions result in a critical slenderness of

$$\left(\frac{K L_{cr}}{r_x}\right)^2 = \pi^2 \frac{E_{st}}{\sigma_y} \quad \ldots \ldots \ldots \ldots \ldots (8.6)$$

which when solved for $L_{cr}$ gives

$$L_{cr} = \frac{b\pi}{K} \sqrt{\frac{E_{st}}{12 \sigma_y}} \quad \ldots \ldots \ldots \ldots \ldots (8.7)$$

in which $K$ = effective length factor taken as 0.8 (see Art. 6.3); $L_{cr}$ = critical length for lateral buckling of compression flange; $b$ = width of flange; $r_x$ = radius of gyration of flange = $b/\sqrt{12}$; $E_{st}$ = strain-hardening modulus of steel; and $\sigma_y$ = yield stress of steel assumed in the design.

By substituting the mechanical properties, $E_{st}$ (assumed to be 800 ksi) and $\sigma_y$ (assumed to be 36 ksi), the critical length

$$L_{cr} = 5.3b \quad \ldots \ldots \ldots \ldots \ldots \ldots (8.8)$$

is obtained for fully strain hardened compression flanges of ASTM A36 type steel. This expression neglects any restraint to buckling offered by the web. It contains some restraint offered by adjacent portions of the flange. For other grades of steel, appropriate values would be substituted in Eq. 8.7 (see Art. 5.1).

Frequently it will be found that $L_{cr}$ given by Eq. 8.8 will be less than the value obtained from the original haunch layout. In such a case, additional points of lateral support would be provided. Alternatively the flange thickness or the depth of the haunch at Section 2 (Fig. 8.6) could be increased. Ref. 8.9 suggests methods for accomplishing such modifications.

The shear stresses in the web and flange forces around the corner panel BDFE (Fig. 8.6) are of the same character as those shown in Fig. 8.2(d) for a square corner, and would result in deformation similar to that in Fig. 8.2(e) when the forces exceed the shear strength of the panel. The problem may be examined in more general form with the aid of the sketch of a haunched knee of a gable bent as shown in Fig. 8.7. In this knee, the forces on the panel BDFE are to be determined. For the most severe loading, the cross sections BD and BE will be fully yielded and the total area of the flanges at these sections will be stressed to $\sigma_y$. At the re-entrant corner B, the inner flanges will have an unbalanced component of force in the direction of BF in the absence of a web stiffener. This unbalanced component of flange force would have to be carried by the web. The web could be fully yielded due to bending stresses at point B, so it is advisable to neglect the carrying capacity of the web and furnish a symmetrical pair of diagonal stiffeners along FB.

At the outer corner, F, the situation is slightly different because part of the flange force could be carried by shear in the web along lines EF and DF, thus reducing the components of flange force to be carried by the

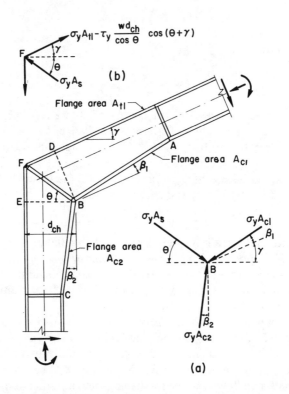

FIG. 8.7.—DIAGONAL STIFFENER FORCES IN A GABLED TAPERED HAUNCH

diagonal stiffeners at F. For this reason, the selection of diagonal stiffeners will usually be governed by equilibrium at the re-entrant corner B.

The maximum possible forces in the two flanges and in the diagonal stiffener at corner B are shown in Fig. 8.7(a). The required area of the diagonal stiffener may be determined from an equation of equilibrium of horizontal components of these forces as

$$\sigma_y A_s \cos \theta - \sigma_y A_{c1} \cos (\beta_1 + \gamma) + \sigma_y A_{c2} \sin \beta_2 = 0 \quad \ldots \ldots (8.9)$$

Then

$$A_s = \frac{A_{c1} \cos (\beta_1 + \gamma) - A_{c2} \sin \beta_2}{\cos \theta} \quad \dots \dots \quad (8.10)$$

in which   $A_s$ = area of a symmetrical pair of diagonal stiffeners;
$A_{c1}$ = area of inner flange of rafter haunch;
$A_{c2}$ = area of inner flange of column haunch;
$\gamma$ = angle of inclination of rafter;
$\theta$ = angle of slope of diagonal stiffener;
$\beta_1$ = angle of taper of rafter haunch; and
$\beta_2$ = angle of taper of column haunch.

In Fig. 8.7(b) the maximum possible forces at the outer corner, $F$, are shown. Equilibrium of horizontal components gives

$$\sigma_y A_{t1} \cos \gamma - \tau_y \frac{w d_{ch}}{\cos \theta} \cos (\theta + \gamma) \cos \gamma - \sigma_y A_s \cos \theta = 0 \quad \dots \quad (8.11)$$

Substituting $\tau_y = \sigma_y / \sqrt{3}$ and solving for the required stiffener area gives

$$A_s = \left( \frac{A_{t1}}{\cos \theta} - \frac{w d_{ch} \cos (\theta + \gamma)}{\sqrt{3} \cos^2 \theta} \right) \cos \gamma \quad \dots \dots \quad (8.12)$$

in which   $A_{t1}$ = area of outer flange of beam haunch;
$w$ = web thickness of haunch; and
$d_{ch}$ = depth of column haunch at section EB (Fig. 8.7).

If Eq. 8.12 should result in a zero or negative value for $A_s$, the implication is that the shear capacity of the web is adequate to transmit the outer flange force, and that diagonal stiffeners are needed only to transmit the unbalance of the inner flange force. Since in any case the web will carry some force, Eq. 8.10 based on equilibrium at the inner corner will control for ordinary haunch proportions rather than Eq. 8.12.

Transverse stiffeners at the junctions of the tapered and prismatic sections (points A and C) may be designed to carry the unbalance of the flange force due to the sudden change in direction. Since the angles $\beta_1$ and $\beta_2$ are generally quite small, the size of the stiffeners usually will be governed by minimum size requirements.

A series of tests of haunched corner connections has given experimental results agreeing well with the concepts just outlined (8.10). Moment-rotation curves for these tests are shown in Fig. 8.8. Specimens 44 and 45 were made with the critical length of compression flange approximately equal to that given by Eq. 8.8. Specimen 44 was not braced against twisting at the inner corner, whereas specimen 45 was braced. Specimen 45 performed satisfactorily, whereas specimen 44 buckled before it reached the computed maximum load, although it exhibited considerable postbuckling strength. Specimens 46 and 47 had compression-flange lengths greater than that given by Eq. 8.8, but were modified by increasing the haunch

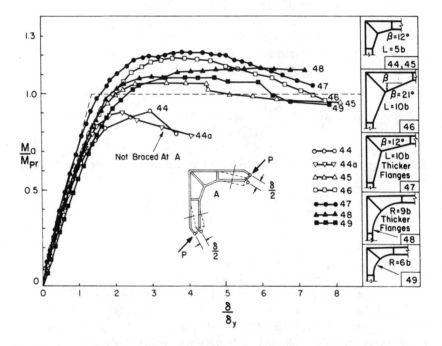

FIG. 8.8.—MOMENT-ROTATION CURVES FOR HAUNCHED CONNECTIONS (A7 STEEL)

depth and by increasing the flange thicknesses, respectively. These specimens also performed satisfactorily in that they met the requirements stated earlier.

The results of these tests indicate that safe and adequate connections may be made by meeting the requirements derived by the theory. In summary, the following suggestions are made with regard to proportioning of tapered haunched connections:

---

**TAPERED HAUNCHES**

*Required Plastic Modulus:*

The plastic modulus should be checked for resistance to the applied moment at the deep end and the shallow end of each haunch.

*Local Buckling:*

The recommendations of Chapter 6 should be followed to assure that premature local buckling of flanges will not occur.

*Lateral Buckling:*

The critical unbraced length of a compression flange which may be strained to the point of strain hardening throughout its entire length without premature lateral buckling is conservatively estimated as

$$L_{cr} = 5.3 \, b \quad \cdots\cdots\cdots\cdots \quad (8.8)$$

for A36 steel. For other grades of steel, $L_{cr}$ can be calculated by substituting appropriate mechanical property values into Eq. 8.7.

The critical unbraced length of a compression flange may be increased substantially by increasing the angle of taper $\beta$ or by increasing the thickness of the flanges.

*Diagonal Web Stiffeners:*

To resist an unbalance of inner flange forces and reinforce the web against undue shear deformation, a symmetrical pair of diagonal stiffeners may be provided having a total area

$$A_s = \frac{A_{c1} \cos (\beta_1 + \gamma) - A_{c2} \sin \beta_2}{\cos \theta} \quad \cdots\cdots \quad (8.10)$$

Diagonal stiffeners should be welded to the web and to both flanges.

*Transverse Stiffeners:*

Transverse stiffeners at the junctions of the tapered haunch and prismatic section serve to carry the unbalance of the inner flange force due to the sudden change in direction. Minimum size requirements will usually govern the thickness.

---

## 8.5   CURVED HAUNCHES

In Fig. 8.9 are shown the layout and the applied forces for a typical curved haunch. The haunch must be designed to withstand the plastic hinge moment of the beam at its connection to the haunch and any larger moment which develops in the haunched portion as a result of the moment gradient.

As with tapered haunches, the three main problems to be considered in the design of curved haunches are: (1) resistance to bending in the haunch, (2) resistance to local and lateral buckling, and (3) shear stresses in the corner panel BDFE (Fig. 8.10).

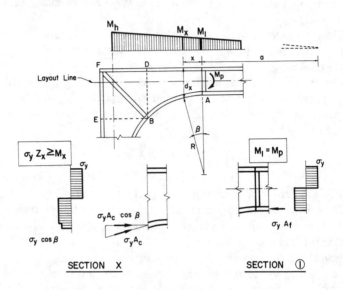

FIG. 8.9.—FORCES ON A CURVED HAUNCH

The plastic moment of resistance at any cross section $x$ of the haunch perpendicular to the layout line is (Fig. 8.9)

$$M_{px} = \sigma_y Z_x \quad \ldots \ldots \ldots \ldots \ldots \ldots (8.3)$$

As in tapered haunches, increasing the thickness of the curved flange would compensate for the reduction in effective section due to the inclination $\beta$ of the flange, and would make the section effectively symmetrical about its half depth. The theoretically required thickness is given by (8.9)

$$t_c = \frac{t_t}{\cos \beta} \quad \ldots \ldots \ldots \ldots \ldots (8.4a)$$

in which $t_c$ = thickness of the compression flange plate and $\beta$ = central angle between point of tangency and given section of knee. For all practical cases, the controlling angle $\beta$ will be small (approximately 12°), and symmetry can be assumed without increasing the compression flange thickness. Assuming symmetry, the section modulus at any section $x$ is

$$Z_x = bt_t (d_x - t_t) + \frac{w}{4} (d_x - 2 t_t)^2 \quad \ldots \ldots \ldots (8.5)$$

in which $d_x$ = depth of haunch at any section $(x)$ = $d + R (1 - \cos \beta)$; $R$ = radius of curvature of inner flange; and $x = R \sin \beta$.

Eq. 8.5 may be substituted into Eq. 8.3 for $M_{px}$ and the result equated to $M_x$, the applied moment which must be resisted. Solving for the thickness of the tension flange gives

$$t_t = \frac{d_x - \sqrt{d_x^2 \left(\dfrac{b}{b-w}\right) - \dfrac{4 M_x}{\sigma_y (b-w)}}}{2} \quad \ldots \ldots \ (8.13)$$

At some station along the haunch defined by a controlling value of the angle $\beta$, the values of $d_x$ and $M_x$ will require a maximum flange thickness. For values of the radius of flange curvature and distance to the inflection point that would be encountered ordinarily in practice, the controlling angle $\beta$ has been found to be about 12° (8.7).

The resistance to local buckling of the flanges of curved haunches may be assured by following the recommendations of Chapter 6.

Lateral stability of curved haunches is dependent upon the resistance to buckling of the compression flange perpendicular to the plane of the web. Ref. 8.9 contains an approximate solution obtained by analyzing the problem as the buckling of a curved beam simply supported at the points of tangency and at the diagonal stiffener. To simplify the analysis the curved flange is conservatively assumed to have a uniform stress distribution over its whole area and length. The tangent modulus equation for the buckling of fully strain hardened steel plates gives, for the critical arc length of flange (8.9, 6.26)

$$\left(\frac{KL}{r_x}\right)_{cr} = \left(\frac{KR\alpha}{r_x}\right)_{cr} = \pi \sqrt{\frac{E_{st}}{\sigma_y}} \ldots \ldots \ldots (8.14)$$

in which    $L_{cr}$ = critical arc length for lateral buckling of compression flange = $(R\alpha)_{cr}$;

      $\alpha$ = central angle of curved flange between points of lateral support (it is equal to the angle $[45° - (\gamma/2)]$ in Fig. 8.10 unless there are additional points of lateral support between A and B); and

      $r_x$ = radius of gyration of compression flange in strong direction = $b/\sqrt{12}$.

The critical arc length when expressed in terms of the flange width becomes (for ASTM A36 type steel)

$$(R\alpha)_{cr} = L_{cr} = 5.3 b \ldots \ldots \ldots \ldots (8.8)$$

This solution assumes a pin-ended condition. Since some end restraint would be provided by the adjoining beam segment, and since the stress distribution is not actually uniform along the curved inner flange, a moderate increase is provided by using the effective length factor, $K$, in the critical arc length. For a 90° connection, Eq. 8.8 reduces (approximately) to

$$R = 7b \quad \ldots \ldots \ldots \ldots \ldots \quad (8.15)$$

If for some reason it is desired to increase the radius above the value given by Eq. 8.15, additional points of support may be added to decrease

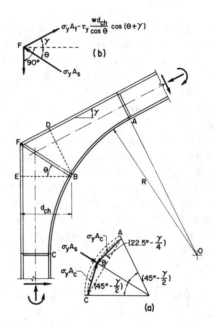

FIG. 8.10.—DIAGONAL STIFFENER FORCES IN A GABLED CURVED HAUNCH

the critical arc length according to Eq. 8.8. Other possible measures are to change the radius of gyration by increasing the flange width $b$, or by changing the shape of the flange cross section. Also, the strains in the flange could be controlled by increasing the flange thickness.

An additional problem not encountered with tapered haunches is the cross bending of the curved flange. Cross bending is a phenomenon in which radial components of force in the curved flanges tend to bend the flange edges toward the web. It has been shown (8.9) that cross bending will have only a negligible effect on haunch behavior if the connection is proportioned so that

$$\frac{b^2}{2\,Rt} \leqq 1 \quad \ldots \ldots \ldots \ldots \ldots \quad (8.16)$$

The effect of shear force on the web will be discussed with the aid of Fig. 8.10 showing a gabled haunch. In the two segments of the haunch bounded by cross sections perpendicular to the layout lines at A and D and at E and C, the problem may be dismissed with the observation that the web area is equal to or greater than the web area of the adjacent prismatic beam which carries the same shear force. In the corner panel BDFE, the forces are similar to those in the tapered haunch described in Art. 8.3, and therefore Eq. 8.12 would indicate the necessary stiffener size at the outer corner, F.

A second reason for using diagonal stiffeners in the corner panel is to resist web buckling due to the radial component of force from the curved inner flange. An approximation of the required stiffener size may be determined by neglecting the radial compression resistance of the web and assuming that the diagonal stiffeners resist two components of inner flange force directed along chords between AB and BC as shown in Fig. 8.10(a). Summing the forces in a radial direction gives

$$\sigma_y A_s = 2\,\sigma_y A_c \sin\left(22.5° - \frac{\gamma}{4}\right) \quad \ldots \ldots \ldots \quad (8.17)$$

in which $A_c$ = area of inner flange. Hence

$$A_s = 2 A_c \sin\left(22.5° - \frac{\gamma}{4}\right) \quad \ldots \ldots \ldots \ldots \quad (8.18)$$

Eq. 8.18 will tend to control the design of diagonal stiffeners for most curved haunches rather than Eq. 8.12. In the case of steeper gables (large $\gamma$), it is possible that Eq. 8.12 may require larger stiffeners.

Results of tests of curved connections (8.10) are given in Fig. 8.8. Test 49 was made on a specimen which had the maximum unsupported flange length recommended by Eq. 8.8, and it performed well. Test 48 was performed on a specimen with a greater unsupported compression flange length, but with the flange thickness increased to reduce strains. This specimen also performed satisfactorily, but had somewhat less rotation capacity. Results of some earlier tests shown in Fig. 8.3 give an opportunity to observe the effect of radius of curvature on rotation capacity. Connection H with $R = 5.5\,b$ had somewhat less capacity. Connection G with $R = 8\,b$ had the least rotation capacity, and might be considered inadequate. Connection J, of a slightly different design, had $R = 3.4\,b$, and exhibited good rotation capacity.

## CURVED HAUNCHES

### Required Plastic Modulus:

The plastic modulus furnished at any point in the haunch must be adequate to resist the applied moment at that point. For typical values of $R$ and moment gradient, the central angle $\beta$ to the section controlling the thickness of the flange is about 12°. If the web of the haunch is no thinner than the web of the beam, the thickness of flange required to provide an adequate plastic modulus is given by

$$t_t = \frac{d_x - \sqrt{d_x^2 \left(\dfrac{b}{b-w}\right) - \dfrac{4\,M_x}{\sigma_y\,(b-w)}}}{2} \quad \dots\dots (8.13)$$

### Lateral Buckling:

The critical unbraced length of a curved compression flange strained to the point of strain hardening without premature lateral buckling is conservatively estimated as

$$L_{cr} = (R\alpha)_{cr} = 5.3\,b \quad \dots\dots\dots (8.8)$$

for A36 steel. For other grades of steel, $L_{cr}$ can be calculated by substituting appropriate values into Eq. 8.14.

The critical unbraced length of a compression flange may be increased by increasing the thickness of the flanges.

### Cross Bending:

The effect of cross bending on connection behavior will be negligible if

$$\frac{b^2}{2\,Rt} \leq 1 \quad \dots\dots\dots\dots (8.16)$$

### Diagonal Web Stiffeners:

To reinforce the web against buckling due to radial compression in the curved inner flange, a symmetrical pair of diagonal stiffeners may be provided having a total area

$$A_s = 2\,A_c \sin\left(22.5° - \frac{\gamma}{4}\right) \quad \dots\dots\dots (8.18)$$

For steep gabled haunches the diagonal stiffener thickness should also be checked by means of Eq. 8.12.

## 8.6  BEAM-TO-COLUMN CONNECTIONS

Fig. 8.11 shows three common types of beam-to-column connections used on planar structures. The function of the "Top" and "Interior" connections is to transmit moment from one beam to another, the column carrying any unbalanced moment. The "Side" connection transmits beam moment to the upper and lower columns. The design problem is to provide sufficient stiffening material so that the connection will transmit the moment. Some columns are sturdy enough to carry full-moment beam connections without stiffening. Other columns require stiffening of their webs or flanges to aid in carrying the concentrated forces from the flanges of the connected beams.

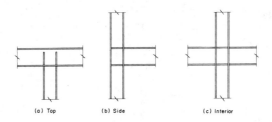

(a) Top          (b) Side          (c) Interior

FIG. 8.11.—TYPES OF BEAM-TO-COLUMN CONNECTIONS

Studies on the design and the behavior of full moment interior beam-to-column connections are reported in Refs. 8.11 and 8.12. Further studies are now in progress on beam-to-column connections to evaluate the effect of axial load and strain hardening on the connection behavior (8.13). Studies by Popov have shown that connections whose proportions met the applicable provisions contained in this Manual subjected to repeated applications of the limit load perform satisfactorily (6.80).

In treating problems relating to beam-to-column connections, the case of connections without stiffening will be examined as to the adequacy or inadequacy of the connections, and then some methods of providing necessary stiffening will be presented.

No systematic research has been undertaken on connections that are designed to transmit less than the full plastic moment. If a reduced moment capacity is used, provisions must be made to assure satisfactory rotation capacity.

**Columns Without Stiffeners.**

In Fig. 8.12(a) are shown schematically the moments and forces on a typical interior beam-to-column connection. In Fig. 8.12(b), the effect of a beam moment on a column is shown as a couple composed of the two flange forces, the beam web forces being of secondary importance. Significant effects of the beam flange forces can occur in two regions in the column. The first region is the column web, where yielding may be accompanied by buckling due to the beam compression flange force or by fracture due to the beam tension flange force. The second region is the column flange, where bending may contribute to the fracture of welds connecting the beam flange to the column flange.

The tensile force in the beam flange tends to pull the outstanding column flanges, as shown in Fig. 8.13. At the toes of the column flanges, flexibility allows the beam and column flanges to deform together. How-

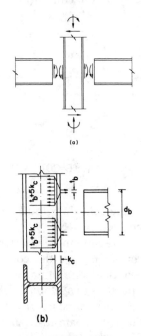

(a)

(b)

FIG. 8.12.—FORCES ON BEAM-TO-COLUMN CONNECTIONS

ever, at the middle of the column flange where it is restrained by the column web, deformation is restricted, and fracture is most likely to start there.

A column without stiffeners must be able to maintain static equilibrium in regions of both web yielding and flange bending. Stresses in the column caused by a concentrated beam flange force will spread out as they penetrate into the column. Because of this, the intensity of stress decreases with deeper penetration. If the spread of stresses is insufficient to reduce their intensity to the yield level at the depth of the base of the column flange fillet ($k$-depth), the web will not be able to provide sufficient reactive resistance to the beam flange force. This effect is most serious in the region stressed by the beam compression flange. Rational analysis of the spread of stress in a wide-flange section is difficult and is usually replaced by a linear assumption based on test results. Ref. 8.12 gives the results of several tests on connections where the beam and column have comparable proportions. It is recommended that the stress in the column be assumed to be distributed on a 2.5:1 slope from the point of contact to the column "$k$-line." As shown in Fig. 8.12(b), this assumption implies that the force of a beam flange is resisted by a length of column web equal to $(t_b + 5\,k_c)$ at the column "$k$-line," in which $t_b$ = the beam flange thickness, and $k_c$ = the column fillet depth. For equilibrium, the resistance of the effec-

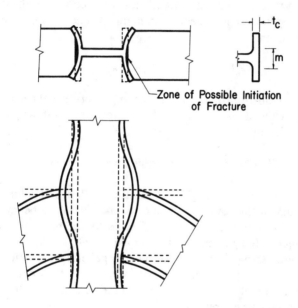

FIG. 8.13.—COLUMN FLANGE BENDING IN TENSION REGION

tive area of the web must equal or exceed the applied concentrated force of the beam tension or compression flange.

$$\text{Column web resistance} = \sigma_y\,w_c\,(t_b + 5\,k_c) \quad \ldots\ldots \quad (8.19)$$

$$\text{Beam flange force} = \sigma_y\,A_f \quad \ldots\ldots\ldots \quad (8.20)$$

which gives

$$\sigma_y\,w_c\,(t_b + 5\,k_c) \geq \sigma_y\,A_f \quad \ldots\ldots\ldots \quad (8.21)$$

in which $w_c$ = column web thickness and $A_f$ = area of one flange of beam. If the column web resistance is insufficient to carry the beam flange forces, stiffeners must be provided.

Static equilibrium in cases where the column flange thickness is small involves the consideration of bending in the column flange due to the beam tension or compression flange forces. The analysis is further complicated by the fact that the flange bending occurs in two directions, both longitudinal and transverse to the axis of the member, as can be visualized from Fig. 8.13. To solve the problem it is necessary to make assumptions regarding the distribution of the beam flange force on the column flange, the extent of the zone of bending in the column flange, and the effect of the central portion where the column flange joins the column web. It may be assumed that the fully yielded beam flange puts a line load on the column flange. For the beam

$$\text{Beam flange force} = \sigma_y A_f \quad \ldots \ldots \ldots \ldots \text{(8.22)}$$

The thick center portion of the column flange between the ends of the fillets may be assumed to resist the beam flange force with an axial force as if it were rigid. Thus

$$\text{Column flange direct resistance} = \sigma_y t_b m \quad \ldots \ldots \text{(8.23)}$$

in which $m$ = distance between fillet extremities of flange of column.

The remainder of the column flange resistance is due to bending of the projecting portion of the flange, and is affected by the projecting width of flange, thickness of flange, length of line load, length of the zone affected by bending, and strength of the material. In general, the action can be looked on as a case of plate bending, with the flange thickness being the most important geometrical property. The force of resistance to the beam flange line load may be expressed by

$$\text{Column flange bending resistance} = c_1 \sigma_y t_c^2 \quad \ldots \ldots \text{(8.24)}$$

in which $c_1$ is a coefficient depending on the width of column and beam flanges, extent of two-way bending, distance between column flange fillets, and boundary conditions.

To develop the full yield strength of the beam flange, the column flange resistance must be at least equal to it. Thus

$$\sigma_y A_f = \sigma_y t_b m + c_1 \sigma_y t_c^2 \quad \ldots \ldots \ldots \ldots \text{(8.25)}$$

If the column flange resistance is found to be insufficient, the column flange is too thin, and stiffening is required. This effect is most serious in the region stressed by the beam tension flange.

In Ref. 8.12, Eq. 8.25 is evaluated by means of "yield line theory,"* assuming a plate bending mechanism which extends for a length of column flange equal to 12 $t_c$. Additional assumptions of the relative dimensions of beams and columns are made in such a way as to assure a conservative result. From this combination of assumptions, the column flange thickness to resist a given beam flange area is obtained as

$$t_c \geqq 0.4 \sqrt{A_f} \quad \ldots \ldots \ldots \ldots \ldots (8.26)$$

Results of tests showed that connections proportioned according to Eq. 8.26 carried the plastic moment of the beam satisfactorily. Fig. 8.15 shows the results of tests on connections designed to meet the appropriate design criteria. The "A" tests are those without stiffeners which satisfied both Eq. 8.21 and Eq. 8.26.

### Columns With Stiffeners.

If the column web thickness satisfies Eq. 8.21, column stiffeners are not needed adjacent to the beam compression flange. If the column flange

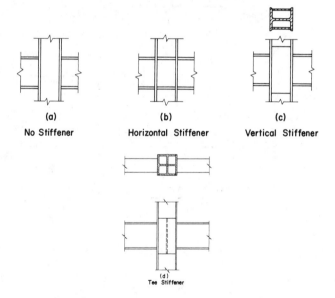

| (a) | (b) | (c) |
| :-: | :-: | :-: |
| No Stiffener | Horizontal Stiffener | Vertical Stiffener |

(d)
Tee Stiffener

FIG. 8.14.—STIFFENING OF BEAM-TO-COLUMN CONNECTIONS

thickness satisfies Eq. 8.26, column stiffeners are not needed adjacent to the beam tension flange. If the column proportions fail to satisfy either of these equations, however, stiffeners should be provided. Three types of stiffeners are shown in Fig. 8.14, the horizontal stiffener, the vertical stiff-

*Yield line theory is an upper-bound plastic analysis of bending of plates in which plastic hinges are assumed to form along lines in a plate to form a mechanism.

ener, and the tee stiffener. All three types of stiffeners may be proportioned by considering the additional amount of resisting force required to achieve equilibrium. They should also be proportioned to maintain stability under their full load.

Horizontal stiffeners preferably should be furnished in symmetrical pairs opposite both beam flanges. They should be welded to the column flange and web by either groove or fillet welds. Vertical stiffeners of the type shown in Fig. 8.14(c) should also be furnished in symmetrical pairs, and should be deep enough to allow the beam flange force to be dispersed in the stiffener in the same manner in which it is assumed to be dispersed in the web in Eq. 8.19.

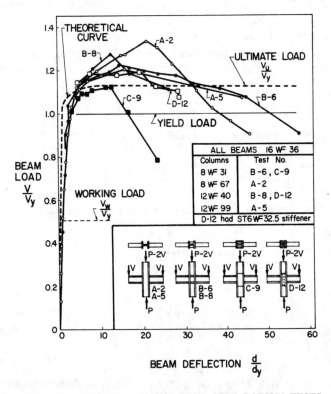

FIG. 8.15.—RESULTS OF TWO-WAY CONNECTION TESTS

Results of tests on connections using both types of stiffening are given in Ref. 8.12. Some of them are shown in Fig. 8.15. These tests and tests without stiffening were used to help establish semiempirical methods of deciding the need for stiffeners and the proportioning of stiffeners to resist thrusts of beam flanges. If the moments applied by the beams to the columns were unsymmetrical, the same methods would be appropriate. A detailed evaluation of the beam and column flange width has not been made.

**Critical Parts of Connections.**

The preceding analyses have shown that the use of stiffeners may depend either on compression in the column web (Eq. 8.21) or on tension normal to the column flange (Eq. 8.26) resulting from the end moments of the beams. For most of the rolled column sections normally only one type of failure need be checked, depending on the proportions of the column. The sections controlled by each type of failure may be tabulated, thus simplifying design.

Eq. 8.21 states that a connection will need stiffeners in the compression region if

$$A_f > w_c(t_b + 5\ k_c) \qquad \dots\dots\dots\dots (8.27)$$

From Eqs. 8.26 and 8.27 this connection will need stiffeners in the tension region if

$$t_c < 0.4\ \sqrt{w_c(t_b + 5\ k_c)} \qquad \dots\dots\dots\dots (8.28)$$

that is

$$\frac{t_c}{\sqrt{k_c\,w_c}} < 0.4\ \sqrt{5 + \frac{t_b}{k_c}} \dots\dots\dots\dots\dots (8.29)$$

For all practical combinations of rolled beams and columns that might be used in this type of connection

$$0.2 < \frac{t_b}{k_c} < 0.8 \dots\dots\dots\dots\dots\dots (8.30)$$

By taking $t_b/k_c = 0.2$, it is seen that this connection will need stiffeners in the tension region if

$$\frac{t_c}{\sqrt{k_c\,w_c}} < 0.91 \qquad \dots\dots\dots\dots\dots (8.31)$$

By taking $t_b/k_c = 0.8$, it is seen that the connection will not need stiffeners in the tension region if

$$\frac{t_c}{\sqrt{k_c\,w_c}} > 0.96 \qquad \dots\dots\dots\dots\dots (8.32)$$

Fig. 8.16 shows a plot of the values of $t_c/\sqrt{k_c\,w_c}$ for all wide-flange columns in the 8-in., 10-in., 12-in., and 14-in. series. It can be seen that in many cases the column need only be checked for compression. For values

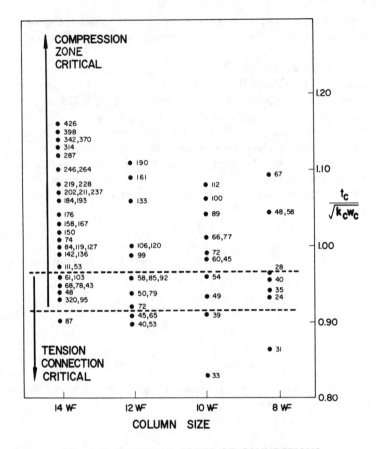

FIG. 8.16.—CRITICAL PARTS OF CONNECTIONS

of $t_c/\sqrt{k_c\,w_c}$ between 0.91 and 0.96 the need for column stiffening will depend on the beam, and both tension and compression should be checked.

**Shear Stiffening.**

When the moments in the two beams at an interior connection differ by a large amount, they may cause large shears in the column web, tending to deform the web in the same manner as in a corner connection [Fig. 8.2(e)]. With such an unbalance of moments, the shear in the web should be checked, and if necessary, diagonal stiffeners or a doubler plate should be added (1.2). In Fig. 8.17(a) the shears and moments acting on a typical connection are shown. Fig. 8.17(b) is a free body diagram of the forces acting on the column web just below the top flange stiffener. The forces are $V$, the horizontal shear present in the column above the connection, and two tensile flange forces, $T_1$ and $T_2$. The flange forces are obtained approximately by dividing the moment in the respective beams by the beam depths. The net result of these forces must be resisted by a shear stress $\tau$ acting on an area of column web equal to $w_c d_c$. Thus

$$\tau \, w_c \, d_c = \frac{M_2}{d_b} - \frac{M_1}{d_b} - V \dots \dots \dots (8.33)$$

Assuming that $\tau_y = \sigma_y/\sqrt{3}$, the required web thickness to resist shear is

$$w_c = \frac{\sqrt{3}}{\sigma_y d_c} \left( \frac{M_2}{d_b} - \frac{M_1}{d_b} - V \right) \dots \dots \dots (8.34)$$

when the directions of moments and shears are as shown in Fig. 8.17(b). If the actual web thickness of the column is less than that in Eq. 8.34, diag-

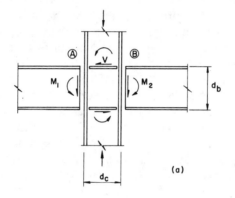

FIG. 8.17a.—SHEAR AND MOMENT ON CONNECTION WITH UNEQUAL MO-MENTS ON BEAMS

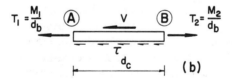

FIG. 8.17b.—FREE BODY DIAGRAM OF FORCES ACTING ON TOP STIFFENER AND COLUMN WEB

onal stiffeners similar to those in Fig. 8.2(f) or web doubler plates, vertical stiffeners, or tees could be used to carry the excess shearing force. The special case of a "one-sided" beam-to-column connection is obtained when $M_1$ equals zero.

In tall buildings large columns are used in the lower stories. Such members commonly have very large flanges. In these cases, it is not reasonable to assume that the web alone resists the beam flange forces and shear. The column flanges will also provide resistance to the applied forces in an amount equal to the thickness of web times the depth of flanges. As noted in Chapter 6, the combined shear and direct stress in the flanges can be carried because of the strain hardening characteristics of steel. The experimental work to date has been undertaken on connections in which the column web depth was about 95% of the column depth. The flange would offer little resistance to shear in these cases.

**Four-Way Beam-to-Column Connections.**

Frequently additional beams must be framed into a single joint on a column, forming a four-way beam-to-column connection. Two beams may be framed into a column web either by direct welding or by plate plus seat type of connections. When connections such as these are used, the question has been raised as to whether the triaxial stresses in the column web might cause premature failure, or, on the other hand, whether a beneficial effect might be obtained through the partial stiffening action of the beams framing into the column web. A limited number of tests have been made on four-way connections. In the specimens tested, there was no adverse effect of triaxial stresses indicated (8.12).

Sketches of some of the four-way connections tested are shown in Fig. 8.18. The direct-welded type, shown in Fig. 8.18(a), had a column web thickness meeting the requirement of Eq. 8.21, and hence the column web required no reinforcement to prevent crippling due to the forces applied to the column flanges by the beams. The addition of two more identical beams, welded directly to the column web, appeared to stiffen the web. In the second type of connection [Fig. 8.18(b)], the horizontal plates which served as top plate and seat plate for the beams framing into the column web also served as stiffeners for the column. Because the beams framing into the web were not as deep as those welded to the column flanges, the bottom stiffener was 4 in. away from its ideal location opposite the lower flange of the deeper beam. However, the connection performed satisfactorily. The connection in Fig. 8.18(c) used split-tee sections for stiffeners in the same way that vertical plates had been used in two-way connections. The stems of the tees served to support both the stiffeners and the column web. The flanges of the split tees served as suitable surfaces to which beams could be directly welded to complete the connection. The performance of this connection was also satisfactory. The four-way connection tests of Ref. 8.12 were performed with considerable axial load in the columns so that the results could reflect the influence of this practical loading situation. All of these tests were performed under a symmetrical moment condition.

For the design of four-way connections, Ref. 8.12 recommends that the connection of the beams to the column flange be designed exactly as in a two-way connection as if the beams framing to the column web were not

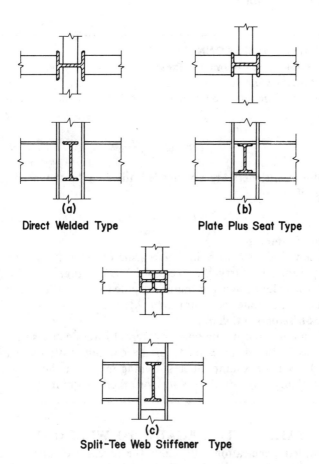

(a)
Direct Welded Type

(b)
Plate Plus Seat Type

(c)
Split-Tee Web Stiffener  Type

FIG. 8.18.—TYPES OF FOUR-WAY INTERIOR BEAM-TO-COLUMN CONNEC-TIONS

present. Test specimens of four-way connections designed on this assumption performed even better than comparable two-way connections because of additional restraints.

---

**BEAM-TO-COLUMN CONNECTIONS**
**(Beams Joined to Column Flanges)**
**Unstiffened Columns:**
Column stiffeners are not needed adjacent to the beam compression flanges if

$$w_c \geqq \frac{A_f}{t_b + 5 k_c} \quad \ldots \ldots \ldots \ldots \ldots \ (8.21)$$

Column stiffeners are not needed adjacent to the beam tension flanges if

$$t_c \geqq 0.4 \sqrt{A_f} \ldots \ldots \ldots \ldots \ldots (8.26)$$

**Column Stiffeners**
Column stiffeners at points of bearing of beam flanges should be proportioned to carry the excess of beam flange force over that which the column web and flange are able to carry. (Stiffeners should also be proportioned so as not to buckle.)
**Shear Stiffening in Column**
When unbalanced moments or external forces cause shear stresses in excess of the shear capacity of the column, stiffening should be provided for the column. Such stiffening may take the form of diagonal stiffeners, web doubler plates, or other possibilities.

---

## 8.7 DETAILS WITH REGARD TO WELDING

In complete penetration butt welds the forces are carried primarily in compression or tension, and are limited by the tensile or compressive resistance of the base metal or weld metal, depending on which is least. Since the weld metal normally used in any joint is stronger than the base metal, the strength of butt welds should be calculated on the basis of the yield strength of the base metal.

The ultimate strength of fillet welds subjected to shear alone is dependent upon the strength of the weld metal and the direction of applied load, which may be parallel or transverse to the weld. In both cases the weld fails in shear, but the plane of rupture is not the same. Longitudinal fillet welds provide the lower bound for weld strength. All experimental studies have shown that transverse welds are somewhat stronger. Hence, the results of studies of longitudinal welds were selected as the basis for design recommendations since they provide the lower bound of weld strength. The results can then be applied to fillet welds in general without regard to the direction of loading.

Early tests on low carbon steels connected by manual arc fillet welds showed that the ultimate strength of fillet welds based on the minimum throat area was 70% to 75% of the tensile strength of the deposited metal (8.14, 8.15, 8.16). More recent tests on low carbon and alloy steels have given comparable strengths (8.17).

It was recognized early that shear yielding was not critical in fillet welds because the material strain hardened without large over-all deformations occurring.

The shear strength of the weld $\tau_f$ as analyzed from the early data (8.14, 8.15, 8.16) and from more recent work (8.17) is

$$\tau_f \approx 0.70 \; \sigma_f \; \ldots \ldots \ldots \ldots \ldots \ldots (8.35)$$

in which $\sigma_f$ = minimum tensile strength of the welding rod. In plastic design, the design shear stress values, $\tau_u$, for the factored load should assure the attainment of the member strength without premature failure of the weldment or connection. From the tests described in Ref. 8.17 and from past experience, a minimum factor of safety of 2.5 was selected to determine the allowable shear stress for welds. Comparing this with the value of 1.70 for flexural members, this means a further reserve at the plastic limit load of about 1.45. Alternatively, this can be considered as providing a reduction factor against the ultimate strength of the weld. The reduction factor is equal to the reciprocal of the reserve factor of safety at the plastic limit load (1/F.S.). Applying this to the ultimate shear strength, $\tau_f$, of the weld would yield a nominal shear stress for analysis at the plastic limit load of

$$\tau_u = 0.70 \; (0.70 \; \sigma_f) \cong 0.50 \; \sigma_f \; \ldots \ldots \ldots \ldots (8.36)$$

The value used in allowable-stress design is directly compatible, of course, with the suggested ultimate load values. The shear stress can be used regardless of the direction of the applied load with respect to the weld.

If fillet welds are subjected to eccentric loads that produce a combination of bending and shearing stresses, they can be proportioned conservatively on the basis of a direct vector addition of the stresses.

The results of tests (8.18, 8.19) on vertical weld groups (E60 electrodes and A7 steel) subjected to combined bending and shear are plotted in Fig. 8.19. These tests show that the use of a direct vector addition of the shear forces on the weld is a conservative approach to the design of eccentrically loaded fillet welds.

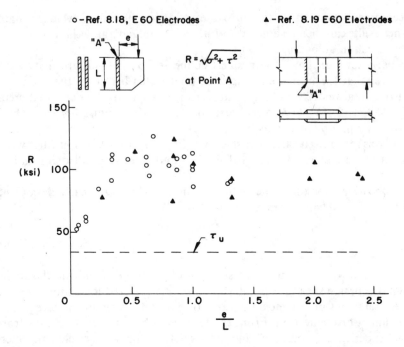

FIG. 8.19.—FILLET WELDS SUBJECTED TO BENDING AND SHEAR

---

**WELD STRESSES**

***Butt Welds*** may be assumed capable of developing on their minimum throat section the tensile yield stress of the base metal.

***Fillet Welds*** should develop the required maximum strength of the base metal when made by electrodes of comparable strength. The plastic design stress value should be

$$\tau_u = 0.50 \ \sigma_f \qquad \ldots \ldots \ldots \ldots (8.36)$$

in which $\sigma_f$ = the tensile strength of the weld metal.

---

## 8.8 DETAILS WITH REGARD TO BOLTING

Bolted joints in plastic design will probably have their greatest application as field joints for the erection of structures. The forces acting on the joint are resisted by the fasteners in either tension or shear.

The shear strength of a high-strength bolt is determined by the location of the shear planes. If a shear plane intersects the bolt threads, only the root area is effective in resisting the shear. The shear strength of high-strength bolts was observed to be about 60% of the tensile strength (8.20).

For high-strength bolts in tension, the maximum stress is limited by the ultimate tensile strength of the steel, $\sigma_f$, applied to the stress area.* The ratio of the stress area to the nominal bolt area for 1/2-in. to 1-in. bolts varies from 0.725 to 0.773. Therefore, the maximum strength may be expressed as 75% of the tensile strength of the bolt materials. Studies on both A325 and A490 bolts have shown that the tensile strength is not affected by installation (8.21, 8.22, 8.23).

The nominal stresses to be used at the design ultimate or factored load should assure that the plastic moment of adjoining members will be developed without premature failure of the connections. An approach for developing suitable "design ultimate" stresses can be based on past practice—as was done in establishing the appropriate factors for flexural members. The case of fasteners in shear will be considered as an example.

As shown in Ref. 8.24, the stresses used in past designs of both riveted and bolted joints have resulted in a variable factor of safety ranging from 2.0 to 3.3. Since the value 2.0 has existed in the largest (and therefore most important) joints, a value of 2.0 seems to be the maximum factor of safety that should logically be required for joints with bolts in shear. Since the factor of safety with respect to beam failure is 1.70, this means that the *added* reserve inherent in past practice is $2.0/1.70 \cong 1.20$; the joints have been designed to be 20% stronger than the members joined.

It has been shown that allowable shear stress of 30 ksi in A325 bolts and 40 ksi in A490 bolts provides a factor of safety of 2.0 against failure. Using these values and the added reserve factor of 1.20 gives design ultimate shear stresses of 50 ksi and 70 ksi, respectively, for the two grades of high-strength bolts.

Alternatively, the design ultimate shear stress could be determined from an analysis that proceeds along the following lines. The design ultimate shear, $\tau_u$, can be determined from

$$\tau_u = \frac{\text{F.S. beam}}{\text{F.S. bolted shear joint}} \times \bar{\tau}_f \quad \ldots \ldots \ldots (8.37)$$

in which $\bar{\tau}_f$ = average shear failure stress in a bolted joint. The minimum average shear failure stress corresponds to

$$\bar{\tau}_f = 0.8\,\tau_f \quad \ldots \ldots \ldots \ldots \ldots (8.38)$$

in which $\tau_f$ = the shearing strength of a bolt.

The reduction in bolt strength recognizes the influence of geometrical

---

*Stress area is calculated as

$$A_t = 0.7854 \left(D - \frac{0.9743}{n}\right)^2$$

in which $D$ = the nominal bolt size and $n$ = threads per in.

factors, such as joint length in large splices, and the strengthening effect of splice material which forces the plastic hinge to form outside the joint and subjects the joint to larger forces.

Since the shear strength of a bolt is

$$\tau_f = 0.65 \, \sigma_f \quad \dots \dots \dots \dots \dots \quad (8.39)$$

in which $\sigma_f$ = the tensile strength of the bolt, the design ultimate shear, $\tau_u$, can be expressed as

$$
\left.
\begin{aligned}
\tau_u &= \frac{\text{F.S. beam}}{\text{F.S. bolted shear joint}} \times \frac{\bar{\tau}_f}{\sigma_f} \times \sigma_f \\[2mm]
\tau_u &= \frac{1.70}{2.00} \times 0.8 \times 0.65 \times \sigma_f \\[2mm]
\tau_u &\cong 0.45 \, \sigma_f
\end{aligned}
\right\} \quad \dots \dots \quad (8.40)
$$

If one followed the concept of safety factors as used in allowable-stress design, the F.S. ratio could be termed a "stress reduction factor," and this procedure has been followed in "Load Factor Design for Steel Highway Bridges" (8.25). The same result, however, would be obtained.

For bolts in tension

$$
\left.
\begin{aligned}
\sigma_u &= \frac{\text{F.S. beam}}{\text{F.S. bolt in tension}} \times 0.75 \, \sigma_f \\[2mm]
\sigma_u &= \frac{1.70}{2.20} \times 0.75 \, \sigma_f \\[2mm]
\sigma_u &\cong 0.60 \, \sigma_f
\end{aligned}
\right\} \quad \dots \dots \quad (8.41)
$$

For bolts that are subjected to tension and shear, an ellipse has been fitted to the test data (8.26). The test results for bolts with threads excluded from the shear plane and bolts with threads in the shear plane are compared with an interaction curve in Fig. 8.20. It is apparent that good agreement exists. Also, the root area is seen to provide an adequate measure of resistance when a shear plane intersects the bolt threads.

For bolts subjected to combined tension and shear, the shear stress component should not exceed

$$\tau < \sqrt{\tau_f^2 - (0.6 \, \sigma)^2} \, . \, \dots \dots \dots \dots \quad (8.42)$$

in which $\sigma$ = tensile stress due to the applied load.

The suggested stress for bolts in tension is nearly equal to the value one would obtain by factoring the currently used allowable stress by the usual factor, 1.65. The resulting design value would be 0.54 $\sigma_f$, whereas the suggested value is 0.60 $\sigma_f$. The same reduction factor of 0.75 was applied to shear.

Tests have shown that flexural members can be proportioned to resist bending on the basis of the gross cross section as long as the holes do not deduct an excessive amount of moment capacity from the section (8.27, 8.28). Bolt holes had no appreciable effect on the test behavior even

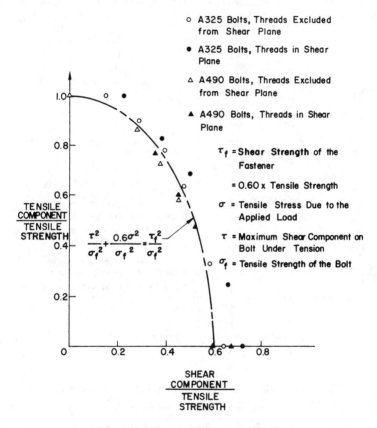

FIG. 8.20.—INTERACTION CURVES

though 25% of the plastic bending strength was removed. This is illustrated in Fig. 8.21, which shows that $M_{pr}$ of the net section is not the governing plastic moment. This is the result of the recognized effect of the strain hardening (8.29).

For tension members and the tension flange of flexural members, the reduction in area caused by bolt holes can be neglected provided the net section has sufficient strength to "develop" gross section yielding. Failure of the member and suitable deformation capacity would only occur after gross section yielding. If the maximum permitted load on the net area of the tension flange or tension member is taken 85% of the tensile strength, then

$$\frac{A_n}{A_g} \geq \frac{\sigma}{0.85\,\sigma_f} \quad \cdots\cdots\cdots\cdots\cdots \quad (8.43)$$

If the net to gross area ratio satisfies Eq. 8.43, the full moment capacity or tensile strength (based on the gross area) can be used to resist the applied

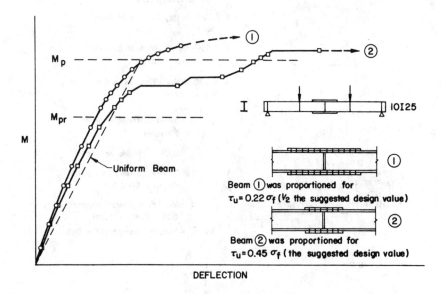

FIG. 8.21.—MOMENT-DEFLECTION BEHAVIOR OF BEAM SPLICES

loads. If the net to gross area ratio violates Eq. 8.43, the effective area of the tension flange or member should be taken as the product of the gross area times the ratio $\left(\dfrac{A_n/A_g}{\sigma/0.85\,\sigma_f}\right)$. The coefficient 0.85 corresponds to the ratio of $\sigma_u/\sigma_y$ of A572 steel.

Tests of beam splices and beam-to-column connections have shown that bolted joints can develop the full plastic moment of the connected members (8.27, 8.28, 8.30). Fig. 8.22 gives the general layout of joints which are capable of developing satisfactory strength. Bolts have been subjected to shear and to tension depending on the connection type.

**Bolted Splices.**

At maximum load bolts proportioned on the basis of 75% of their shear strength were able to develop the plastic moment. Fig. 8.21 compares the

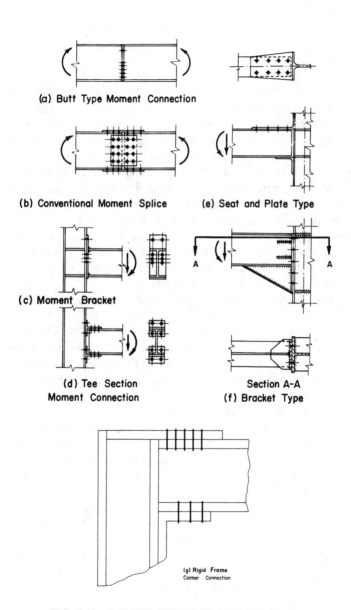

(a) Butt Type Moment Connection

(b) Conventional Moment Splice

(e) Seat and Plate Type

(c) Moment Bracket

A        A

(d) Tee Section
Moment Connection

Section A-A
(f) Bracket Type

(g) Rigid Frame
Corner Connection

FIG. 8.22.—BOLTED MOMENT CONNECTIONS

behavior of beams proportioned with the bolts at 38% and 75% of their shear strength. Both were able to develop the full plastic moment in the connected members. In the first case no slip developed, whereas in the second case slip occurred but did not prevent attainment of the plastic moment. In Fig. 8.21, $M_{pr}$ is with the holes removed.

The suggested design value of 0.45 $\sigma_f$ given by Eq. 8.40 provided satisfactory connection behavior, as illustrated by Beam 2 in Fig. 8.21. The beam was able to develop its full plastic moment capacity. Also, note that slip did not prevent the member from developing the plastic moment strength of the beam. The deviation from the idealized moment-deflection relationship was no worse than that exhibited by experiments on plain rolled shapes (see Fig. 6.7). At about twice the theoretical plastic moment deflection the plastic moment was achieved. The slips that developed in the shear splices only caused a rounding of the moment deflection relationship that is directly analogous to the shape of the exact moment curvature relationship (Fig. 2.3). The moment in the bolted splice also rapidly approaches the plastic moment. In most cases it will provide a beneficial effect, because it will permit a more favorable distribution of moment and does not require as much rotation capacity.

Web splices have resisted the applied shear without adverse effect (8.28, 8.31).

Beam splices (8.27, 8.28), as illustrated in Fig. 8.22(b), rigid frame corner connections (8.32, 8.33), as illustrated in Fig. 8.22(g), and splice plates have all demonstrated the ability to develop the desired strength when the fasteners have been proportioned to resist the plastic moment at the suggested design levels.

### T-Stub Flange-to-Column Connections.

A considerable amount of work has been undertaken during the past ten years on beam-to-column connections fastened with high-strength bolts (8.27, 8.28, 8.30). A commonly used connection incorporates a T-stub to transfer the beam moments into the column. On the beam compression flange, the T-stub acts much like a bearing pad, so that only column web crippling or crippling of the T-stub web can occur. Eq. 8.21 can conservatively be used to evaluate the adequacy of the column web for this situation. The T-stub connecting the beam tension flange is more critical. Particular attention must be paid to the tensile forces in the bolts connecting the T-stub flange to the column face. Because of distortion of the column or T-stub flanges, prying forces develop.

In Fig. 8.23 are shown schematically the forces and distortions of a simple T-stub. Under zero applied load, $T$, the tension in each bolt is $T_o$, the initial clamping force. When the external load is applied, the flange deflects, causing prying forces to develop. A semiempirical estimate of the prying force $Q$, developed in Ref. 8.28, is

$$Q = \left[ \frac{\dfrac{l}{2} - \dfrac{wt^4}{30\,ab^2\,A_b}}{\dfrac{a}{b}\left(\dfrac{a}{3b} + 1\right)\dfrac{wt^4}{6\,ab^2\,A_b}} \right] F \quad \ldots \ldots \ldots (8.44)$$

in which

$Q$ = prying force;

$w$ = length of T-stub;

$a$ = distance from center of bolt to edge of plate;

$b$ = distance from center of bolt to edge of fillet of connected part;

$A_b$ = nominal bolt area;

$t$ = thickness of T-stub flange; and

$F$ = average force per bolt ($T/n$).

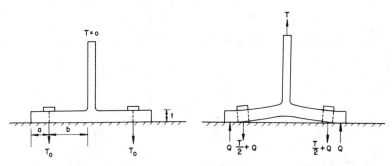

(a) Forces and Deformations in Unloaded T-Stub     (b) Forces and Deformations in Loaded T-Stub

FIG. 8.23.—ASSUMED FORCES AND DEFORMATIONS IN T-STUBS

Fig. 8.24 compares the observed bolt force with the computed tension based on Eq. 8.44. It is seen that Eq. 8.44 is in reasonable agreement with the test results.

Because of the complexity of the analytical solution given by Eq. 8.44, several variables were evaluated to establish their significance. This study showed that prying action could be approximated with reasonable accuracy using

$$Q = \left(\frac{3b}{8a} - \frac{t^3}{20}\right) F \quad \ldots \ldots \ldots \ldots \ldots (8.45)$$

A comparison of the simplified expression given by Eq. 8.45 with Eq. 8.44 is given in Fig. 8.25. The approximation is usually a conservative estimate of the prying force for all bolt diameters.

In arriving at a simple analysis of the T-stub flange, the approach suggested by Schutz (8.30) seems reasonable. The equations for the required

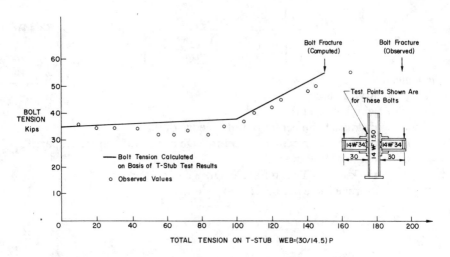

FIG. 8.24.—COMPARISON OF COMPUTED AND OBSERVED BOLT FORCES

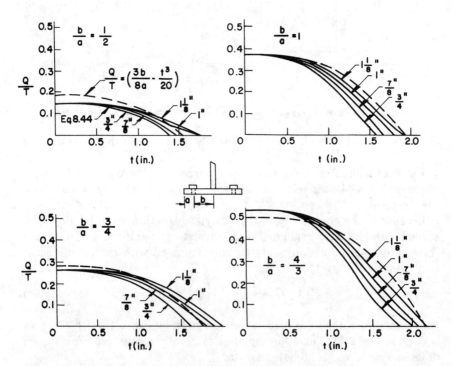

FIG. 8.25.—COMPARISON OF DESIGN RECOMMENDATIONS WITH SEMI-EMPIRICAL FORMULA ($w = 3.5$ IN.)

thickness can be determined by considering plastic hinges to form in the flange, as shown in Fig. 8.26. The force in the flange is given by

$$T \approx \frac{M_p}{d_b} \quad \dots\dots\dots\dots\dots (8.46)$$

in which $d_b$ = the beam depth. Now, the plastic hinges forming in the flange adjacent to the web and bolts have values of

$$M_{pw} = \frac{wt^2\sigma_y}{4}$$

and $\qquad\qquad\qquad\qquad\qquad\qquad\left.\begin{array}{c}\\ \\ \\ \\ \end{array}\right\} \quad \dots\dots\dots\dots (8.47)$

$$M_{pb} = \frac{kwt^2\sigma_y}{4}$$

in which $k$ provides for the presence of the bolt holes. Tests reported in Ref. 8.28 have shown that $k$ can be taken as unity because strain hardening enables the flanges to resist a continuously increasing load. Failure ultimately occurs by fracture of the T-web or a bolt. Thus

$$M_{pw} = M_{pb} = M_{pt} \dots\dots\dots\dots\dots (8.48)$$

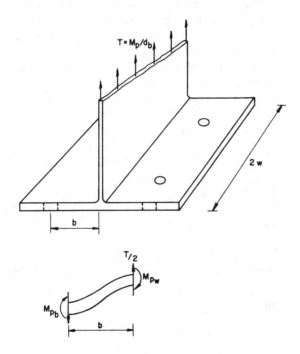

FIG. 8.26.—SYSTEM OF FORCES ACTING ON TEE FLANGES

The simple mechanism that is formed enables one to evaluate the required flange thickness

$$M_{pw} + M_{pb} \approx \frac{Tb}{2} \quad \ldots \ldots \ldots \ldots \quad (8.49)$$

Therefore, the minimum thickness can be obtained from

$$\left.\begin{array}{c} \dfrac{2\,wt^2\,\sigma_y}{4} = \dfrac{M_p\,b}{2\,d_b} \\[2em] \text{or} \\[1em] t = \sqrt{\dfrac{M_p\,b}{wd_b\,\sigma_y}} \end{array}\right\} \quad \ldots \ldots \ldots \ldots \quad (8.50)$$

Eq. 8.50 can be used to make an initial selection of the T-stub. However, it is more likely that prying action will control, so that it may be necessary to increase the flange thickness if it is necessary to minimize the prying effect given by Eq. 8.45.

**End Plate Connections.**

End plates welded to beam ends were suggested in Refs. 8.27, 8.30, and 8.31 for a variety of types of connections. For example, moment brackets, butt-type beam splices, and beam-to-column connections (see Fig. 8.22) were tested to provide an indication of their behavior and performance.

These studies have all indicated that the shear force can be transmitted by the friction developed between the end plate and the element to which it is connected. Its resistance to slip can be evaluated in terms of the bolt preload and the nominal slip coefficient.

The tests have also indicated that when end plates extend beyond the tension flange, as shown in Fig. 8.22(c), the bolts which are chiefly effective in resisting the tension-flange force are those adjacent to the tension flange. Refs. 8.28 and 8.30 have suggested that the bolts and the part of end plate at the tension flange can be treated as an equivalent T-stub connection. Eq. 8.45 and 8.50 can be used to evaluate the adequacy of the T-stub and the bolt forces. For large beams additional bolts can be used to develop the tension in the inner portions of the web. The test results have indicated that connections designed on this basis will provide adequate strength.

Excessive thickness of the end plate can cause difficulties when attached to stiff beams and columns. The high-strength bolts may not be able to pull the connected parts together. When this condition exists, shims should be provided.

**BOLT STRESSES**
*High-Strength Bolts in Tension:*

$$\sigma_u = 0.60\,\sigma_f \quad \ldots \ldots \ldots \ldots \quad (8.41)$$

in which $\sigma_f$ = the tensile strength of the bolt. The bolt area is taken as the nominal area.

*High-Strength Bolts in Shear:*

$$\tau_u = 0.45\,\sigma_f \quad \ldots \ldots \ldots \ldots \quad (8.40)$$

in which $\sigma_f$ = the tensile strength of the bolt. The bolt shear area is taken as the nominal area when the shear plane intersects the shank. The root area is used when the shear plane intersects the threads.

For combined tension and shear, bolts shall be proportioned so that the shear stress does not exceed

$$\tau < \sqrt{\tau_f^2 - (0.6\,\sigma)^2} \quad \ldots \ldots \ldots \quad (8.42)$$

in which $\sigma$ = tensile stress due to the applied load.

The tension due to prying action can be computed from

$$Q = \left(\frac{3b}{8a} - \frac{t^3}{20}\right) F \quad \ldots \ldots \ldots \quad (8.45)$$

**BOLTED BEAM-TO-COLUMN CONNECTIONS**

The provisions of Art. 8.6 apply for column stiffeners and for shear stiffening of the columns.

*T-Stub Flange.*

The minimum thickness of T-stub flanges is

$$t = \sqrt{\frac{M_p\,b}{wd_b\,\sigma_y}} \quad \ldots \ldots \ldots \ldots \quad (8.50)$$

# CHAPTER 9.—DEFLECTIONS

## 9.1 INTRODUCTION

Although strength to carry the load is the primary matter of importance in most structures, certain problems related to deflections do concern the structural engineer. The deflection may exceed established limits set up by a building code or specification. Deflections may hinder the operation of moving parts or the closing of doors, or they may cause the cracking of plaster in finished ceilings. In some structures, such as tall building frames, calculations of strength require that deflections ($P \Delta$ effect) be taken into account. Also deflection control is needed to limit the "drift" (lateral deflection) of the building. In some cases it is necessary to estimate the deflections to assure that racking against adjacent buildings will not occur. Thus, it is desirable to have methods for calculating the deflections of structures.

This chapter will outline the basic problem of structural deflections. It will discuss briefly the calculation of deflections in the elastic range. The calculation of deflections at ultimate load will be covered in more detail. Illustrative examples will show that the deflections at working load of structures designed plastically usually are no greater than those of structures designed on an allowable-stress basis.

The calculation of the deflections of continuous structures at working loads, whether designed elastically or plastically, is cumbersome. Usually such calculations may be dispensed with because sufficient experience has been gained with the particular type of structure to indicate that the deflections will not be excessive. The use of electronic computers makes the task much easier.

Structural deflections are in essence calculated by integration, with appropriate boundary conditions, of the differential equation

$$\frac{d^2y}{dx^2} = \phi \quad \ldots \ldots \ldots \ldots \ldots \ldots (9.1)$$

in which $y$ = deflection from original straight line of member; $x$ = distance along member; $d^2y/dx^2$ = approximate curvature of member (the approximation is valid when slope and deflection are small); and $\phi$ = curvature caused by bending (thus it is a function of moment which in turn is a function of $x$; in the elastic range $\phi = M/EI$).

There are many methods of solving Eq. 9.1 in both the elastic and plastic ranges. The methods differ principally in the means of expressing $\phi$

213

and in the methods of handling boundary conditions. In the following sections, a number of these methods will be discussed.

## 9.2 CALCULATION OF DEFLECTIONS IN THE ELASTIC RANGE

Methods for calculating deflections in the elastic range are available in texts on structural theory, so these methods will not be explained here. To make a precise calculation of deflections at working load of structures proportioned by plastic design it would be necessary to use one of these methods. (As will be seen later, an upper bound to this deflection may be determined without resorting to the elastic analysis of the indeterminate structure.)

One thing elastic methods have in common is that they express the curvature $\phi$, for use in Eq. 9.1, as

$$\phi = \frac{M}{EI} \quad \dots \dots \dots \dots \dots \dots \dots (9.2)$$

in which $M$ = bending moment as a function of $x$; $E$ = Young's modulus of elasticity; and $I$ = moment of inertia of the cross section of the member.

A second feature of most of the elastic methods is that expressions giving the slope at all points of a deflected member are continuous functions. Connections between members are usually designed to be fully rigid or completely free.

Certain of the methods also are adaptable for the consideration of factors contributing to deflection which ordinarily are neglected in the study of rigid frame structures. These factors are the deflections caused by axial force and shear force. In the consideration of stability problems, the second-order moment terms resulting from deflections cause changes in the equilibrium conditions.

## 9.3 CALCULATION OF DEFLECTIONS IN THE PLASTIC RANGE

Several methods for calculating the deflections of structures in the plastic range are available. Five of these methods are outlined, discussed, and compared with experimental results in Ref. 9.1. In these methods, the moment-curvature relationship derived from the elastic and plastic stress-strain relationship is substituted in Eq. 9.1 and, using appropriate boundary conditions, slopes and deflections are obtained by integration. The methods differ (1) in the number of assumptions made in the moment-curvature relationship to simplify the computation, (2) in the degree of refinement used in defining boundary conditions at plastic hinges, and (3) in the computational procedures used for execution of the integration. Table 9.1 outlines the salient features of the five methods. Fig. 9.1 shows

TABLE 9.1—SUMMARY OF METHODS FOR CALCULATING DEFLECTIONS IN THE PLASTIC RANGE

| Method (1) | $M$-$\phi$ relationship (2) | Spread of plastic zone (3) | Strain hardening (4) | Handling of boundary conditions (5) | Remarks (6) |
|---|---|---|---|---|---|
| Numerical integration | "Exact" | Considered | Considered | Trial and error needed to fit B.C. for redundant structure | Most precise |
| Mathematical integration | Simplified to functions expressable mathematically | Considered | Considered | Trial and error | |
| $\phi$-area | Simplified | Neglected | Considered | Trial and error | |
| Simple plastic theory | Simplified | Considered | Neglected | Trial and error where moment is constant | |
| Plastic hinge method | $\phi = M/EI$ | Neglected | Neglected | Direct | Large error in curvature for section with constant moment |

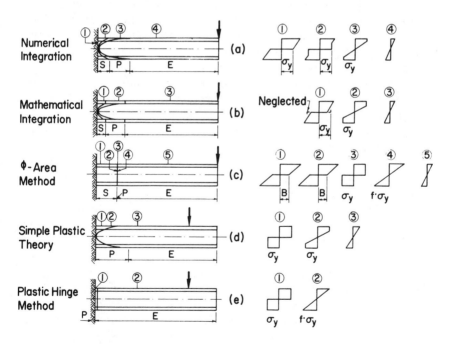

FIG. 9.1.—STRESS DISTRIBUTIONS ASSUMED FOR CALCULATING DEFLECTIONS OF BEAMS BEYOND THE ELASTIC LIMIT

the stress distribution associated with the assumptions for each of the methods. The simplest approach, the "plastic hinge" method, is most suitable for structural engineering applications. The additional work involved in the theoretically more "exact" methods is not justified by the accuracy gained except for special purposes.

The "plastic hinge" method assumes that the structure has only elastic regions and localized plastic hinges. This allows the use of the curvature equation in the form given as Eq. 9.2. The boundary conditions are then changed to allow for freedom of rotation at plastic hinges. As was pointed out in Ref. 1.27, the controlling boundary condition for deflection just prior to formation of a mechanism is continuity at the last plastic hinge to form.* Any of the well-known methods of calculation of deflection in the elastic range may then be used with suitable handling of the boundary conditions. Methods which have shown promise are "slope deflection," "moment area," "conjugate-beam," and the "method of virtual work." Some advantages of the "plastic hinge" method are that it obviates the necessity of knowing the $M$-$\phi$ relationship beyond the elastic limit, and, for certain continuous beams, makes use of the deflection formulas tabulated in structural handbooks and usually available in the design office.

The other four methods discussed in Ref. 9.1 are "simple plastic theory," "$\phi$ area," "mathematical integration," and "numerical integration." These methods utilize more accurate representations of the moment-curvature relationship and properties of the steel to obtain a small increase in accuracy of the calculated deflections. However, this increase in accuracy is gained at the expense of a considerable increase in complexity. A trial-and-error process must be used, not only to determine the boundary conditions (last plastic hinge), but also to determine the moment and curvature. For this reason, these methods have only been used in the calculation of deflections of very simple structures such as continuous beams and rectangular portal frames (9.1, 9.2, 9.3). For more sophisticated moment-curvature relationships with more complicated structures the use of digital computers has been required (9.4, 9.5).

Deflections of more complicated structures have been calculated by the "plastic hinge" method with reasonable agreement between calculations and tests. For most practical cases, therefore, the "plastic hinge" method is recommended for deflection calculations (1.27, 5.13, 9.5, 9.6, 9.7).

In some cases the effect of strain hardening in strengthening and stiffening plastic hinges could markedly affect the distribution of internal moments, the stability of frames, and the occurrence of local buckling (2.16). The discussion and references of Art. 2.3 provide an introduction to the

---

*An exception occurs when hinge rotation has occurred at one or more sections where the bending moment at ultimate load is less than the fully plastic value. For a discussion of this phenomenon see Ref. 1.6.

handling of these problems in the calculation of deflections in the plastic range.

Digital computer programs can be formulated which apply each of the methods listed above for determination of the deformed shape of members loaded into the inelastic range. Programs using numerical integration have been most helpful in computing Column Deflection Curves applicable for design aids in a large variety of beam-column problems (1.33). In the computation of deflections for more complex structures, the normal capacity of computing equipment frequently requires a compromise between refinement of the moment-curvature relationship for individual members and the ability to handle a larger number of members. Here again the "plastic hinge" method has been found to be most practical for deflection computations (3.9, 9.8, 9.9).

## 9.4  SAMPLE CALCULATION OF DEFLECTION AT ULTIMATE LOAD

### Slope-Deflection Method.

In this section, the approximate deflection at ultimate load of the simple portal frame shown in Fig. 9.2(a) will be calculated. The assumptions used will be those given in Art. 9.3 for the "plastic hinge" method. One method of calculation is to make use of the slope-deflection equation (1.2, 1.6, 1.27, 3.1, 9.6)

$$\theta_A = \theta'_A + \frac{\Delta}{\ell} + \frac{\ell}{3EI}\left(M_{AB} - \frac{1}{2}M_{BA}\right) \quad \ldots \ldots (9.3)$$

(See Fig. 9.3 for nomenclature. Clockwise $M$ and $\theta$ are positive. When the equation is used in this form, $EI$ must be constant in segment $AB$.)

The mechanism and moment diagram at ultimate load are given in Fig. 9.2(b) and 9.2(c), respectively. In Fig. 9.2(d) are given free body diagrams of the portions of the frame. To solve for the deflections $\delta_V$ and $\delta_H$, two boundary conditions are needed. One of these is that $\theta_{21}$ equals $\theta_{23}$ because of continuity at joint 2. The second boundary condition depends on whether the last plastic hinge forms at section 3 or section 4. A trial solution of the problem will be made for each of these assumptions, and then the correct solution will be selected.

**Continuity at Section 2.**— $(\theta_{21} = \theta_{23})$

$$\theta_A = \theta'_A + \frac{\Delta}{\ell} + \frac{\ell}{3EI}\left(M_{AB} - \frac{M_{BA}}{2}\right)$$

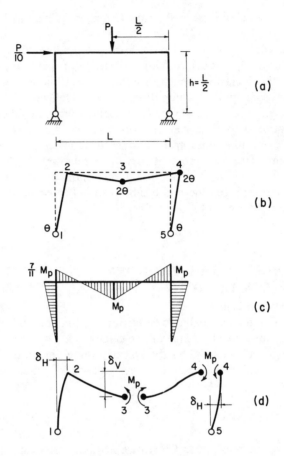

FIG. 9.2.—DEFLECTION OF PORTAL FRAME AT ULTIMATE LOAD

First, considering segment 2-1 and using the moments of Fig. 9.2(c)

$$\theta_{21} = 0 + \frac{\delta_H}{\dfrac{L}{2}} + \frac{\dfrac{L}{2}}{3EI}\left(\frac{7}{11}M_p - 0\right)$$

$$\theta_{21} = \frac{2\,\delta_H}{L} + \frac{7}{66}\frac{M_p L}{EI}$$

Next, considering segment 2-3

$$\theta_{23} = 0 + \frac{\delta_V}{\dfrac{L}{2}} + \frac{\dfrac{L}{2}}{3\,E\,I}\left(-\,\frac{7}{11}\,M_p + \frac{1}{2}\,M_p\right)$$

$$\theta_{23} = \frac{2\,\delta_V}{L} - \frac{1}{44}\,\frac{M_p\,L}{E\,I}$$

Equating $\theta_{21}$ and $\theta_{23}$

$$\frac{2\,\delta_H}{L} + \frac{7}{66}\,\frac{M_p\,L}{E\,I} = \frac{2\,\delta_V}{L} - \frac{1}{44}\,\frac{M_p\,L}{E\,I}$$

$$\delta_V = \frac{17}{264}\,\frac{M_p\,L^2}{E\,I} + \delta_H \quad \ldots\ldots\ldots\ldots (9.4)$$

This gives one desired relationship for $\delta_V$ and $\delta_H$ which applies for either of the following trial solutions.

**Trial at Section 3.**—$(\theta_{32} = \theta_{34})$
Considering segment 3-2

$$\theta_{32} = 0 + \frac{\delta_{V3}}{\dfrac{L}{2}} + \frac{\dfrac{L}{2}}{3\,E\,I}\left(-\,M_p + \frac{7}{22}\,M_p\right)$$

$$\theta_{32} = \frac{2\,\delta_{V3}}{L} - \frac{5}{44}\,\frac{M_p\,L}{E\,I}$$

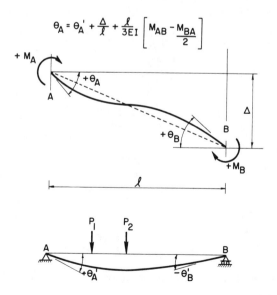

$$\theta_A = \theta_A' + \frac{\Delta}{\ell} + \frac{\ell}{3EI}\left[M_{AB} - \frac{M_{BA}}{2}\right]$$

FIG. 9.3.—NOMENCLATURE FOR SLOPE-DEFLECTION EQUATION

Considering segment 3-4

$$\theta_{34} = 0 - \frac{\delta_{V3}}{\frac{L}{2}} + \frac{\frac{L}{2}}{3EI} \left( M_p - \frac{1}{2} M_p \right)$$

$$\theta_{34} = -\frac{2\,\delta_{V3}}{L} + \frac{1}{12} \frac{M_p L}{EI}$$

In the above expressions, $\delta_{V3}$ is the vertical deflection with continuity assumed at section 3.

Equating $\theta_{32}$ and $\theta_{34}$

$$\frac{2\,\delta_{V3}}{L} - \frac{5}{44} \frac{M_p L}{EI} = -\frac{2\,\delta_{V3}}{L} + \frac{1}{12} \frac{M_p L}{EI} \quad \dots \dots (9.5)$$

Thus

$$\delta_{V3} = \frac{13}{264} \frac{M_p L^2}{EI}$$

and from Eq. 9.4

$$\delta_{H3} = -\frac{1}{66} \frac{M_p L^2}{EI} \quad \dots \dots \dots \dots (9.6)$$

These values for $\delta_V$ and $\delta_H$ would be the correct values for the deflections at ultimate load if the last plastic hinge formed at point 3.

**Trial at Section 4.**—($\theta_{43} = \theta_{45}$)

Considering segment 4-3

$$\theta_{43} = 0 - \frac{\delta_{V4}}{\frac{L}{2}} + \frac{\frac{L}{2}}{3EI} \left( M_p - \frac{1}{2} M_p \right)$$

$$\theta_{43} = -\frac{2\,\delta_{V4}}{L} + \frac{1}{12} \frac{M_p L}{EI}$$

Considering segment 4-5

$$\theta_{45} = 0 + \frac{\delta_{H4}}{\frac{L}{2}} + \frac{\frac{L}{2}}{3EI} \left( -M_p - 0 \right)$$

$$\theta_{45} = \frac{2\,\delta_{H4}}{L} - \frac{1}{6} \frac{M_p L}{EI}$$

Equating $\theta_{43}$ and $\theta_{45}$ and solving simultaneously with Eq. 9.4 gives

$$\delta_{V4} = \frac{25}{264} \frac{M_p L^2}{EI}$$

and

$$\delta_{H4} = \frac{1}{33} \frac{M_p L^2}{E I} \quad \ldots \ldots \ldots \ldots \ldots \text{(9.7)}$$

The deflections calculated assuming continuity at section 4 are larger than those obtained on the basis of continuity at section 3. Consideration of the rotations at section 4 when continuity is assumed at section 3 shows that an impossible reverse "kink" would occur at section 4. Because of this reverse "kink," the assumption resulting in such a solution is discarded. Therefore, the deflections assuming continuity at section 4 are the correct deflections at ultimate load. It has been established elsewhere (1.27) that the correct set of calculated deflections will be the largest set from any series of calculations based on different assumptions of the last plastic hinge. The last plastic hinge to form will be the hinge at which continuity is assumed in calculating the largest deflection.

**Dummy Load Method.**

Another example of the calculation of deflection at ultimate load will be given using the "dummy load" method, which is a variation of the "virtual work" method. This method is used in many textbooks on structures—for instance, Ref. 9.10. In plastic range applications, the moment-curvature relationship boundary conditions will be treated according to the assumptions of the plastic hinge method.

The operations of the method are as follows: (1) the moments $M$ due to the applied loads are determined, and (2) a dummy unit load is applied to the unloaded structure at the point of the desired deflection and in the direction of the desired deflection. A set of moments $m$ in equilibrium with the unit load is then determined.

Additional special conditions used to adapt this method for the solution of deflections at ultimate load are:

1. All members are assumed to be fully elastic between plastic hinges.
2. Continuity is assumed at the last plastic hinge.
3. The dummy load is applied to an auxiliary structure with frictionless hinges assumed at all but the last plastic hinge.
4. If the location of the last plastic hinge is unknown, a solution must be made for each assumed last plastic hinge.

After applying these conditions, the deflection at the unit load due to the original applied loads is determined from a virtual work equation of the form

$$\delta (1^k) = \int \phi \, m \, ds = \int \frac{M m}{E I} ds \quad \ldots \ldots \ldots \text{(9.8)}$$

in which

$\delta$ = deflection in direction of unit load;

$M$ = moments in structure due to applied loads;

$m$ = moments in auxiliary structure in equilibrium with unit load;

$ds$ = distance along member;

$E$ = Young's modulus of elasticity; and

$I$ = moment of inertia of member.

Eq. 9.8 is integrated over the whole structure, using intervals where all functions exist and are piecewise continuous. By defining limits at joints, concentrated loads, and hinges, the discontinuities in the curvature functions are readily handled.

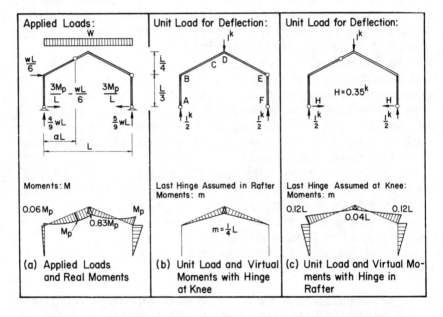

FIG. 9.4.—LOADS AND MOMENTS FOR DUMMY LOAD SOLUTION OF DEFLECTION

The vertical deflection at ultimate load of the ridge of the gabled frame in Fig. 9.4(a) will be calculated. The locations of the plastic hinges and the $M$ moment diagram due to the applied loads are shown in Fig. 9.4(a). The necessary additional relationships from the analysis are

$$w L^2 = 16.84 \ M_p$$

and

$$\alpha = 0.355$$

$$\left.\rule{0pt}{60pt}\right\} \qquad \ldots \ldots \ldots (9.9)$$

The last plastic hinge may occur either at the leeward knee or in the windward rafter. By making two deflection calculations, one assuming each hinge in turn to be the last, the correction deflection will be determined.

In Fig. 9.4(b), a unit load is applied at the ridge of the structure with a frictionless hinge assumed at the knee. In other words, there is continuity in the windward rafter in which the last plastic hinge is assumed to occur. The resulting reactions due to the unit load and the $m$ moments are also shown. Moments $M$ and $m$ are inserted in Eq. 9.8 with the proper expressions for $ds$

$$\delta_D = \int_A^B \frac{M\,m}{EI}\,ds + \int_B^D \frac{M\,m}{EI}\,ds$$

$$+ \int_F^E \frac{M\,m}{EI}\,ds + \int_E^D \frac{M\,m}{EI}\,ds \quad \ldots \ldots \ldots \ldots (9.10)$$

in which the limits of integration indicate the applicable points on the structure of Fig. 9.4(b)

$$\delta_D = 0 + \frac{1}{EI}\int_O^{L/2}\left(-M_p + \frac{wL^2}{18} + \frac{4}{9}wLx - \frac{3}{2}\frac{M_p x}{L} - \frac{wx^2}{2}\right)\left(\frac{1}{2}x\right)\frac{\sqrt{5}}{2}\,dx$$

$$+ 0 + \frac{1}{EI}\int_O^{L/2}\left(-M_p + \frac{5}{9}wLx - \frac{3}{2}\frac{M_p x}{L} - \frac{wx^2}{2}\right)\left(\frac{1}{2}x\right)\frac{\sqrt{5}}{2}\,dx \quad \ldots \ldots (9.11)$$

Performing the indicated integration and substituting Eq. 9.9 results in

$$\delta_D = 0.1012\,\frac{M_p L^2}{EI}. \ldots \ldots \ldots \ldots \ldots (9.12)$$

Instead of having a hinge at the knee, the structure with the dummy load in Fig. 9.4(c) has a hinge in the windward rafter. The structure in this condition behaves as a three-hinged arch with the $m$ moments and reactions shown. Using these $m$ moments with the $M$ moments of Fig. 9.4(a), a second expression for deflection is obtained as

$$\delta_D = \int_A^B \frac{M\,m}{EI}\,ds + \int_F^E \frac{M\,m}{EI}\,ds + \int_B^C \frac{M\,m}{EI}\,ds$$

$$+ \int_C^D \frac{M\,m}{EI}\,ds + \int_E^D \frac{M\,m}{EI}\,ds \quad \ldots \ldots \ldots \ldots (9.13)$$

$$\delta_D = \frac{1}{EI} \int_0^{L/3} \left( -\frac{3 M_p x}{L} + \frac{w L x}{6} \right) (-H x) dx$$

$$+ \frac{1}{EI} \int_0^{L/3} \left( -\frac{3 M_p x}{L} \right) (-H x) dx$$

$$+ \frac{1}{EI} \int_0^{\alpha L} \left( -M_p + \frac{w L^2}{18} + \frac{4}{9} w L x - \frac{3}{2} \frac{M_p x}{L} - \frac{w x^2}{2} \right)$$

$$\left( \frac{1}{2} x - \frac{H x}{2} - \frac{H L}{3} \right) \left( \frac{\sqrt{5}}{2} dx \right)$$

$$+ \frac{1}{EI} \int_0^{L/2 - \alpha L} \left( M_p + \frac{4}{9} w L x - w \alpha L x \right.$$

$$\left. - \frac{w x^2}{2} - \frac{3}{2} \frac{M_p x}{L} \right) \left( \frac{1}{2} x - \frac{H x}{2} \right) \left( \frac{\sqrt{5}}{2} dx \right)$$

$$+ \frac{1}{EI} \int_0^{L/2} \left( -M_p + \frac{5}{9} w L x - \frac{3}{2} \frac{M_p x}{L} \right.$$

$$\left. - \frac{w x^2}{2} \right) \left( \frac{1}{2} x - \frac{H x}{2} - \frac{H L}{3} \right) \left( \frac{\sqrt{5}}{2} dx \right) \quad \dots \dots (9.14)$$

Integrating and substituting for $w$, $\alpha$, and $H$ results in

$$\delta_D = 0.0159 \frac{M_p L^2}{EI}. \quad \dots \dots \dots \dots (9.15)$$

Since the larger of the two calculated deflections is the correct one, then

$$\delta_D = 0.1012 \frac{M_p L^2}{EI}. \quad \dots \dots \dots \dots (9.16)$$

The conclusion that the largest calculated deflection based on a given ultimate moment diagram is the correct deflection is explained in Ref. 1.6. It is stated that "any incorrect solution can be found from the correct solution by superposing the displacements and hinge rotations due to a backwards motion of the collapse mechanism." Additional references are available on finding the last plastic hinge (9.11, 9.12).

## 9.5 HINGE-BY-HINGE CALCULATIONS OF DEFLECTIONS

Occasionally, and especially for research purposes, it becomes desirable to construct the load-deflection (or load-rotation) curve for a structure.

This is done by means of a hinge-by-hinge procedure, because the load-deflection behavior is approximately linear between the formation of successive plastic hinges (9.13). The calculations to be discussed here will be based only on the plastic hinge method.

As an example, consider the deflection under load of the built-in beam in Fig. 9.5(a). In the elastic range, the load-deflection curve follows the line 0-a. The curve will cease to follow line 0-a when the moment at the left support reaches $M_p$. This point is designated by A on the solid curve.

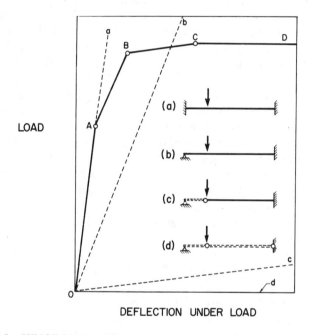

LOAD

DEFLECTION UNDER LOAD

FIG. 9.5.—HINGE-BY-HINGE LOAD-DEFLECTION CURVE OF A BEAM

Thereafter the moment at the left support cannot increase, but the moments can increase at every other point in the beam. The subsequent increment of deflection of the beam will then be the same as the propped cantilever of Fig. 9.5(b). The elastic load-deflection relationship of structure (b) when standing by itself is given by the line 0-b. The increment of deflection of the original beam is determined according to the line AB drawn parallel to 0-b. The magnitude of the increment of load corresponding to AB is determined by considering the moment under the load. A certain moment corresponding to point A exists under the load in the original structure (a). The difference between this moment and $M_p$ is made up by the moment under the load of auxiliary structure (b). The increment of load is the amount required to raise the moment of auxiliary structure (b) from zero to the amount of the original difference from $M_p$, and the increment of deflection of the auxiliary structure (b) caused by this increment of load.

At this stage, there are plastic hinges both at the load and at the left support. Consequently, no increase in moment can occur at either of these points. The auxiliary structure of Fig. 9.5(c) will be used to determine the next increment of load and deflection in the same manner as was done for the first two increments. The load at the end of the third step will be based on the moment at the right support as summed up for the three cases.

The final stage of the load-deflection curve is the horizontal portion CD representing deflection without increase of load. This can be represented schematically by structure (d) which has three hinges. Neglecting catenary effects, the load deflection of structure (d) is represented by baseline d.

In summary, the load-deflection curve of a structure loaded to ultimate load may be obtained by superimposing on the elastic load-deflection curve of the primary structure portions of the elastic load-deflection curves of auxiliary structures. The number of auxiliary structures will be the same as the number of plastic hinges.

The same procedures may be followed for rigid frame structures. Fig. 9.6 shows the load-deflection curve of a gabled portal frame and the load-deflection curves of the necessary auxiliary structures (9.6). The deflection at point (4) in Fig. 9.6 is the same as would be obtained by the methods of Art. 9.4.

Hinge-by-hinge deflection calculations have made it possible to verify that certain amounts of support settlement and rotation or semirigidity of joints may be present without increasing the deflection at which a mechanism forms, even though elastic range deflections are altered (9.14).

Digital computers have made possible the hinge-by-hinge analysis of much more complicated rigid frames, apparently limited only by the ingenuity of the programmer in conserving sufficient space for his problem on the computer (3.9, 9.9). The plastic hinge method is usually relied upon to simplify the handling of the moment-curvature relationship.

The advent of widespread use of digital computers has initiated a change in formulation of solutions of structural problems whereby increasing use of matrix operations is prevalent. This will eventually allow the solution of a large variety of engineering problems using routines for matrix operations as a universal language which need not be translated for different engineering or scientific disciplines. It is likely that all computers will have programs for matrix operations, even though they might not have programs for particular structural problems.

Studies of the plastic design of multistory frames have posed an even more challenging problem, that of the second-order load-deflection relationship in the inelastic range. The horizontal displacement of the frame due to wind loads results in an additional overturning moment due to the gravity loads acting in a displaced position. This overturning moment imposes additional bending moments on all beams and columns in the structure. The dependence of the final bending moments upon the final deflec-

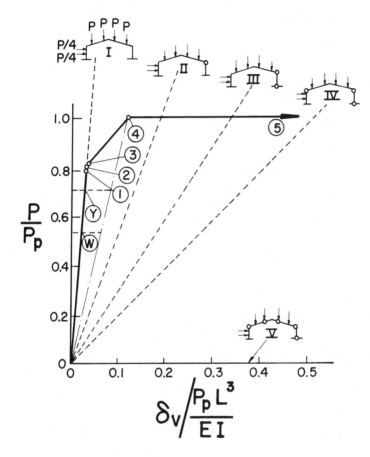

FIG. 9.6.—HINGE-BY-HINGE LOAD-DEFLECTION CURVE OF A PORTAL FRAME

tion of the structure requires trial-and-error procedures for which iterative calculation capabilities of computers are ideally suited. Several programs for second-order load-deflection relationships have been prepared (3.10, 6.89, 9.8, 9.15–9.19). In at least one of these, iterative procedures for solving the deflections of one story at a time have made possible the calculation of the second-order load-deflection relationship including the effects of column shortening for a 24-story 3-bay frame on a computer of 32k capacity (9.8).

A few tests have been made on structures loaded to produce a substantial second-order effect (6.89, 9.20).Fig. 9.7 shows the test results, as well as the first- and second-order load-deflection curves for a 3-story 2-bay frame (9.20). The substantial reduction in strength for the second-order case shows the necessity of considering this action in the design and analy-

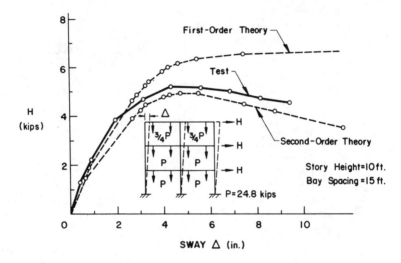

FIG. 9.7.—TEST RESULTS COMPARED WITH FIRST- AND SECOND-ORDER THEORY FOR A 3-STORY UNBRACED FRAME

sis of unbraced multistory frames (6.82). Second-order curves are not straight line relationships, but are shown that way because a limited number of points was used to define the relationship.

## 9.6 APPROXIMATE DEFLECTION AT WORKING LOAD

It has been suggested (9.21) that an upper bound for the deflection at working load may be obtained by dividing the calculated deflection at ultimate load by the load factor.* Calculations were made to compare this type of estimate with calculated and measured deflections at working load. Bar graphs showing these comparisons for five structures are given in Fig. 9.8. Each deflection is plotted as a percentage of the calculated deflection, $\delta_p$, at limit load. Thus, the upper bound to deflection estimated at working

---

*The intersection of the dot-dash line 0–4 in Fig. 9.6 with the horizontal line indicating the magnitude of $P/P_p$ is a graphical representation of this upper bound for deflection at working load of a single-span gabled frame.

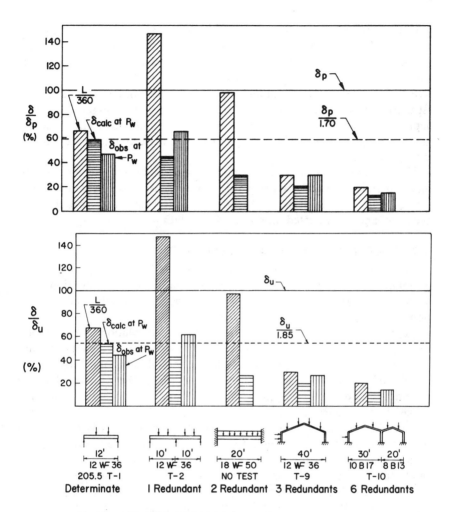

FIG. 9.8.—COMPARISON OF DEFLECTIONS AT WORKING AND ULTIMATE LOADS WITH ESTIMATED WORKING LOAD DEFLECTION

load is always 59% of $\delta_p$ when the load factor is 1.70. The deflection calculated from an elastic analysis at the plastic design working load and an observed deflection at working load from a test are shown where available. For a further comparison, a bar showing 1/360 of the span is plotted to the same scale as the deflections.**

The bar graphs show that the estimate of deflections made by dividing $\delta_p$ by the load factor is more and more in error as the number of statically

---

**The value $L/360$ is used not because it is particularly recommended on a scientific basis, but because it is frequently used in specifications.

indeterminate reactions increases. Whereas the approximate estimate is very good for one redundant, the estimate is four times the actual deflection at working load for the structure with six redundants. This estimate would imply excessive deflection, whereas the actual deflection here was well below $L/360$. Unfortunately, no simple rule can be established for estimating how much in error the original calculation might be. Much depends on the order of formation of the plastic hinges. In any structure in which all plastic hinges form simultaneously, the estimate will equal the true deflection.

The approximate procedure suggested is satisfactory whenever the estimated deflection calculated from this procedure does not exceed the prescribed deflection limitation. Otherwise it is necessary to resort to more accurate (and complicated) methods of calculation.

## 9.7 DEFLECTION AS A LIMITATION

One of the most important questions about deflections in plastic design is whether or not they will constitute an undue design limitation. The answer to this question on the basis of available test results and calculations is: no.

Admittedly, on the basis of the few tests and calculations for examples shown, it cannot be stated that all possible combinations have been studied. Variations in load and span do change the relationships. However, it is believed on the basis of the studies which have been made that the statements made here apply to typical cases and also to cases within the range of practical extremes.

Consider the case shown in Fig. 9.9 (1.2). The problem is to design a beam to carry a given load on a given span. First, picture the beam being designed as simply-supported, this being the standard with which the safety factor is compared in plastic design. The rolled section required would be an 18 **WF** 50, and the load-deflection curve would be as shown by curve I in Fig. 9.9. A horizontal mark on the graph indicates the value of the working load, and a vertical mark indicates the deflection which is equivalent to $1/360$ of the span.

Next consider a fixed-ended beam designed to carry the same load on the same span according to elastic design. Because of the negative moment at the fixed ends, only a 16 **WF** 36 would be required. The load-deflection curve would be as given by curve II in Fig. 9.9. It is seen that the deflection at working load is considerably less than that of the simply-supported beam. The elastically designed beam with fixed ends would support a much greater ultimate load than would the simple beam. This indicates that, although both beams are designed for the same working load and both are "safe," the built-in beam has an excess margin of safety against ultimate load.

The third case in Fig. 9.9 indicates an even more economical solution by plastic design. Here only a 14 **W** 30 is required. The load-deflection curve shows that the load capacity is equal to that of the simple beam. Though the deflection at working load for case III is greater than for case II, it is considerably less than for case I and would be acceptable. This and similar comparisons show that deflections at working load in plastically designed

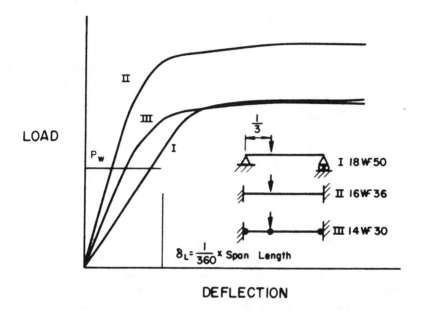

DEFLECTION

FIG. 9.9.—LOAD-DEFLECTION RELATIONSHIP FOR THREE DIFFERENT BEAM DESIGNS FOR SUPPORTING THE SAME LOAD

continuous structures are usually less than what engineers have accepted in the past for simply connected structures having the same spans.

For a particular type of structure, design guides to limit deflections can be formulated in terms of maximum ratios of span-to-depth of member. It can be shown that merely limiting the span-to-depth ratio to less than some simple value will assure that working load deflections are kept below a desired limit for a large range of practical structures. An illustration follows.

The live load deflection at a point on any structure can be expressed in the form

$$\delta = C_2 \frac{P_L L^3}{E I} \quad \ldots \ldots \ldots \ldots \ldots (9.17)$$

Assume that the structure is designed for a plastic moment to support a total load $P_r$ as expressed by

$$M_P = C_1 F P_r L = \sigma_y f \, \frac{I}{\dfrac{d}{2}} \quad \dots\dots\dots \quad (9.18)$$

in which    $P_L$ = live load (working);
$\quad\quad\quad\quad$ $P_r$ = total dead plus live load (working);
$\quad\quad\quad\quad$ $C_1$ = moment coefficient depending on support and load conditions ($C_1$ = 1/8 for uniformly loaded simple beams);
$\quad\quad\quad\quad$ $C_2$ = deflection coefficient depending on support and load conditions ($C_2$ = 5/384 for uniformly loaded simple beams);
$\quad\quad\quad\quad$ $F$ = load factor; and
$\quad\quad\quad\quad$ $f$ = shape factor.

By eliminating $I/L$ from Eqs. 9.17 and 9.18 the following expression for limiting $L/d$

$$\frac{L}{d} = \frac{\delta}{L} \, \frac{E}{\sigma_y} \, \frac{F}{2f} \, \frac{C_1}{C_2} \, \frac{P_r}{P_L} \quad \dots\dots\dots \quad (9.19)$$

can be obtained. If typical values of $\delta = L/360$, $E = 29{,}000$ ksi, $F = 1.7$, and $f = 1.14$ are used, the values of $C_1/C_2$ and $P_r/P_L$ still need to be assigned. Exact values can be assigned for a specific structure. A crude conservative value will be assigned to cover a wide range of structures. For several examples of indeterminate beams and single-story portal frames, $C_1/C_2$ can be shown to lie between 9.8 and 28, with most values near 16. If live load is estimated to be two-thirds of total load at most and the most conservative values of all other functions are used, Eq. 9.19 becomes

$$\frac{L}{d} = \frac{882}{\sigma_y} \quad \dots\dots\dots\dots \quad (9.20)$$

Such an equation would serve the same purpose as is served by the deflection recommendations given in the AISC Specification for allowable-stress design. Maximum $L/d$ ratios of 18 to 25 would be indicated as reasonable.

The major drawback of such simplified equations is that so many of the governing factors lose their identity. The limiting $L/d$ could increase by 60% even if the restraint conditions $C_1/C_2$ improved only to the average value of 16 listed above. Conversely, an especially efficient design where live load could be greater than two-thirds of total load might result in excessive deflection unless stiffness were increased.

The above discussion is applicable primarily for calculating the vertical deflection of simple beams, continuous beams, and beams as part of frames. The lateral deflection of structures due to wind and other loads is discussed in Chapter 10.

## 9.8  ROTATION REQUIREMENTS

In addition to the problem of deflections in plastic design, the rotations at plastic hinges must also be considered. For example, in the beam of Fig. 9.5, it is the inelastic rotation at the left support which allows redistribution of moments to the load point and right support of the member, thereby making possible the increase in load from points A to D. Similarly, in any continuous structure, some rotation must take place at the first plastic hinges to form, except in the case where all hinges form simultaneously. The measure of this required rotation is referred to as the "hinge angle." It is of interest to determine the hinge angle that would be required in structures in order to formulate certain secondary design guides which depend upon this function.

The hinge angle may be calculated as part of the deflection calculations described in Art. 9.4. The results of numerous hinge angle calculations are presented in Ref. 9.3. Some of these results have been used in the determination of the required lateral bracing for bending members given in Art. 6.3 (6.17).

In some cases, the calculated hinge angle required to form a mechanism may be quite large, implying a limitation on the design. However, practical considerations suggest that nearly the same load-carrying capacity may exist with a much lower hinge angle requirement. In Fig. 9.10 is plotted the theoretical load versus hinge rotation function $H$ at the first plastic hinge of a two-span frame. Seven labelled points on the curve indicate the formation of seven plastic hinges in reaching the mechanism state. Point (7) is the hinge angle that would be calculated in a rotation requirement study. Note, however, that at the formation of the next-to-last plastic hinge, point (6), the load is 98.2% of the maximum load. To attain this load, the required rotation is only 0.54 $M_p L/(E I)$, or about one-third of the amount calculated as needed to reach a complete mechanism at the plastic limit load [1.52 $M_p L/(E I)$]. Assurance of reaching 98% of a predicted load, along with a reasonable load factor or safety factor, is generally accepted as good engineering practice. Thus, it is seen that the problem of large required rotation in highly redundant structures is not as serious as might first be suspected.

Experimental verification that a structure may behave quite satisfactorily, even though it may not meet the full rotation requirements, is given in Ref. 5.13. A test was performed on the two-span frame of Fig. 9.10. Although the frame did not quite attain the computed ultimate on the basis of a 40 ksi coupon stress, it reached 97.4% of this value, or well in excess of an ultimate load based upon a 33 ksi yield point (Fig. 9.11). Observa-

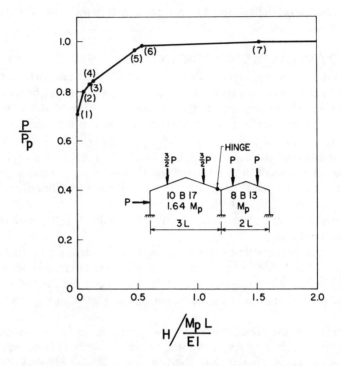

FIG. 9.10.—HINGE ANGLE REQUIRED FOR A 2-SPAN PORTAL FRAME

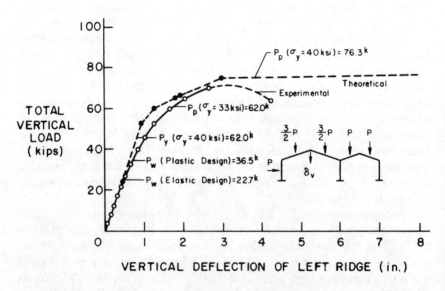

FIG. 9.11.—EXPERIMENTAL LOAD-DEFLECTION CURVE OF 2-SPAN PORTAL FRAME

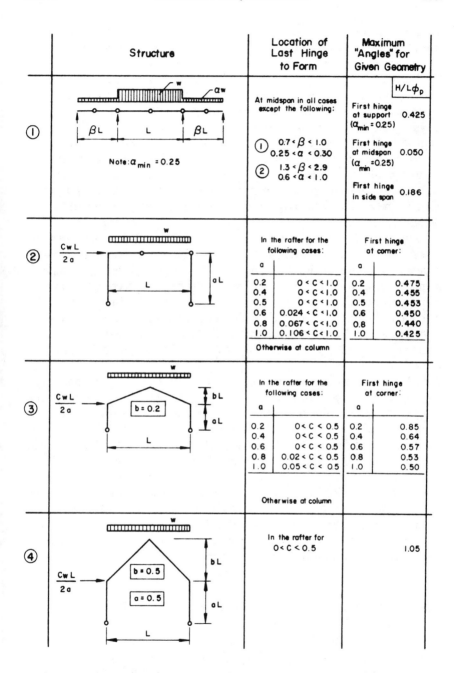

FIG. 9.12.—LOCATION OF LAST HINGE TO FORM IN SEVERAL PRACTICAL STRUCTURES; MAXIMUM VALUES OF THE FUNCTION $H/L\phi_p$ FOR THE SAME STRUCTURES

tions indicated that six of the seven plastic hinges were formed before lateral buckling occurred due to the instability of a lateral support which was made very flexible for test purposes. There is every reason to believe that with adequate lateral support the seventh plastic hinge would have formed, and an even greater load would have been reached due to strain hardening. For highly indeterminate multispan frames, large hinge angles may be required for the full development of a mechanism. For these same frames, however, the load at the formation of the next-to-last hinge is almost as great as the maximum load, whereas the rotation at that instant is substantially less, as in the case shown in Fig. 9.10. Hence a lower limit for rotation capacity requirement, suitable for general design purposes, need not be related to the large theoretical rotations associated with highly redundant frames.

Some examples of the size of maximum hinge angles and their location in a few structures are given in Fig. 9.12 (1.2). Typically, the first hinge occurs at a joint or a support. Therefore the largest hinge angle requirements occur at points where the moment gradient is steepest. Steep moment gradient improves lateral stability (see Art. 6.3). In the few cases where the first hinge forms in a region of near constant moment, the required hinge angles are fortunately small. The order of magnitude of hinge angles reported in the literature varies from 0.02 radians to 0.15 radians (6.17, 9.5).

A deflection study of unbraced multistory frames showed that hinge angles required according to a first-order computation could be quite large, with trends similar to that shown in Fig. 9.10 (9.18). However, a second-order analysis (more realistic for such frames) indicates that the maximum load on the structures is reached due to instability at much smaller deflections than that necessary to form a complete mechanism. Plastic hinges were not called upon to rotate to a large extent in this case, so the ordinary lateral bracing requirements for members would probably still be valid. This study also considered the effect of axial deformation of the members. The effect was found to increase working load deflection over that predicted by ignoring member shortening, but the deflection curves at maximum load tended to converge.

## 9.9  CONSIDERATION OF DEFLECTIONS IN MULTISTORY FRAMES

Calculation of deflections for multistory frames is complicated by the considerable redundancy of the frames, and by the necessity of considering the second-order effects as discussed in Arts. 9.5 and 9.8. It was formerly thought that unequal axial deformations of columns could contribute to serious reduction in the strength of frames. Recent studies indicate that the strength of unbraced frames may not be affected as severely as was previously expected, but that deflections in the working range are increased substantially (9.18).

Deflections of braced frames have been shown to depend on the axial deformations of columns, girders, and bracing members (9.22). Additional discussion of deflection considerations in multistory frames is presented in Chapter 10.

Occasionally, the beam-to-column connections in multistory frames may exhibit concentrated rotations due to high shearing strains in the column web. The possibility that such rotations may influence frame strength adversely should not be overlooked. Some references are available on this topic (6.73, 9.23).

# CHAPTER 10.—MULTISTORY FRAMES

## 10.1 INTRODUCTION

The basic theorems of plastic analysis presented in Chapter 2 apply to structural members and frames stressed primarily in bending—members in which the axial loads are small. Under these conditions it is satisfactory to formulate equilibrium equations on the undeformed configurations of the structure. The maximum load that the structure can carry is the plastic limit load.

A different situation exists for multistory frames where the frame must carry large gravity loads in addition to lateral loads. The secondary overturning moments caused by the gravity loads acting through the lateral deflections of the frame can significantly alter the equilibrium relationships of the undeformed frame. The effect of the secondary overturning moments, termed the "$P\Delta$ effect," is to reduce the strength and stiffness of the frame to resist gravity and lateral loads, which can lead to instability failure (1.33).

For purposes of analysis and description of frame behavior, two types of multistory frames are identified: "braced frames" where the primary resistance to lateral loads, frame buckling, and frame instability is provided by a vertical bracing system (see Fig. 10.3, for example), and "unbraced frames" in which the bending resistance of the frame members themselves must account for the total frame strength and stiffness in resisting lateral loads and frame instability.

The basic task of extending plastic design to multistory frames has been to identify the possible modes of failure, to develop dependable analytical methods for predicting them, and to verify these predictions by experiments. Research spanning the last decade and completed since the 1961 edition of this Manual has provided the background needed to apply the plastic design concept to braced and unbraced multistory frames (1.33).

Several multistory frames have already been designed by the plastic method—and with significant savings in weight (1.34, 10.1, 10.2, 10.3). Chapters 5, 7, and 9 of this Manual summarize much of the theoretical and experimental research that was the basis for these applications.

An important development is the extension of provisions for plastic design to include braced multistory frames in the 1969 edition of the AISC Specification (4.18). Further research and design experience may modify some details of current thinking in this rapidly expanding application of plastic design, but the basic concepts are now evident.

Research on unbraced frames is in progress and is nearing the stage where it can be applied in practice (1.33, 6.102, 10.4 through 10.11). Current research work is concentrated on the development of simplified and computerized procedures for design office use, and on experiments to confirm these procedures.

The purpose of this chapter is to present a summary of the methods and concepts useful in the design of braced and unbraced multistory frames, and to give a description of the behavior of braced and unbraced frames under gravity loads and under combined gravity and lateral loads. Detailed descriptions of the design procedures are available elsewhere (1.33, 9.22, 10.4, 10.5, 10.6, 10.12).

**Behavior of Frames Under Gravity and Lateral Loads.**

Braced and unbraced frames under gravity loads alone may become unstable in one of two ways: either by frame instability or by frame buckling. These conditions may be described as follows.

1. For symmetrical frames subjected to unsymmetrical gravity loads or for unsymmetrical frames, lateral deflection will occur from the first application of load. At first these lateral or sway deflections will increase nearly linearly with the applied gravity load. (In the research into the maximum strength behavior of multistory frames and the plastic design procedures described herein, no distinction is made between the terms lateral deflection, sway, or drift whether resulting from gravity or lateral loads.) As loading increases, $P\Delta$ effects and yielding will cause the sway deflections to increase more rapidly than before. At a certain critical value of the load called the "stability limit load," the frame will continue to sway without further increase in the load. A frame that becomes unstable in this manner is said to have failed by frame instability. Fig. 10.1(a) illustrates this type of behavior for a symmetrical frame under unsymmetrical gravity load.

2. For symmetrical frames subjected to symmetrical gravity loads it is possible that for a given value of load the frame may pass from a symmetrical stable configuration to an unsymmetrical unstable configuration characterized by a large lateral deflection. This behavior is analogous to that of a centrally loaded column, in which bifurcation of equilibrium is possible at a certain critical load. A frame that becomes unstable in this manner is said to have failed by frame buckling. Fig. 10.1(b) illustrates this type of behavior for a symmetrical frame under symmetrical gravity loads.

In the more general case an unbraced frame will resist combined gravity and lateral loads, and at a lower load factor. For unbraced frames subjected to combined loads, lateral deflections will occur from the first application of load. Initially the loads and resulting lateral deflections will be nearly proportional. As the applied loads increase, however, $P\Delta$ effects and yielding will cause the lateral deflections to increase at a greater rate than the rate of loading until, at the stability limit load, the frame will continue to sway without further increase in the load. Fig. 10.2 illustrates this type of behavior, also designated as frame instability.

Unlike an unbraced frame under gravity loads, the stability limit load of an unbraced frame under combined loads depends on the sequence of application of the combined loads (1.33). Ref. 9.8 presents an elastic-plastic

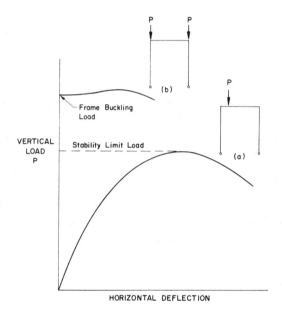

FIG. 10.1.—FRAME BUCKLING AND FRAME INSTABILITY UNDER GRAVITY LOADS

method for the determination of the stability limit load under proportional gravity and lateral loads. However, the proportional loading case may not always be realistic for practical frames. It is not likely that the gravity loads on the floors of a multistory building will be increasing at the same rate as the wind loading on the surface of the building. It is much more likely that the gravity loads will remain virtually constant while the wind load increases from zero to maximum. As a result, recent theoretical and experimental research has concentrated on the study of frame behavior under nonproportional combined loads (6.89, 10.5, 10.8, 10.10).

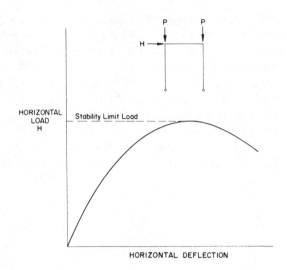

FIG. 10.2.—FRAME INSTABILITY UNDER COMBINED LOADS

## 10.2  FRAMING SYSTEM AND ASSIGNMENT OF LOADS FOR BRACED FRAMES

This section describes a structural framing system that is used frequently in the United States for the plastic design of braced multistory building frames. The assignment of gravity and lateral loads to braced frames is also discussed. The types of construction and connections for plastically designed frames are discussed in Chapters 4 and 8.

The framing system for a braced multistory frame consists of a planar rectangular frame with rigid beam-to-column connections. The frame also has an uninterrupted vertical bracing system. This means that at least one bay of each story must be braced. The beams, columns, and bracing in each braced bay comprise the vertical bracing system. This concept is illustrated in Fig. 10.3 where, for example, diagonal X and K bracing are used. The vertical bracing system is assumed to be the primary element which controls lateral deflection of the frame under the applied lateral loads.

It is common practice not to brace every parallel frame which occurs within the length of a multistory building but only a sufficient number of frames to assure adequate lateral strength and stiffness of the building. Braced frames are often used at or near the ends of a building. Additional braced frames are sometimes used on the perimeter of the core area. The term "supported bent" is used to describe the planar unbraced frames which are placed between the braced frames. These frames are designed primarily to resist gravity loads. They derive most of their lateral support through the diaphragm action of the continuous floor and roof systems which in turn are laterally supported by the braced frames. Fig. 10.4 shows a typical floor framing plan of a multistory building which has braced frames and supported bents.

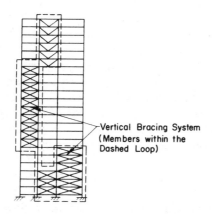

Vertical Bracing System
(Members within the Dashed Loop)

FIG. 10.3.—UNINTERRUPTED VERTICAL BRACING SYSTEM

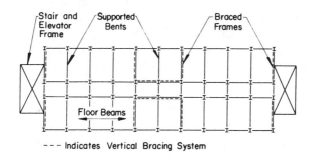

Stair and Elevator Frame

Supported Bents

Braced Frames

Floor Beams

--- Indicates Vertical Bracing System

FIG. 10.4.—TYPICAL FLOOR FRAMING PLAN

The continuous floor and roof systems usually consist of joists and slabs perpendicular to, and supported by, the beams of the braced frames and supported bents. Simple shear connections can be used at the ends of the floor and roof joists.

The gravity loads to be carried by a particular braced frame consist of the concentrated reactions from adjacent floor and roof joists. If the spacing of these joists is sufficiently small, the gravity loads may be considered distributed along the beams of the braced frame. Since the supported bents are assumed to resist no lateral loads, the lateral load per story to be carried by a particular braced frame is to be computed using a width equal to the average spacing of adjacent braced frames and a height equal to the story height. All lateral loads are assumed to be concentrated at the exterior joints of the braced frame.

In design calculations, a braced frame is treated as a planar structure. All loads are assumed to act in the plane of the structure and the resulting deformations are confined to the same plane. Individual members in the frame are assumed to be braced in the perpendicular direction so that they can not fail by lateral or lateral-torsional buckling. The floor system can usually be designed to provide adequate lateral bracing for the beams. Lateral bracing of the columns can also be provided at the floor levels by the floor system or the spandrel beams. In some instances, additional bracing may be required between floor levels in order to achieve the maximum in-plane strength. (The decision to provide this lateral bracing should be carefully reviewed, because the option of selecting different column shapes which require no additional bracing may be a more economical solution.)

The planar frame assumption described above is somewhat restrictive and cannot be applied without modifications to buildings using "two-way rigid" framing systems. Current research on the inelastic biaxial bending of restrained columns will be of value in formulating future design recommendations for such frames. Plastic design recommendations in England are in part based on two-way rigid frame action under the factored gravity loads with the lateral forces resisted by bracing (10.13). The column design for biaxial bending and the two-way rigid beam-to-column connection design are somewhat more involved for this type of framing. A brief discussion on columns subjected to biaxial bending has been given in Art. 7.6, and a design approach can be developed along the same line.

---

**BRACED FRAMES**
*Framing System:*
A braced frame consists of a planar rectangular frame with rigid beam-to-column connections. The frame also has an interrupted vertical bracing system containing diagonal X or K bracing. Other bracing configurations are sometimes used. Deformations of individual members are confined to the plane of the frame.
*Assignment of Loads:*
The beams and columns of the braced frame support the gravity loads transmitted from the adjacent floor and roof systems. The vertical bracing system resists the applied lateral loads.

## 10.3   VERTICAL BRACING SYSTEM

### Functions and Design Concept.

The vertical bracing system in a braced frame consists of the bracing members plus the beams and columns of each braced bay. This is illustrated in Figs. 10.3 and 10.5, in which the members within the dashed loops comprise the vertical bracing system. As illustrated in these figures, the bracing members may be confined to only one bay or may extend across more than one bay as shown in the lower stories of the frame in Fig. 10.3.

The vertical bracing system has two primary functions: (1) it is designed to provide adequate stiffness at working lateral loads, and (2) it is designed

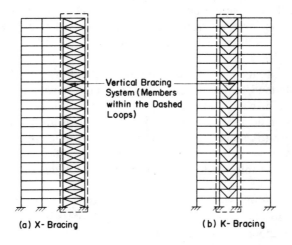

(a) X- Bracing                    (b) K- Bracing

FIG. 10.5.—VERTICAL BRACING SYSTEMS EMPLOYING INTERNAL X AND K BRACING

to prevent frame instability under combined gravity and lateral loads, and to prevent frame buckling and frame instability under gravity loads alone.

For design purposes a braced frame can be treated as two separate load-carrying systems: a rigid frame plus a vertical bracing system. The beams and columns of the braced bays will be common to both systems. The rigid frame can be proportioned initially for the gravity loads. All lateral loads as well as frame stability requirements are then assigned to the vertical bracing system. The design problem is simplified since all beams having the same span and gravity loading (except for the beams in the braced bays) can be designed alike.

The above remarks refer primarily to those structures in which the vertical bracing system has a lateral strength and stiffness much greater than those of the rigid frame. In this case the lateral resistance of the rigid frame may be discounted with no great loss in economy. Many structures, however, are composed of rigid frames coupled with vertical shear-wall systems consisting entirely of masonry or concrete shear walls, reinforced concrete elevator shafts, stairwalls, etc. In these cases the lateral resistance of the rigid frames may form a considerable portion of the total lateral strength of the structure, and this contribution cannot be disregarded.

A limited amount of research has been performed on the maximum strength of frames with vertical shear-wall systems (10.14). The relatively flexible shear-wall system, to some extent, dominates the lateral deflection pattern, and the interaction between the frames and the shear-wall system may change the force distribution significantly. A design method which accounts for this interaction has been developed and is being checked experimentally (10.15).

In a vertical bracing system containing diagonal bracing [Fig. 10.5(a)], the diagonals tend to be slender. Hence, their capacity is considerably larger in tension than in compression, and it is customary to assume that only the tension diagonals are active. If the diagonals are erected under an initial prestress to reduce sag, the compression diagonal will remain active until the net prestress is overcome. As a result, smaller diagonal bracing members are possible (10.16). Design examples for diagonal bracing are given in Ref. 1.33.

In a K-bracing system [Fig. 10.5(b)], both diagonals share in resisting horizontal loads. Gravity loads also cause axial forces in the K-braces and beams. Since the K-braces support the beams at midspan, the effective beam span and required plastic moment capacity are reduced. Design examples for K-bracing and braced beams are included in Ref. 9.22.

### $P\Delta$ Effects.

One of the functions of the vertical bracing system is to resist frame instability caused by the $P\Delta$ effect, which can reduce the strength and stiffness of the frame when considering the combined loads.

Fig. 10.6(a) shows the deformed configuration of columns of height $h$ from one story of a braced frame. The story is subjected to an applied lateral force, $\Sigma H$, and applied gravity loads, $\Sigma P$, as shown. Each column is required to resist its proportionate share of the moments $M + M_\Delta$ and shears $Q + Q_\Delta$ produced by the applied loads, as well as the $P\Delta$ effect. The subscript $\Delta$ indicates that these moments and shears arise due to the $P\Delta$ effect, which must be superimposed on the moments, $M$, and shears, $Q$, produced by the applied loads. Considering the $P\Delta$ effect separately, the columns of Fig. 10.6(a) resist an external moment of $\Sigma P\Delta$. This resistance is provided by column end moments, $M_\Delta$, and shears, $Q_\Delta$, as shown in Fig.

10.6(a). Equilibrium requires that

$$\Sigma P\Delta = \Sigma Q_\Delta h + \Sigma M_\Delta \ldots \ldots \ldots \ldots (10.1)$$

in which the end moments and shears are summed across the story. Neglecting any bending stiffness provided by the diagonal bracing in a braced frame, the moments $M_\Delta$ must be resisted by the adjacent beams and col-

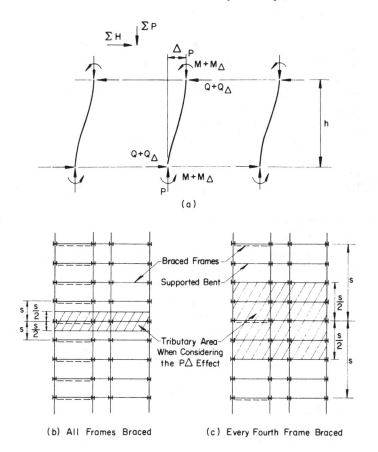

(a)

(b) All Frames Braced        (c) Every Fourth Frame Braced

FIG. 10.6.—DETERMINATION OF $P\Delta$ EFFECT FOR A BRACED FRAME

umns (assuming rigid connections), and the shears $Q_\Delta$ by the vertical bracing system.

Conservatively, it may be assumed that all beam-to-column joints in the braced frame are pinned. The total $P\Delta$ effect, therefore, must be resisted by the vertical bracing system alone. Thus

$$\Sigma Q_\Delta = \Sigma P \frac{\Delta}{h} \ldots \ldots \ldots \ldots \ldots (10.2)$$

The $P\Delta$ effect for a braced frame can therefore be represented as a horizontal shear $\Sigma Q_\Delta$ in the vertical bracing system termed the "$P\Delta$ shear." The total shear to be resisted by the vertical bracing in one story is the sum of the wind shear and the $P\Delta$ shear in that story.

$$\Sigma H = \Sigma Q + \Sigma Q_\Delta \quad \dots \dots \dots \dots (10.3)$$

Several observations are pertinent:

1. In Eq. 10.2, $\Sigma P$ is to be taken as the total gravity load (at working or factored levels) above the story under consideration which contributes to the $P\Delta$ effect. This concept is illustrated in Figs. 10.6(b) and 10.6(c). The gravity load contributing to the $P\Delta$ effect is computed using the tributary area of the braced frame. The tributary area of a braced frame is computed using a width equal to the width of the braced frame between exterior columns and a length equal to the average spacing of the adjacent braced frames [$S/2 + S/2$ in Figs. 10.6(b) and 10.6(c)].

2. If the floor system can be assumed to provide essentially rigid diaphragm action, then the relative displacements of the levels immediately above and below a given story in both the braced frame and the adjacent supported bents will be equal, assuming no torsional mode exists. In this case, $\Sigma P$ in Eq. 10.2 is taken as the total gravity load above the story within the tributary area of the braced frame (Fig. 10.6), and $\Delta$ is the relative displacement of the level immediately above and below a given story in the braced frame.

3. Also, if rigid diaphragm action of the floor system can be assumed, then the relative displacement $\Delta$ of two adjacent levels of the braced frame will include only the effect of elongation and/or shortening of the bracing, beams, and columns in the vertical bracing system (10.4, 10.17). Fig. 10.7 shows the contribution of each of these factors to the lateral deflection of the frame. Estimates of the $P\Delta$ effect that consider only brace deformations are obviously incomplete, because they ignore the deformations of the beams and columns.

4. If rigid diaphragm action can not be assumed, the $P\Delta$ shears must be computed separately for the braced frame and each supported bent, then combined to give the total $P\Delta$ shear which the braced frame must resist, in addition to the applied lateral loads. In general, a decrease in diaphragm stiffness will result in increased $P\Delta$ shears.

5. The $P\Delta$ effect will result in a nonlinear relationship of load versus lateral deflection under increasing applied loads, and will lead eventually to failure by instability. The tendency for instability failure of a braced frame will increase with increased slenderness of the ver-

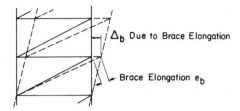

(a) Lateral Frame Deflection Due to Brace Elongation

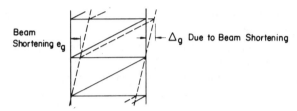

(b) Lateral Frame Deflection Due to Beam Shortening

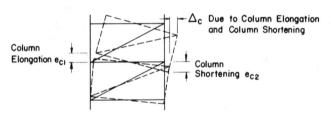

(c) Lateral Frame Deflection Due to Column Elongation and Shortening

FIG. 10.7.—FACTORS CONTRIBUTING TO LATERAL DEFLECTION OF VERTICAL BRACING SYSTEM

tical bracing system (total height divided by the width). This is due to the larger sway deflections associated with more slender vertical bracing systems. The sway deflection of a braced frame depends primarily upon the axial stiffnesses of all the members in the vertical bracing system, which can remain virtually unchanged until axial loads approach the yield load, $P_y$, an event that may not occur until relatively late in the loading process.

6. Although the possibility that frame instability may occur before the attainment of the design ultimate load should be checked in each design, it is possible that for the combined load condition, applicable to high-rise tower type buildings at least, a suitable drift limitation at the working load level will limit the reduction of load-

carrying capacity due to frame instability. This approach was
suggested in Chapter 7 of Ref. 1.33 as an approximate method for
calculating bracing forces. Further research is required to establish
the limits within which such a technique is applicable.

---

**VERTICAL BRACING SYSTEM**
   The vertical bracing system, in addition to supporting the applied
gravity loads, performs the following functions in a braced frame.

   1. Provides adequate stiffness to resist the applied lateral loads
      plus $P\Delta$ shears.
   2. Prevents frame instability under gravity and combined gravity
      and lateral loads.
   3. Prevents frame buckling under gravity loads.

---

### Design of Vertical Bracing System.

   The design of diagonal bracing members is discussed in Ref. 1.33. Two
methods of considering the $P\Delta$ shears are presented there. In both methods a value is assigned to the sway deflection $\Delta$ which occurs at the design
ultimate value of the gravity or combined loads, so that the $P\Delta$ shear can
be included in the subsequently determined strength and stiffness requirements for the diagonal bracing. The two methods differ only in the conditions used to establish $\Delta$.

   In the first method it is assumed that $\Delta$ is the sway deflection that would
result from tension yielding of the diagonal bracing. This value is determined from the geometry of the braced panel and the yield-stress level of
the bracing members. The contribution to $\Delta$ from the axial deformations
of the beams and columns in the vertical bracing system is neglected.
Strength and stiffness requirements for the diagonal bracing which are
based on this method will be sufficiently accurate providing that the axial
deformations of the beams and columns in the vertical bracing system are
small. This, however, will not generally be the case for a slender vertical
bracing system, or if the ratio of $\Sigma Q_\Delta$ to the applied story shear is large.

   In the second method a maximum lateral working load deflection is
assumed at the working load. This assigned value of sway deflection includes the effect of axial deformations of all the members in the vertical
bracing system, but does not include the $P\Delta$ effect. A linear relationship
is then assumed between the lateral loads and the resulting lateral deflections. The working load deflection times the load factor for the combined
loading condition plus an arbitrary estimated adjustment for the nonlinear
$P\Delta$ effects then gives the desired estimate of the sway deflection $\Delta$ at the

design ultimate load. The value $\Delta = 0.004\ h$ is suggested in Refs. 1.33 and 9.24 for the particular case in which a working load deflection of from $0.0020\ h$ to $0.0025\ h$ is used. This method of computing the strength requirements for the diagonal bracing requires that the strength versus stiffness relationship for the particular braced frame under design be checked for the combined loading condition. If this relationship is known, a working load deflection can be assigned and an adjustment for $P\Delta$ effects considered such that the bracing design is always conservative. Research is currently in progress at Lehigh University to establish the required strength-stiffness relationships for braced frames.

**Design Recommendations.**

The following design recommendations extend the concepts discussed in Ref. 1.33 to include the effects of the lateral loads and $P\Delta$ shears on the lateral stiffness of the vertical bracing system under working loads and the strength and stability of the bracing system under design ultimate loads.

It is suggested herein that the vertical bracing system be considered in design as containing one or more vertical pin-connected cantilever trusses which are subjected to gravity and lateral loads. These cantilever trusses will occur either singly, as shown in Fig. 10.5, adjacent to each other, as shown in the bottom three stories of the frame in Fig. 10.3, or in a more complex pattern, as shown in Fig. 10.3. In the following, design equations are presented only for the single vertical cantilever truss in the vertical bracing system. The concepts presented may be extended to the other cases by considering indeterminate truss analysis.

Three separate design conditions are to be considered. The design equations to be presented are in terms of the bracing area requirement, $A_b$, since the initial selection of beams and columns is controlled by the factored gravity loads (L.F. = 1.70). Only diagonal X bracing is considered.

**Design Condition 1: Lateral Stiffness Under Working Loads.**—Consider the braced panel ABCD of length $L$ and height $h$ shown in Fig. 10.8. With the direction of the working gravity and lateral loads as shown, diagonal BC of length $L_b$ and area $A_b$ is subjected to tension. It is conservatively assumed that diagonal AD cannot resist compression. The lateral deflection $\Delta$ of point B relative to point D will be determined by the elongation or shortening of only those members shown by heavy lines in Fig. 10.8. Only the change in length of these members due to lateral loads plus $P\Delta$ shears need be considered.

The required area $A_b$ of the tension diagonal brace BC can be found as

$$A_b = \frac{F_b L_b^2}{EL\Delta - \sigma_g L^2 - Ee_c h} \qquad \dots \dots \dots (10.4)$$

in which     $E$ = modulus of elasticity;

                 $F_b$ = tension force in diagonal BC (Fig. 10.8) due to lateral loads plus $P\Delta$ shear;

                 $e_c$ = sum of elongation of column CE plus shortening of column DF (Fig. 10.8) due to lateral loads plus $P\Delta$ shear;

                 $\sigma_g$ = axial compressive stress in beam CD (Fig. 10.8) due to lateral loads plus $P\Delta$ shear; and

                 $\Delta = \Delta_b + \Delta_g + \Delta_c$ (see Fig. 10.7).

In a typical design situation the maximum value of $\Delta$ under the working loads would be specified (for example, $\Delta = 0.002h$). The magnitude of the

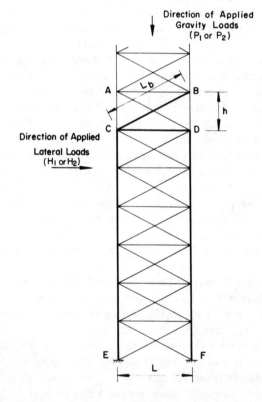

FIG. 10.8.—MEMBERS OF VERTICAL BRACING WHICH CONTROL LATERAL STORY DEFLECTION

$P\Delta$ shear can therefore be calculated, since the total gravity load $\Sigma P$ (L.F. = 1.0), above the story under consideration, contributing to the $P\Delta$ shear in the story is known. From the known lateral load $\Sigma H$ and

$P\Delta$ shear $Q_\Delta$, $\sigma_g$ and $e_c$ can be calculated. Eq. 10.4 will therefore determine the required area of the tension diagonal brace.

For unusually small or restrictive values of $\Delta$, or for very tall and slender vertical bracing systems, it may not be possible to keep within the limiting working load value of $\Delta$ using a bracing member of reasonable area, especially in the upper stories of the frame. To decrease the lateral deflection it may be necessary to increase the areas of the beams in the vertical bracing system, or to increase the areas of the columns in the lower stories of the vertical bracing system, or both.

**Design Condition 2: Strength and Stability Under Design Ultimate Loads.**—In order to maintain sufficient axial stiffness of the members of the vertical bracing system, it is suggested that the axial force in each member be arbitrarily limited to not more than 0.85 times its axial yield load, for the following reasons:

1. To limit the reduction of axial stiffness that comes about as a result of partial yielding due to combined axial force and residual stress.
2. To provide a reserve of plastic moment capacity for resisting the secondary moments in the vertical bracing system that are neglected by virtue of the assumption that this system is considered as a pin-connected truss for analysis.
3. To limit the extent to which lateral-torsional buckling may influence the behavior of laterally unbraced compression members in the vertical bracing system.

Insofar as axial loads and deformations are concerned, the vertical bracing system will remain essentially elastic if this limit on axial loads is not exceeded at the design ultimate value of combined gravity and lateral loads. Plastic hinges may form, but their influence on axial stiffness will be minor, because they usually are confined to short regions near the joints. Hence, elastic calculations will give a reasonable approximation of the lateral deflections of the vertical bracing system under the lateral loads and $P\Delta$ shears.

**Strength Requirement.**—Under the combined loading condition (L.F. = 1.30) the vertical bracing system must resist the applied lateral loads plus $P\Delta$ shears. Referring to Figs. 10.7 and 10.8, the required area $A_b$ of the diagonal brace BC can be found as

$$A_b = \frac{L_b}{0.85\,\sigma_y L}\,\Sigma H_1 + \left( \frac{L_b^3}{EhL^2} + \frac{L_b\,\sigma_g}{0.85\,\sigma_y Eh} + \frac{L_b\,e_c}{0.85\,\sigma_y L^2} \right) \Sigma P_1 \ . \ . \ (10.5)$$

in which  $\Sigma H_1$ = story shear due to the applied lateral loads (L.F. = 1.30);
  $\Sigma P_1$ = total applied gravity load above the story which contributes to the $P\Delta$ shear in the story (L.F. = 1.30); and

$\sigma_y$ = yield stress level of the diagonal brace. All other terms have been defined previously.

In this case, the story deflection $\Delta$ corresponding to the design ultimate load is unknown. Therefore, both $\sigma_g$ and $e_c$ in Eq. 10.5 are unknown. However, a first approximation of $\sigma_g$ and $e_c$ can be determined using the bracing areas found from Eq. 10.4 and a stress level of 0.85 $\sigma_y$ in each diagonal brace. Eq. 10.5 therefore will enable the designer to determine whether the bracing members required for working loads are also adequate for the design ultimate loads. Research has shown that for many braced frames the deflection limitations under working loads are likely to govern the design (1.33).

**Frame Stability Requirement.**—The vertical bracing system must provide sufficient lateral stiffness to prevent frame buckling or frame instability under the gravity loads alone (L.F. = 1.70). Although the applied lateral loads are zero, any initial out-of-straightness of the frame will generate $P\Delta$ shears which must be resisted by the vertical bracing system. The required area $A_b$ of the diagonal tension brace can be determined from Eq. 10.5 as

$$A_b = \left( \frac{L_b^3}{EhL^2} + \frac{L_b \sigma_g}{0.85 \, \sigma_y \, Eh} + \frac{L_b e_c}{0.85 \, \sigma_y \, L^2} \right) \Sigma P_2 \quad \ldots \ldots (10.6)$$

in which the terms are as defined above, and $\Sigma P_2$ = total gravity load above the story which contributes to the $P\Delta$ shear in the story (L.F. = 1.70); $e_c$ = sum of elongation of column CE plus shortening of column DF (Fig. 10.8) due to $P\Delta$ shear; and $\sigma_g$ = axial compressive stress in beam CD (Fig. 10.8) due to $P\Delta$ shear.

In Eq. 10.6, $e_c$ and $\sigma_g$ are computed corresponding to an assumed stress level of 0.85 $\sigma_y$ in each diagonal brace.

**Design Condition 3: Brace Slenderness Requirement.**—It is usually required that the slenderness ratio of the tension diagonal brace be less than a certain value to prevent vibration and "slapping." The AISC Specification provides for a maximum slenderness ratio of 300 for tension bracing members. This design condition can be expressed as

$$r_b \geq \frac{L_e}{300} \quad \ldots \ldots \ldots \ldots \ldots (10.7)$$

in which $r_b$ = the radius of gyration of the bracing member and $L_e$ = the effective length of the diagonal brace between points of support, as defined by the AISC Specification (4.18).

**Contribution of Frame Stiffness.**—The frame itself will contribute to the resistance to horizontal loads. This contribution has been disregarded in all the previous discussions on bracing design. However, it is sometimes desirable to include the frame resistance to shear in computing the axial force in the beams in the braced bay when the final design of the beams is performed. The shear resistance, $H_F$, of the frame at a given story is given approximately by (1.33)

$$H_F = \frac{12\,ER}{h}\ \Sigma\ \frac{k_C}{1 + \dfrac{4\,k_C}{k_B}} \qquad \ldots \ldots \ldots \ldots (10.8)$$

in which the last term in Eq. 10.8 is calculated for each column in the story and the resulting values summed across the story; and in which

$E$ = modulus of elasticity;

$h$ = height of the story under consideration;

$R$ = chord rotation of the columns in the story (can be assumed to equal the chord rotation of the vertical bracing system under the combined loading condition);

$k_C$ = $I_C /h$ for a particular column in the story;

$k_B$ = $I_B /L$ for a particular beam in the story;

$I$ = moment of inertia of a beam ($I_B$) or a column ($I_C$) in the story; and

$L$ = span of beam for which $I_B$ is obtained.

This approximation is for a regular rectangular frame and uses the assumptions that the beam end moment is shared equally by the column above and below, and that the moment at the bottom of the lower column is the same as that at the top. (That is, the inflection point is assumed to be at midheight of the column.)

When the columns have considerably greater stiffness than the beams, as would be the case in the lower stories of a tall frame, then the equation for shear resistance can be simplified to

$$H_F = \frac{3\,ER}{h}\ \Sigma\ k_B \qquad \ldots \ldots \ldots \ldots \ldots (10.9)$$

If the contribution of frame stiffness is considered in the design, the bending moments resulting from frame action must be considered when designing the columns.

## VERTICAL BRACING SYSTEM DESIGN

The vertical bracing system is to be designed as a vertical cantilever, pin-connected truss to resist the applied loads plus the $P\Delta$ shears.

The following equations are recommended for establishing the required area, $A_b$, of the diagonal tension bracing members.

**Design Condition 1: Lateral Stiffness Under Working Loads.—**

$$A_b = \frac{F_b L_b^2}{EL\Delta - \sigma_g L^2 - Ee_c h} \quad \cdots \cdots \cdots (10.4)$$

**Design Condition 2: Strength and Stability Under Design Ultimate Loads.—**

**Strength Requirement:**

$$A_b = \frac{L_b}{0.85\,\sigma_y L}\,\Sigma H_1 + \left(\frac{L_b^3}{EhL^2} + \frac{L_b\,\sigma_g}{0.85\,\sigma_y Eh}\right.$$

$$\left. + \frac{L_b e_c}{0.85\,\sigma_y L^2}\right)\,\Sigma P_1 \quad \cdots \cdots \cdots (10.5)$$

**Stability Requirement:**

$$A_b = \left(\frac{L_b^3}{EhL^2} + \frac{L_b\,\sigma_g}{0.85\,\sigma_y Eh} + \frac{L_b e_c}{0.85\,\sigma_y L^2}\right)\,\Sigma P_2 \quad \cdots (10.6)$$

**Design Condition 3: Brace Slenderness Requirement.—**

$$r_b \geq \frac{L_e}{300} \quad \cdots \cdots \cdots \cdots (10.7)$$

**Contribution of Frame Stiffness:**

The lateral shear resistance, $H_F$, of a story of the rigid frame may be included when determining the total frame resistance to lateral loads and $P\Delta$ shears as

$$H_F = \frac{12ER}{h}\,\Sigma\,\frac{k_C}{1 + \dfrac{4\,k_C}{k_B}} \quad \cdots \cdots \cdots (10.8)$$

For large values of $k_C/k_B$, Eq. 10.8 can be simplified to

$$H_F = \frac{12ER}{h}\,\Sigma\,k_B \quad \cdots \cdots \cdots (10.9)$$

## 10.4   THE SUBASSEMBLAGE CONCEPT FOR BRACED FRAMES

For braced frames the vertical bracing system resists the combined gravity and lateral loads, and provides stiffness against frame instability under the gravity loads alone. As a result, the frame member sizes are selected primarily to resist gravity loads. The beams can be selected on the basis of their mechanism load. The columns are then designed to resist the axial force from the stories above and the bending moment transmitted from the adjacent beams.

An important aspect of the design procedure for the columns of braced frame is the inclusion of the axial force effect in determining their moment-carrying capacity. As described in Art. 7.2, the presence of axial force causes a reduction of the moment capacity in two ways. First, the plastic moment of the cross section is reduced. Second, the column deflections, when combined with the axial load, generate an additional moment. This secondary moment may lead to instability failure of the column (see Art. 7.4). For the case of constant axial thrust and increasing end moment, the complete response of a column can be represented by its moment-rotation $M$-$\theta$ curves. This is accomplished by developing appropriate "subassemblages" or "limited frames" for the columns being designed.

### Subassemblages in Braced Frames.

In braced frame design a subassemblage is defined as a structural system consisting of two or more colinear and adjoining column segments and their adjacent beams, as shown in Fig. 10.9. Fig. 10.9 illustrates the selection of subassemblages for the design of an interior column AB subjected to checkerboard gravity loading and for the design of an exterior column CD under full gravity loading.

The interior subassemblage containing column AB also includes the adjacent beam and column segments framing into joints A and B. The beams at joints A and B which are loaded by the full gravity load $w_D + w_L$ are to fail by forming beam mechanisms with plastic hinges at the column faces and one at the center as shown in the figure. Known maximum moments are therefore applied at the joints. At each joint this moment is to be resisted by the columns above and below, and also by the remaining beam which carries only dead load, $w_D$. To maintain equilibrium of the joint, the resisting moment provided by the two columns and the remaining beam must be greater than the applied moment.

Fig. 10.10 illustrates the procedure for determining the total resisting moment of joint B. The procedure involves the construction of separate moment-rotation curves for the three members which resist the applied moment, $M_e$. These curves are then added graphically to obtain the combined $M$-$\theta$ curve. The peak of the combined curve determines the maximum total resisting moment of joint B. (It should be noted in Fig. 10.10

that the resisting moment of the joint can still increase even after one of the members has reached its maximum capacity.)

Previous studies have shown that the columns in interior subassemblages are likely to be bent into single curvature under checkerboard loading if the beams in the adjacent bays have about the same length and if the dead and live loads are the same in each bay (1.33). Therefore, in de-

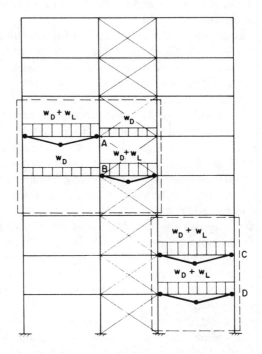

FIG. 10.9.—INTERIOR AND EXTERIOR SUBASSEMBLAGES IN A BRACED MULTISTORY FRAME

sign calculations the moment-rotation curves for symmetrical single curvature bending are often used. To facilitate the design process, a set of $M$-$\theta$ curves covering a wide range of columns has been prepared (1.33). Typical moment-rotation curves are shown in Fig. 10.11.

The exterior subassemblage containing column CD (Fig. 10.9) also includes the adjacent beam and column segments framing into joints C and D. Both beams are loaded by the full gravity load and are expected to fail almost simultaneously. Equal bending moments are therefore transmitted to the two joints, resulting in double curvature bending of the columns. At each joint the applied moment is resisted only by the two columns

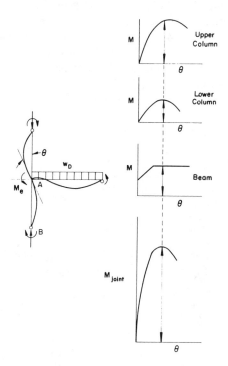

FIG. 10.10.—RESISTING MOMENT OF AN INTERIOR SUBASSEMBLAGE

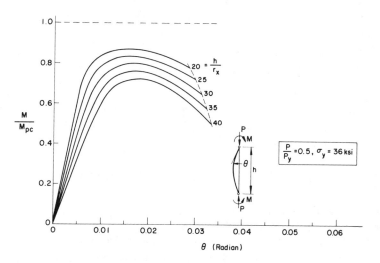

FIG. 10.11.—TYPICAL MOMENT-ROTATION CURVES

framing into the joint. Fig. 10.12 shows the procedure for determining the total resisting moment of joint D, a procedure that is identical with that discussed previously in connection with Fig. 10.10. The necessary moment-rotation curves have also been prepared for this case (1.33).

Other loading cases for both interior and exterior subassemblages are possible and can also be analyzed using appropriate curves contained in Ref. 1.33. One case for which complete curves are not yet in hand is that

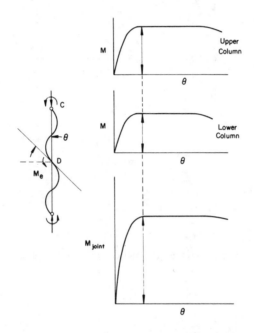

FIG. 10.12.—RESISTING MOMENT OF AN EXTERIOR SUBASSEMBLAGE

of laterally unbraced columns, although information on this topic should soon be available. However, existing curves can be used up to the point at which lateral-torsional buckling begins.

## 10.5 PRELIMINARY DESIGN OF UNBRACED FRAMES

### Design Concepts.

An unbraced frame must be able to resist gravity loads alone or combined gravity and lateral loads plus the additional moments and shears resulting from the $P\Delta$ effect. Also it must be stiff enough so that lateral frame deflections at working loads are within acceptable limits. Unlike braced frames, however, an unbraced frame develops its strength and stiffness entirely from the beams and columns alone.

In plastic design the working loads are multiplied by load factors to obtain the desired design ultimate loads. Since the load factor for gravity load is larger than the load factor for combined load, the top few floors (where the effects of wind are small) will be designed based on gravity loads. With each additional floor, the effect of the wind increases until finally the design of members is controlled by the combined loading case. As shown in Fig. 10.13, between the top several floors controlled by grav-

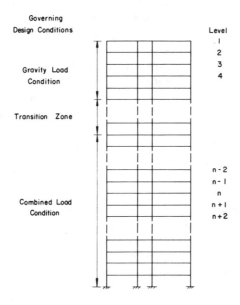

FIG. 10.13.—DESIGN CONDITIONS FOR UNBRACED FRAMES

ity loading and the floors in the middle and lower regions controlled by combined loading, there is a transition zone in which either one can control.

**Design for Gravity Loads.**

The preliminary design of the portion of the frame controlled by the gravity loading condition can be performed by straightforward plastic design procedures. Member sizes can be selected assuming this portion of the frame is braced against lateral deflections. Studies to date (see Art. 10.7) indicate that cladding will tend to reduce the possibility of frame buckling in this portion of the frame before the attainment of the mechanism load.

**Design for Combined Loads.**

In the region controlled by combined loading the preliminary design procedure is more complicated. A part of the loading carried by the members is from the unknown $P\Delta$ effect. One preliminary design procedure involves estimating the $P\Delta$ effect when selecting member sizes based on strength. The frame is then analyzed to determine the adequacy of the members selected considering strength and stiffness against lateral deflection. From the results of the analysis, one or more members may have to be revised. Any revision constitutes another preliminary design which must be analyzed once more.

An alternative design procedure is to first select members to resist gravity load alone (at the reduced load factor). The preliminary frame is then analyzed for its strength and lateral deflection behavior when subjected to combined loading. Member sizes are then revised based on the results of the analysis, thus forming a new preliminary design. Although the latter design method may be conceptually simpler, the former method is more practical, since the use of an initial estimated $P\Delta$ effect usually results in faster convergence. This procedure will be described in the discussions to follow.

Research has indicated that the preliminary design of an unbraced multistory frame for combined gravity and lateral loads can be essentially a three-step process:

Step 1. A preliminary analysis of moments and forces is made, using the moment-balancing technique described in Chapter 3 and further discussed in this article as it pertains to this type of frame. At this stage of design the $P\Delta$ moment in each story is usually not known. As a first try, the lateral deflections of each story corresponding to the mechanism condition, say, for that story are estimated. The $P\Delta$ moments for each story are then calculated and included in the story equilibrium equations. A preliminary design of the frame is performed, resulting in a preliminary selection of all frame member sizes.

Step 2. The lateral load versus sway deflection analysis of each story is then performed. The sway subassemblage method can be used in this step of the design. The analysis is carried out for a nonproportional loading condition where the total gravity loads are held constant while the lateral load is allowed to increase until the stability limit load is reached. The resulting analysis can then be used to check the estimated values of the $P\Delta$ moments which were included in the moment balance in Step 1, as well as to determine the adequacy of the preliminary design on the basis of working load deflections, stability, or other design conditions.

Step 3. A revision of the preliminary design is made if the frame behavior is not as desired. Any revision constitutes another preliminary design and Step 2 is repeated.

*Preliminary Analysis.*—In the design of unbraced frames with reasonably symmetric geometry and with gravity loading, the preliminary architectural and structural considerations up to the tabulation of loads and selection of members would be similar to those used for braced frames. In the design for resistance to combined gravity and lateral loads, different preliminary analysis procedures are required.

Fig. 10.14 shows a free body diagram of the several columns in a story which is subjected to horizontal shear $\Sigma H$ and gravity load $\Sigma P$. The values of $\Sigma H$ and $\Sigma P$ are computed from the loads acting on all the stories above the one shown in Fig. 10.14, a story which has a sway $\Delta$ and a height $h$. The magnitude of $\Sigma H$ and $\Sigma P$ will be computed as discussed in Art. 10.3 for braced frames. The resultant horizontal shear and total gravity load acting together in the deflected position cause an overturning moment which must be resisted by the sum of the column end moments, $\Sigma M_c$.

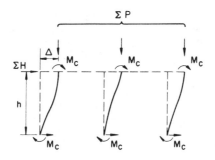

FIG. 10.14.—HORIZONTAL SHEAR EQUILIBRIUM IN A STORY OF AN UNBRACED FRAME

Without knowing the individual end moments, their required sum can be determined from

$$\Sigma M_c = - \left[ (\Sigma H)h + (\Sigma P)\Delta \right] \quad \ldots \ldots \ldots (10.10)$$

Fig. 10.15 shows a free body diagram of floor level $n$. The beams receive column moments from the columns above and below. For an estimate, it is assumed that half the total moments are at the top and bottom of each set of columns (this is tantamount to assuming an inflection point at mid-height). Then (for wind from left) the sum of the clockwise end moments on all beams in a level is

$$\Sigma M_g = - \frac{1}{2} \left[ (\Sigma M_c)_{n-1} + (\Sigma M_c)_n \right] \quad \ldots \ldots \ldots (10.11)$$

in which $n-1$ refers to column moments in the story above and $n$ to those in the story below the beams at floor level $n$. The sway deflection $\Delta$, which

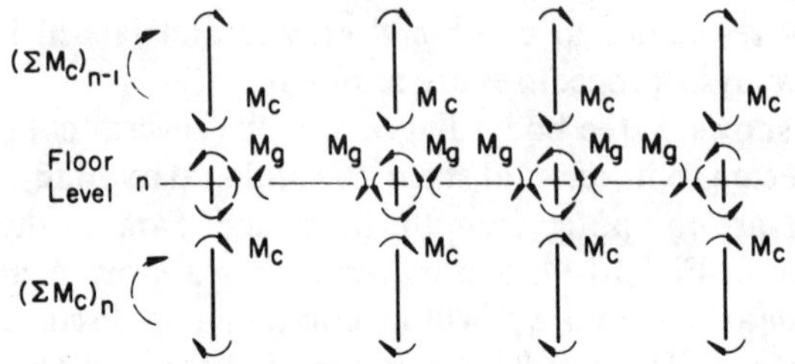

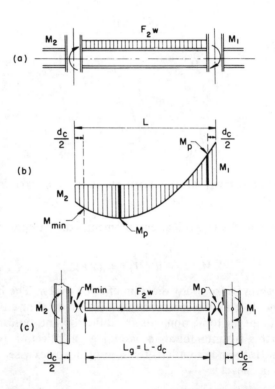

FIG. 10.15.—FREE BODY DIAGRAM AT FLOOR LEVEL $n$

FIG. 10.16.—SWAY MOMENTS ON A TRANSVERSELY LOADED BEAM

affects $\Sigma M_c$ in both Eq. 10.10 and Eq. 10.11, is unknown at the time of the preliminary analysis, but can be estimated so that trial member sizes can be selected and then revised if later deflection checks show this to be necessary.

Once the sum of the required beam end moments is known it can be proportioned to all beams on the level and the selection of beam sizes can begin. This is aided by solutions for the sway resistance of a loaded beam.

Fig. 10.16(a) shows a beam with both uniform load $F_2w$ and sway moments $M_1$ and $M_2$. The plastic limit load is reached when a plastic hinge forms at the leeward column face [Section B in Fig. 10.16(b)] and another at some point between the beam center and the windward column face. Detailed dimensions are shown in the free body diagrams of Fig. 10.16(c). To carry the antisymmetrical wind moments together with the symmetrical gravity moments requires a larger $M_p$ than is required for the gravity loads alone. Equilibrium solutions based on the moment diagram of Fig. 10.16(b) permit the determination of the required plastic moment $M_p$, the moments at both column center lines $M_1$ and $M_2$, and moments at both column faces $M_p$ and $M_{min}$ for a given design ultimate gravity load $F_2w$ and sum of clockwise beam moments $\Sigma M_g$ (in which $\Sigma M_g = M_1 + M_2$). A chart for the determination of these functions is given in Fig. 10.17. In Fig. 10.17 each of the above moments is nondimensionalized by dividing by the moment parameter $M_{pm}$ (defined below), which may be calculated from

$$M_{pm} = \frac{F_2 w L_g^2}{16} \quad \ldots \ldots \ldots \ldots \ldots (10.12)$$

in which

$F_2w$ = factored uniformly distributed load (with factor $F_2 = 1.3$);

$L_g$ = clear span of beam; and

$M_{pm}$ = plastic moment requirement under gravity load alone with a load factor $F_1$ or $F_2$ of 1.3.

The moment functions are plotted against the load parameter $F_1$ which is common to each of the moments. The load parameter $F_1$ serves as a measure of the excess beam capacity which must be supplied to resist wind along with gravity loads. The actual design chart included in Ref. 1.33 contains a family of curves depending on the column depth to column spacing ratio for each of the functions $\Sigma M_g$, $M_1$, and $M_2$. All moment parameters for a given beam lie on a single vertical $F_1$ line.

**Preliminary Design.**—Dashed lines in Fig. 10.17 illustrate the use of the preliminary analysis and the beam selection chart in selecting preliminary beam sizes. The sum of clockwise end moments $\Sigma M_g$ required for a given beam is calculated, keeping in mind the total end moments to be resisted by all the beams given by Eq. 10.11. The upper horizontal dashed line in Fig. 10.17 intersects the $\Sigma M_g / M_{pm}$ curve at the indicated parameter $F_1$ value. A vertical dashed line intersects the straight line for $M_p / M_{pm}$ at a level indicating the required plastic moment to provide the needed sum of end moments. This value is indicated by the lower horizontal dashed line. Fig. 10.18 shows how the beam selection chart may be used further to determine the two beam end moments $M_1$ and $M_2$ (Fig. 10.16) related to

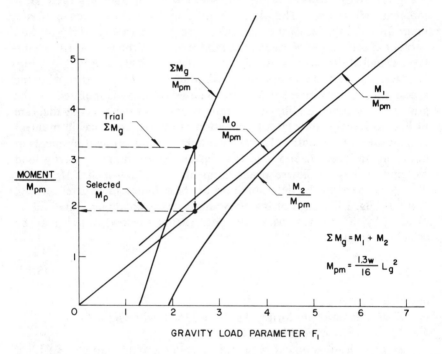

FIG. 10.17.—BEAM SELECTION CHART SHOWING TRIAL SELECTION OF A MEMBER

the center line of the columns. Once the beam size has been selected, the vertical dashed line in Fig. 10.17 may be projected upward and downward to intersect the $M_1 / M_{pm}$ and $M_2 / M_{pm}$ curves as shown in Fig. 10.18. The indicated values give the two resulting beam end moments and, with the already available data, completely define the moment diagram for the beam.

The beam moments thus defined may then be considered with column end moments determined from Eq. 10.10 to obtain a possible complete moment diagram for the story. Fig. 10.19 shows the initial beam moments along with the initial column moments calculated from Eq. 10.10. The

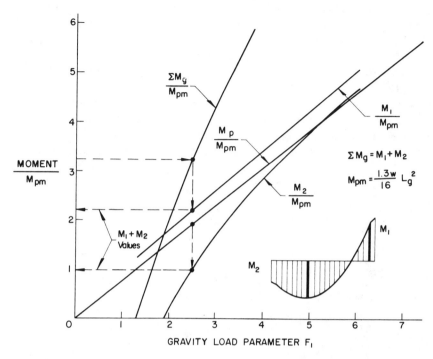

FIG. 10.18.—BEAM SELECTION CHART SHOWING DETERMINATION OF END MOMENTS

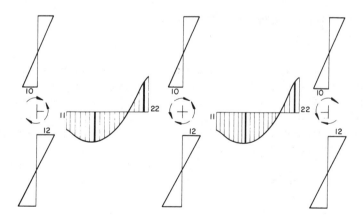

FIG. 10.19.—PRELIMINARY MOMENT DIAGRAMS PRIOR TO MOMENT BALANCE

column end moments in each story were arbitrarily divided equally between all column ends in that story, although other distributions of moment could have been used instead. Examination of the sum of moments
at each joint reveals that the total column moment is too great at the left
joint. There is too little column moment at the center joint. By coincidence
the right-hand joint is in balance.

The moment balancing method presented in Chapter 3 may be used to
put all the joints in balance. This method is simply an orderly process for
calculating and tabulating moment equilibrium at each joint. Fig. 10.20
shows the numerical results of a simple moment balance. It also shows the

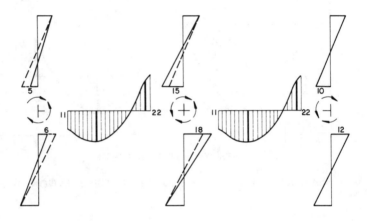

FIG. 10.20.—PRELIMINARY MOMENT DIAGRAMS RESULTING FROM MO-
MENT BALANCE

change in column moment diagrams from the original dashed lines to the
final solid lines, a comparison that shows the physical meaning of the moment balance. Notice that the beam moment diagrams were not changed.
Eqs. 10.10 and 10.11 have been satisfied. Therefore, any increase in moment in one column must be accompanied by an equal decrease in moments among other columns in the same story. Adequate adjustments may
usually be achieved without adjusting column moments at the far ends or
disturbing the equilibrium at another floor. Examination of Fig. 10.20
shows that all these conditions are met.

It is possible to perform the steps of load tabulation and the story equilibrium and moment balancing procedures on a computer, relieving the
designer of these routine calculations. Sufficient data to allow immediate
selection of trial sections can be printed by the computer (10.7, 10.11).

Having obtained the column end moments, it is then possible to select preliminary column sections using the same basic $M_{pc}$ tables and moment-rotation curves as were used for columns in braced frames (Art. 10.4). A further check is needed to determine whether the actual effects of lateral deflection ($P\Delta$ effects) are not greater than were assumed in determining beam and column moments.

---

**UNBRACED MULTISTORY FRAMES**

An unbraced frame consists of a rigid frame in which the bending resistance of the beams and columns alone is used to resist all gravity and lateral loads. $P\Delta$ effects can significantly affect the design of all the beams and columns of unbraced frames. A three-step procedure is used for the design of unbraced frames:

1. The plastic moment balancing technique is used to achieve a statically admissible distribution of bending moments throughout the frame corresponding to the known loads and an estimated $P\Delta$ effect. Selection of columns and beams then follows.
2. The lateral-load versus sway-deflection behavior of each story is then determined using a sway subassemblage method of analysis.
3. A revision of the preliminary design is made if necessary. Any revision constitutes another preliminary design, and Step 2 is repeated.

---

## 10.6   THE SWAY SUBASSEMBLAGE CONCEPT

The response of a story which is subjected to combined loads plus $P\Delta$ moments can be accounted for by the sum of the individual response characteristics of each column in the story. For the case of constant axial thrust and increasing lateral load, the complete response of a column can be represented by its "restrained column curve." Such a curve is shown in Fig. 10.21. It is a graphical description of the nondimensional relationship between lateral load $Q$ and sway deflection $\Delta$ for a particular restrained column with $P/P_y = 0.7$ and $h/r_x = 20$. The restrained column response will be dependent on the magnitude of the axial force $P$, the slenderness ratio of the column $h/r_x$, the yield-stress level of the material $\sigma_y$, the variation of rotational restraint $M_r$ provided by the restraining beams at the top of the column, and the residual stress distribution. To account properly for the behavior of the entire story (which consists of a series of restrained columns) the design method for unbraced frames makes use of the nondimensional $Q$-$\Delta$ curves for each restrained column in the story. In this manner the behavior of a story under combined loads is reduced to that of a "one-story assemblage" of restrained columns. The one-story assemblage is analyzed by developing appropriate "sway subassemblages."

As used in the analysis of one-story assemblages, a sway subassemblage is defined as a structural system in the laterally displaced configuration consisting of the upper half of one story height of a column plus the one or two rigidly connected in-plane beams at the top of the column. The sway subassemblages comprising a one-story assemblage at level $n$ for a 3-bay unbraced multistory frame are shown in Fig. 10.22. The column positions in the story are denoted by A, B, C, and D. The restrained columns of height $h_n/2$ are assumed to be pinned at the bottom. This cor-

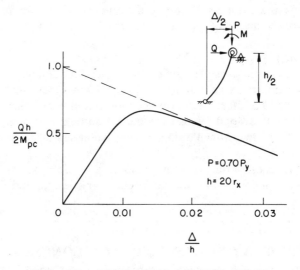

FIG. 10.21.—RESTRAINED COLUMN CURVE

responds to the assumption of an inflection point at the midheight of each column above and below level $n$.

The far ends of the restraining beams are assumed to be subjected to rotational restraints which approximate the effect of the remaining beam and columns in the story. The restrained columns are subjected to axial forces $P$ from above level $n$, and the beam-to-column joint is subjected to a moment $M$ which results from the applied column shear above level $n$. The restraining beams are subjected to gravity loads $w$. These forces and loads may correspond to working load conditions (if working load behavior of the frame is of interest), or they may correspond to the design ultimate loads, or to any other loading condition of interest.

In the analysis procedure, the lateral load, $Q$, versus sway deflection, $\Delta$, of each sway subassemblage is determined (10.5). The lateral load versus sway deflection behavior of the complete story is obtained by a summa-tion of the several sway subassemblage responses $(Q\text{-}\Delta)$. To facilitate the analysis, a set of restrained column curves has been prepared for hand computational use (10.12). A typical nondimensional chart for the analy-sis of a sway subassemblage containing a restrained column with $P = 0.45$ $P_y$ and $h = 22\ r_x$ is shown in Fig. 10.23. Each nondimensionalized load-deflection curve in this chart represents the lateral load $Q$ versus sway deflection $\Delta$ relationship of the restrained column for a particular value of

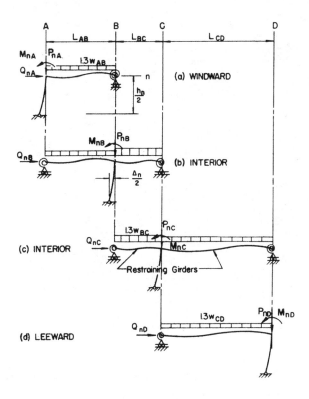

FIG. 10.22.—SWAY SUBASSEMBLAGES FOR A 3-BAY FRAME

elastic rotational restraint $M_r = k\ \theta\ M_{pc}$, in which $k$ = the nondimension-alized restraint stiffness, and $\theta$ = the joint (column top) rotation. This moment is applied at the column top by the adjacent restraining beams. The value of $k$ can vary from zero (no restraint) to infinity (rigid restraint). Termination of elastic rotational restraint can occur when a plastic hinge forms in the restraining beams ($M'_r < 2.0\ M_{pc}$) or when a plastic hinge oc-curs at the top of the restrained column ($M'_r = 2.0\ M_{pc}$). The term $M'_r$ is used to denote particular values of $M_r$ corresponding to the formation of each plastic hinge. Fig. 10.24 illustrates these two possibilities for a re-strained column with rotational restraint $M_r = 160 \ \theta \ M_{pc}$ in which $k = 160$. Curve a-b-c-d represents the load-deflection curve of the restrained column where a plastic hinge at the top of the column results in a mechanism condition. Curve a-b-e results when a plastic hinge forms in the re-

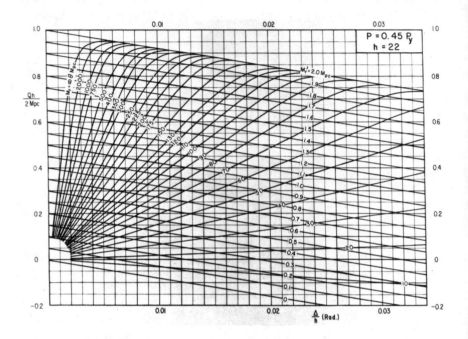

FIG. 10.23.—TYPICAL DESIGN CHART FOR SWAY SUBASSEMBLAGE METHOD OF ANALYSIS

straining beam ($M_r' = 1.5 \ M_{pc}$ is arbitrarily shown in the example) and a mechanism condition results.

The $Q$ versus $\Delta$ response for a one-story assemblage is determined by addition of the sway subassemblage responses in a manner similar to that described in connection with Fig. 10.10 for the joint in a braced frame subassemblage.

The sway subassemblage theory can also be used to assist in selecting the near minimum weight combination of beams and columns in a particular one-story assemblage (10.9). In this procedure, plastic design sections are selected to satisfy the constraints of: (1) No plastic hinges prior to a specified load level; (2) a maximum story sway at the specified load level; and (3) nonlinear elastic behavior. The specified load level will normally be the working load but may be any other desired load level. After the near minimum weight combination of beams and columns has been selected, the stability limit load under combined loads and the working load

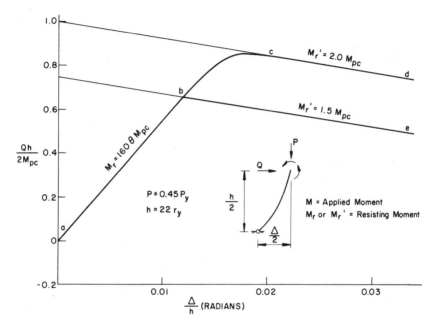

FIG. 10.24.—TYPICAL LOAD DEFLECTION CURVE

deflection under working loads can be checked by the sway subassemblage method of analysis.

**Lateral Load Versus Sway Deflection Analysis.**

After the preliminary design of a frame has been completed, the lateral load versus sway deflection behavior of selected stories in the "middle" and "lower" stories of the frame (region of significant $P\Delta$ effects) can be determined using the sway subassemblage concept. The selection of windward, interior, and leeward sway subassemblages can be made and the rotational restraint provided by the beams can be calculated.

Fig. 10.25 illustrates the procedure for constructing the load-deflection curve of an interior sway subassemblage. The initial part of the curve 0-a is valid prior to the formation of plastic hinges within the sway subassemblage, and is described by the restrained column curve 0-a-e which corresponds to the initial restraint function $M_{r1}$. After the formation of the first plastic hinge at point a, the behavior of the sway subassemblage is described by the curve a-b. Curve a-b is the segment of a'-b' of curve 0-b'-f which corresponds to the reduced restraint function $M_{r2}$. (Restraint function $M_{r1}$ reduces to $M_{r2}$ with the formation of the plastic hinge at point a.) Similarly, with a second plastic hinge at point b, the restraint function further reduces to $M_{r3}$, and the behavior of the sway subassemblage is described by curve b-c, which is segment b″-c″ of curve 0-g. With the formation of a third plastic hinge at point c, a mechanism results, the restraint function reduces to zero, and the load-deflection curve for the sway subassemblage follows the second-order plastic mechanism c″-d.

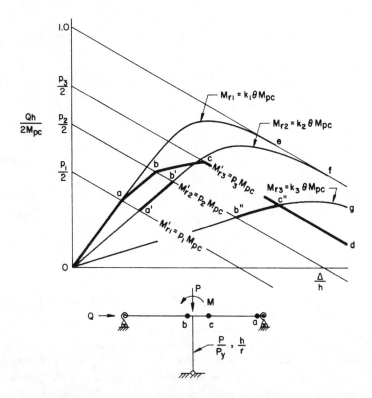

FIG. 10.25.—CONSTRUCTION OF LOAD-DEFLECTION CURVE

Construction of the sway subassemblage load-deflection curves from design charts such as the one shown in Fig. 10.23 requires graphical procedures. This will not be necessary in the computer analysis of a sway subassemblage (10.7). However, in the computer analysis the restrained column curves (of which those shown in Fig. 10.25 are typical) are linearized. For example, point e in Fig. 10.25 would lie on the intersection of a linear projection of curve 0-a with the sloping straight line which passes through the ordinate $Qh/(2M_{pc})$ = 1.0. A similar situation can be described for point f. The resulting inaccuracy, although on the unconservative side, is not large for many sway subassemblages examined. It is smallest when all plastic hinges form in the restraining beams, and largest when a plastic hinge forms at the top of the restrained column.

Fig. 10.26 illustrates the use of the sway subassemblage method for the nonproportional combined load analysis of the one-story assemblage at Level 8 in "Frame B" (1.33, 10.8). The results of the analysis are shown corresponding to the design ultimate value of gravity loads (L.F. = 1.30). The solid curves are the result of hand computations using design charts, whereas the dashed curves are the result of a computer analysis. The individual sway subassemblage curves have been added together as discussed in Art. 10.4 to give the load-deflection curve at Level 8 which was designed using the moment-balancing method. An estimated sway of $0.02h$ was included in the preliminary design in the formulation of equilibrium for purposes of estimating the $P\Delta$ effect corresponding to the mechanism condition. Since a mechanism was reached when $\Delta$ = $0.021h$, the analysis indicates that the $P\Delta$ effect was slightly underestimated in the preliminary design. The stability limit load is 72.5 kips, which exceeds the design ultimate load of 56.1 kips (1.33). The first plastic hinge occurs at approximately 40% of the design ultimate load. This situation can be expected for the nonproportional loading case, even though a proportional load analysis may indicate that no plastic hinges occur before attainment of the working load value of combined loads.

The sway subassemblage analysis is carried out under the assumption of constant gravity loads (axial loads in the columns may vary, however), and monotonically increasing lateral sway displacement. As a result, the lateral-load versus sway-deflection behavior of a one-story assemblage can be obtained for increasing lateral load up to the stability limit load and for decreasing lateral load beyond this point. A similar analysis can also be performed assuming proportional gravity and lateral loads. This procedure involves use of the sway subassemblage method to construct a series of load-deflection curves for a one-story assemblage, where each curve is constructed for a different magnitude of constant gravity load. This set of curves is then used to generate the load-deflection curve of the one-story assemblage for the proportional load case. The resulting proportional loading curve can be compared with the solution obtained by an "exact" second-order elastic-plastic method presented in Ref. 9.8 which has been developed for the proportional loading case.

Fig. 10.27 shows a comparison of the curves obtained by the two methods described above for the one-story assemblage at Level 8 for "Frame B" of Ref. 1.33. The solid curve was obtained using the procedures discussed in Ref. 9.8. The extent of this curve is limited because frame in-

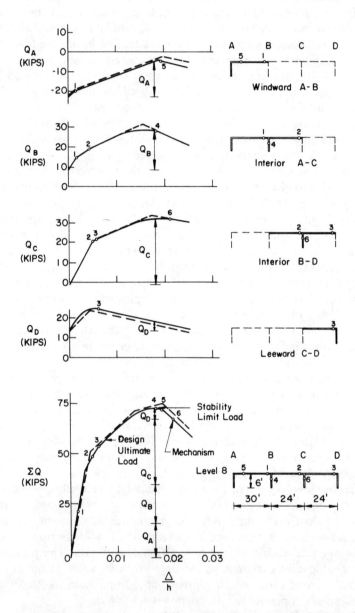

FIG. 10.26.—ANALYSIS OF A 1-STORY ASSEMBLAGE FOR NONPROPOR-
TIONAL LOADING

stability occurred elsewhere in the frame, thus preventing the attainment
of higher load values at Level 8. The analysis of the same assemblage by
the sway subassemblage method is independent of the behavior of other
stories and is shown by the dashed curve in Fig. 10.27. Because of the
assumptions on which the sway subassemblage method is based, this curve
is necessarily approximate. The degree of approximation will, of course,
be a function of how closely the assumptions agree with real frame behavior.

The comparison shown in Fig. 10.27 is close enough for design purposes
and is typical of the agreement obtained between the "exact" and approximate methods for the "middle" and "lower" stories of unbraced frames
(10.8). Thus the sway subassemblage method of analysis may be used to
determine the adequacy of the preliminary unbraced frame design.

Further comparison of Figs. 10.26 and 10.27 indicates that a significant
difference in the stability limit load is possible for Level 8 depending on

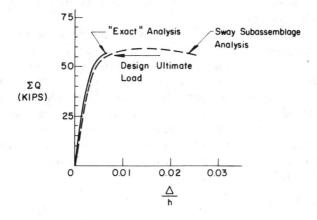

FIG. 10.27.—ANALYSIS OF A 1-STORY ASSEMBLAGE FOR PROPORTIONAL
LOADING

the loading history. In the nonproportional loading case (Fig. 10.26) where
the gravity loads are held constant, the increased moments applied to the
frame beyond the design ultimate load level are a function only of the
increased lateral load $\Sigma Q$ and increased sway deflection $\Delta$. In the proportional loading case (Fig. 10.27) these increased moments are a function not
only of the increased lateral loads $\Sigma Q$ and increased sway deflection $\Delta$,
but also of the increased gravity loads. Thus the increased $P\Delta$ effects resulting from proportional loading tends to reduce the amount of additional lateral load which can be applied to Level 8.

Further discussion can be found in Ref. 10.8.

## 10.7   FINAL ANALYSIS AND DESIGN

For most regular, planar, rectangular, unbraced multistory frames, the three-step preliminary design procedure described in Arts. 10.5 and 10.6 will lead to a satisfactory final design of the frame. The design is based on an equilibrium solution of the structure in which the plastic strength of the members is not exceeded. A lower-bound solution is therefore attained.

A more exact analysis and design of an unbraced frame may be necessary if the frame is irregular or can not be assumed to behave in the manner which was assumed in developing the previously discussed preliminary design techniques. A more precise prediction of frame strength and lateral deflection behavior may also require the use of more exact analytical techniques. The following discussion should be helpful when such analyses are required.

### Gravity Load Condition.

Either frame instability or frame buckling can occur in the upper few stories of unbraced multistory frames and in unbraced frames only a few stories high. In both of these cases member sizes are normally controlled by gravity loading alone.

The instability and buckling behavior of unbraced frames can be analyzed by digital computers (9.8, 9.15). A difficulty encountered in such analyses is the unloading that occurs in some of the previously yielded fibers when frame instability takes place. In an elastic-plastic analysis, this behavior corresponds to plastic hinge unloading. When more than one hinge unloads, the correct order of hinge unloading must be determined. For portal frames the unloading is easier to consider, and hence relatively exact solutions are available (10.18–10.24). At present (1970) these "exact" solutions have not been applied to multistory frame analysis, and therefore elastic-plastic behavior is usually assumed.

The multistory frame buckling problem is under study both experimentally (10.25) and theoretically (6.102, 10.25, 10.26). Ref. 6.102 discusses experiments on two 1-bay, 3-story, pinned-base frames. The beams were designed to fail by beam mechanisms. The columns were designed to carry their axial loads and to have moment capacities sufficient to satisfy the equilibrium requirements at the beam-to-column connections. In each test frame buckling occurred at a load approximately equal to 0.9 of the beam-mechanism load. In a corresponding practical structure there would have been additional stiffness available from the floors, walls, and roof. Partial base fixity has also been found to increase the stiffness of unbraced frames considerably (6.102, 10.27, 10.28).

An exact analysis for the inelastic multistory frame buckling problem is not available. One method of analysis circumvents the unloading problem by approximating the frame buckling load as the limit of frame stability limit loads (6.102). Studies based on this method show the importance of primary bending and the beneficial effects of partial base fixity. The studies indicate that frame buckling is not likely to occur in the upper stories of multistory frames. For frames with only a few stories, frame buckling is not likely to occur if base restraint is provided. If pinned bases are used, however, frame buckling must be considered. The studies did not consider the effects of cladding. However, cladding will tend to restrain the frame, and thus should tend to prevent frame buckling.

**Combined Load Condition.**

The determination of the frame stability load and the lateral deflection behavior up to that load and beyond, if necessary, is possible by a computerized step-by-step second-order elastic-plastic analysis (3.9, 9.4, 9.8, 9.9, 9.15, 9.17, 9.18, 9.19). Some of these computer programs are quite complete and capable of handling relatively large frames. It is possible in some of these programs to include: (1) The instability effects of individual members and of the entire frame; (2) the bending moment caused by relative shortening of the columns; (3) spread of yielding near the plastic hinges; and (4) the influence of strain hardening.

The stability limit load for tall unbraced frames containing high axial loads will be substantially less than the mechanism load predicted by first-order plastic analysis. In addition, the stability limit load (and corresponding lateral deflection) is path dependent. If a second-order elastic-plastic analysis is performed for a frame which was designed using the preliminary design techniques previously discussed, the loading paths should be the same if the results are to be comparable. That is, the more exact analysis method will be required to predict the frame strength and deformation under nonproportional loading as was assumed in the preliminary design of the frame. It is expected that further research will produce computer programs which can provide solutions for extremely complex frames and include more secondary effects, as well as proportional and nonproportional loading of frames.

# APPENDIX I.—SYMBOLS

Although there are exceptions, this list of symbols generally uses lower case letters for linear dimension, capital letters for products of dimensions, and Greek letters for ratios and factors.

| | |
|---|---|
| $A$ | = area of cross section; |
| $A_b$ | = nominal bolt area; |
| | = area of tension diagonal bracing; |
| $A_c$ | = area of steel section or concrete in compression; |
| | = area of sloping (compression) flange plate in tapered or curved haunch; |
| $A_{c1}$ | = area of inner flange of rafter haunch; |
| $A_{c2}$ | = area of inner flange of column haunch; |
| $A_g$ | = gross area; |
| $A_n$ | = net area; |
| $A_s$ | = area of steel section; |
| | = area of symmetrical pair of diagonal stiffeners; |
| | = stress area; |
| $A_t$ | = area of steel section in tension; |
| | = area of straight (tension) flange plate in tapered haunch; |
| $A_{t1}$ | = area of outer flange of beam haunch; |
| $a$ | = depth of rectangular compressive stress block of concrete slab; |
| | = distance from end of cantilever to critical section of beam; |
| | = length from center of bolt to edge of plate; |
| $B$ | = beam-column interaction equation coefficient; |
| $b$ | = flange width; |
| | = breadth of rectangular cross section; |
| | = distance from center of bolt to edge of fillet of connected part; |
| $b'$ | = width of outstanding plate element; |
| $b_o$ | = width of plate simulating flange element of wide-flange shape; |
| $C$ | = compressive force in concrete slab of composite beam; |
| $C'$ | = compressive force in steel section of composite beam; |
| $C_w$ | = warping constant; |
| $C_1$ | = moment coefficient depending on support and load conditions; |
| $C_2$ | = deflection coefficient depending on support and load conditions; |
| $c$ | = distance from centroid to extreme fiber; |
| $D$ | = nominal bolt size; |
| $D_x$ | = $E_x/(1 - \nu_x \nu_y)$; |
| $D_y$ | = $E_y/(1 - \nu_x \nu_y)$; |
| $D_{xy}$ | = $\nu_y D_x$; |
| $D_{yx}$ | = $\nu_x D_y$; |

$d$ = depth of section (subscripts $b$, $c$, and $i$ denote bracing member, column, and member);

$d_{ch}$ = depth of column haunch (Fig. 8.7);

$d_f$ = distance between centers of two flanges;

$d_w$ = web depth of wide-flange shape, $d_w = d - 2\,t$;

$d_x$ = depth of haunch at section $x$ (Figs. 8.6 and 8.9);

$E$ = Young's modulus of elasticity;

$E_{st}$ = strain-hardening modulus;

$E_t$ = tangent modulus;

$E_x$ = tangent modulus in $x$-direction;

$E_y$ = tangent modulus in $y$-direction;

$e$ = distance between resultant concrete compressive force and resultant steel tensile force in composite beam (Fig. 4.2);

= eccentricity;

$e_c$ = sum of elongation of column plus shortening of column due to lateral loads plus $P\Delta$ shear;

$F$ = load factor of safety;

= average force per bolt;

$F_b$ = tension force in diagonal brace due to lateral loads plus $P\Delta$ shear;

$F_v$ = shear strength of fastener;

$F_1, F_2$ = load factors;

$f$ = shape factor, $f = M_p/M_y = Z/S$;

$f'_c$ = ultimate cylinder strength of concrete;

$f_t$ = tensile stress due to the applied load;

$f_v$ = maximum shear component on bolt under tension;

$G$ = modulus of elasticity in shear;

= beam-column interaction equation coefficient;

$G_{st}$ = modulus of elasticity in shear at onset of strain hardening;

$G_t$ = tangent modulus in shear;

$H$ = horizontal reaction or load;

= hinge angle required at a plastic hinge;

$H_B$ = portion of hinge angle that occurs in the critical (buckling) segment of member;

$H_F$ = shear resistance of a frame;

$h$ = story height;

$I$ = moment of inertia (subscripts $x$ and $y$ denote axes, subscripts $b$ and $c$ denote beam and column, and $w$ denotes warping);

= moment of inertia of beam ($I_B$) or column ($I_C$);

$J$ = beam-column interaction equation coefficient;

$K$ = torsion constant;

= beam-column interaction equation coefficient;

= effective column length coefficient;

= spring constant of web;

$K_T$ = St. Venant torsion constant;

$k$ = distance from flange face to end of fillet (subscript $c$ denotes column fillet);

|  | = stiffness factor of a beam (subscripts $\ell$ and $s$ refer to adjacent segments and denote larger and smaller stiffness factors); |
|  | = restraining factor; |
| $k_B$ | = $I_B/L$ for a particular beam in a story; |
| $k_C$ | = $I_C/h$ for a particular column in a story; |
| $L$ | = span length parameter; |
|  | = actual column length; |
|  | = distance between points of lateral support; |
|  | = span of braced bay in the story under consideration; |
| $L_A$ | = length of adjacent segment between points of lateral support; |
| $L_{Acr}$ | = critical length (based on simple span) of adjacent segment; |
| $L_b$ | = length of bracing member; |
| $L_{cr}$ | = critical unsupported length for lateral buckling; |
| $L_e$ | = effective length of diagonal brace between points of support; |
| $L_g$ | = clear span of beam; |
| $L_i$ | = length of member $i$; |
| $L_{\ell cr}$ | = critical length (based on simple span) of adjacent segment (subscript $\ell$ denotes longer critical length); |
| $L_{scr}$ | = critical length (based on simple span) of adjacent segment (subscript $s$ denotes shorter critical length); |
| $\ell$ | = length of segment (slope-deflection equations); |
| $M$ | = bending moment; |
| $M_c$ | = column end moment; |
| $M_{cr}$ | = critical moment of the beam-column in the absence of axial load; |
| $M_E$ | = external moment; |
| $M_{eq}$ | = equivalent end bending moment (subscripts $x$ and $y$ denote axes); |
| $M_g$ | = beam end moment; |
| $M_h$ | = moment at the haunch point; |
| $M_I$ | = internal moment; |
| $M_i$ | = elastic moment at section $i$; |
| $M_L$ | = bending moment about strong axis at $z = L$; |
|  | = lower column end moment; |
| $M_{max}$ | = maximum moment; |
| $M_o$ | = maximum end moment that can be carried by a beam-column; |
|  | = bending moment about strong axis at $z = 0$; |
|  | = maximum moment at the plastic hinge of a beam; |
| $M_p$ | = plastic moment; |
| $M_{pc}$ | = plastic hinge moment modified to include the effect of axial compression; |
| $M_{pi}$ | = plastic moment required for member $i$; |
| $M_{pm}$ | = plastic hinge moment modified to include the effect of axial compression and shear force; |
|  | = plastic moment requirement under gravity load alone with a load factor $F_1$ or $F_2$ of 1.3; |
| $M_{ps}$ | = plastic hinge moment modified to include the effect of shear force; |
| $M_{px}$ | = plastic moment of resistance at section $x$ of a haunch; |
| $M_r$ | = residual moment; |
|  | = initial restraint function; |

$M_s$ = moment at inertia support;

$M_U$ = upper column end moment;

$M_w$ = moment at working (service) loads;

$M_x$ = moment at section $x$ of haunch;

$M_y$ = moment at which yielding first occurs in flexure;

$M_\Delta$ = moment due to $P\Delta$ effect;

$M_1$ =  larger of two end moments on a beam-column;

$M_2$ = smaller of two end moments on a beam-column;

$m$ = moments in a structure in equilibrium with a unit load;

  = distance between fillet extremities of flange of column;

$n$ = threads per inch;

  = number of bolts;

$P$ = concentrated or axial load;

$P_a$ = maximum load for alternating plasticity;

  = allowable load;

$P_{cr}$ = critical load on axially loaded column;

$(P_{cr})_y$ = weak axis critical load of the beam-column in the absence of bending moment;

$P_e$ = Euler buckling load (subscripts $x$ and $y$ denote axes);

$P_L$ = live load (working);

$P_m$ = maximum load;

$P_p$ = plastic limit load;

$P_s$ = stabilizing ("shakedown") load;

  = stability limit load;

$P_T$ = total dead plus live load (working);

$P_t$ = tangent modulus load;

$P_u$ = design ultimate load (factored load);

$P_w$ = working (service) load;

$P_y$ = load on beam when yield stress level is reached in flexure;

  = axial load corresponding to yield stress level, $P_y = A\,\sigma_y$;

$Q$ = prying force;

$Q_\Delta$ = horizontal shear due to $P\Delta$ effect;

$R$ = radius of curved haunch;

  = rotation capacity of a plastic hinge;

  = chord rotation of the columns in a story;

$R_o$ = optimum rotation capacity;

$r$ = radius of gyration (subscripts denote flexural axes);

$r_b$ = radius of gyration of the diagonal brace;

$r_x$ = radius of gyration of compression flange of haunch in strong direction;

$S$ = section modulus, $S = I/c$;

$s$ = distance along member;

$T$ = force;

  = resultant tensile force in composite section;

$T_s$ = horizontal component of diagonal stiffener force;

$T_w$ = web shear force;

$t$ = flange thickness [subscripts $c$ and $t$ denote compression (or column) and tension flange];

|        |                                                                                        |
|--------|----------------------------------------------------------------------------------------|
|        | = over-all thickness of concrete slab; |
| $u, v, w$ | = displacements in $x$, $y$, and $z$ directions, respectively; |
| $V$    | = shear force; |
|        | = vertical reaction; |
| $V_p$  | = shear force that produces full yielding of web; |
| $V_Y$  | = maximum allowable shear force at ultimate load; |
| $v_c$  | = column deflection; |
| $W$    | = total distributed load (subscripts $p$, $w$, and $y$ denote plastic limit, working, and yield loads, respectively); |
| $W_E$  | = external work due to virtual displacement; |
| $W_I$  | = internal work due to virtual displacement; |
| $w$    | = distributed load per unit of length (subscript $p$ denotes plastic limit); |
|        | = web thickness (subscript $c$ denotes column web); |
|        | = length of T-stub flange; |
| $w_r$  | = required web thickness; |
| $x$    | = longitudinal coordinate; |
| $y$    | = transverse coordinate; |
| $y_{\mathbb{C}}$ | = center line deflection; |
| $y_o$  | = distance between centroid and neutral axis; |
|        | = unyielded depth (Fig. 6.1); |
| $Z$    | = plastic modulus (subscripts denote flexural axes, $Z = M_p/\sigma_y$); |
| $Z_x$  | = plastic modulus at section $x$ of a haunch; |
| $z$    | = lateral coordinate; |
|        | = distance along beam; |
|        | = distance along a Column Deflection Curve (CDC); |
| $z_c$  | = distance along column; |
| $\alpha$ | = central angle of curved flange between points of lateral support; |
|        | = proportion of a given length in yielded state; |
|        | = nondimensional parameter locating the position of a plastic hinge; |
|        | = nondimensional load parameter used in cyclic loading studies; |
|        | = slope of a point in a CDC; |
| $\alpha_o$ | = end slope of a CDC; |
| $\beta$ | = angle between two nonparallel flanges (Figs. 8.6 and 8.9); |
|        | = coefficient of restraint; |
|        | = angle of twist about shear center; |
|        | = second nondimensional load parameter used in cyclic loading studies; |
| $\beta_1$ | = angle of taper of rafter haunch (Fig. 8.7); |
| $\beta_2$ | = angle of taper of column haunch (Fig. 8.7); |
| $\gamma$ | = shearing strain; |
|        | = angle of inclination of rafter (Fig. 8.7); |
| $\Delta$ | = virtual displacement; |
|        | = deflection of a joint due to translation; |
|        | = horizontal deflection between the ends of a column; |
| $\Delta M_y$ | = range of moments in which $M\text{-}\phi$ curve is linear; |
| $\delta$ | = deflection (subscripts $u$, $w$, and $y$ denote deflection at ultimate, working, and yield load, respectively); |
| $\epsilon$ | = strain (subscripts denote direction); |

$\epsilon_{cr}$ = critical strain at which local buckling occurs;

$\epsilon_m$ = maximum strain;

$\epsilon_{st}$ = strain at onset of strain hardening;

$\epsilon_y$ = strain corresponding to theoretical onset of plastic yielding;

$\eta$ = reduction factor;

$\theta$ = measured angle change, rotation;

= mechanism angle;

= angle of slope of diagonal stiffener;

$\theta_e$ = maximum elastic rotation;

$\theta_f$ = end slope of a uniformly bent segment at the start of local buckling;

$\theta_L$ = lower end rotation of column;

$\theta_m$ = angle of rotation at maximum load;

$\theta_{max}$ = maximum plastic rotation;

$\theta_p$ = end slope corresponding to elastic theory when $M = M_p$;

$\theta_U$ = upper end rotation of column;

$\theta_u$ = rotation when the maximum capacity reaches $M_p$ on the unloading branch of the $M$-$\theta$ curve;

$\theta_y$ = elastic limit rotation (theoretical);

$\theta'_A$ = rotation of joint $A$ due to transverse loads assuming simply supported ends of member;

$\lambda$ = beam slenderness factor;

$\nu$ = Poisson's ratio;

$\nu_s$ = correction factor for St. Venant torsion;

$\nu_x$ = coefficient of dilation for stress increment in $x$-direction;

$\nu_y$ = coefficient of dilation for stress increment in $y$-direction;

$\nu_\alpha$ = correction factor for partial yielding;

$\nu_\gamma$ = correction factor for restraint;

$\nu_\rho$ = correction factor for moment gradient;

$\rho$ = ratio of smaller end moment to larger end moment for a segment $(-1 \leq \rho \leq 1)$;

$\rho_A$ = ratio of end moments for adjacent segment;

$\sigma$ = normal stress;

$\sigma_a$ = allowable stress;

$\sigma_{cr}$ = critical buckling stress;

$\sigma_f$ = tensile strength of weld metal or bolt;

$\sigma_g$ = axial compress stress in beam due to lateral loads plus $P\Delta$ shear;

$\sigma_r$ = residual stress (subscripts $rc$ and $rt$ denote compression and tension);

$\sigma_u$ = tensile strength;

= design ultimate tensile stress (for bolts);

$\sigma_w$ = allowable (working) stress;

$\sigma_y$ = yield-stress level;

$\tau$ = shear stress;

$\tau_f$ = shear stress of a bolt;

$\tau_o$ = shear stress on neutral axis;

$\tau_u$ = design ultimate shear;

$\tau_y$ = shear yield stress;

$\bar{\tau}_f$ = average shear failure stress in a bolted joint;

$\phi$     = rotation per unit length or average unit rotation, curvature;

$\phi_p$   = $M_p/(EI)$;

$\phi_{st}$ = curvature at strain hardening;

$\phi_y$   = curvature corresponding to first yield in flexure;

$\psi$     = angle as shown in Fig. 7.21; and

$\omega$   = ratio of lateral bending stiffness in the yielded region of beam to its elastic value, $E$.

# APPENDIX II.—GLOSSARY

*Allowable load*—The load which induces the maximum allowable or permitted stress at the critical section.

*Allowable-stress design*—A method of proportioning structures which is based on working loads such that computed stresses do not exceed prescribed values. (The limit of structural usefulness is not specified but is often taken as the yield stress.)

*Bifurcation*—The phenomenon whereby a perfectly straight member under compression may either assume a deflected position or else may remain undeflected; buckling.

*Braced frame*—A frame in which the resistance to lateral load or frame instability is provided by diagonal, K, or other auxiliary system of bracing.

*Buckling load*—The load at which a perfectly straight member under compression assumes a deflected position. Also called critical load.

*Compact shape*—As used in allowable-stress design, a cross-sectional shape which will not experience premature local buckling in the inelastic region. (To be distinguished from "plastic design shapes" which have somewhat more restrictive cross-sectional properties.)

*Design ultimate load (or factored load)*—The working load times the load factor.

*Drift*—Lateral deflection of a building, due to wind or other loads.

*Drift index*—Maximum permitted ratio of lateral deflection to story height.

*Effective length*—The equivalent length $(KL_c)$ used in compression formulas for computing the strength of a framed column. (See Ref. 5.2 for limitations and applications.)

*Effective width*—The reduced width of the plate or slab which, with an assumed uniform stress distribution, produces the same effect on the behavior of a structural member as the actual plate width with its nonuniform stress distribution.

*Factor of safety*—The ratio of a limit of usefulness (be it load, stress, or deformation) to the working or service condition.

*Fatigue*—A fracture phenomenon associated with a cyclic stress condition.

*Frame buckling*—Failure by bifurcation of equilibrium position; applicable to symmetrical frames, with symmetrical gravity load.

*Frame instability*—Attainment of stability limit load as a result of combined effects of loading and lateral deflection; applicable to unsymmetrical frames and to symmetrical frames with unsymmetrical loading.

*Lateral (or lateral-torsional) buckling*—Buckling of a member involving lateral deflection and twist.

*Limit design*—A design based on any chosen limit of usefulness.

*Load factor*—In plastic design, a factor by which the working load is multiplied to determine the design ultimate load. (This choice of terms serves to emphasize the reliance upon load-carrying capacity of the structure rather than upon stress.)

*Local buckling*—The buckling of a compression element which may precipitate the failure of the whole member.

*Maximum load (ultimate load)*—Plastic limit load or stability limit load, as defined (also the maximum load-carrying capacity of a structure under test).

*Mechanism*—An articulated system able to deform without a finite increase in load. It is used in the special sense that the linkage may include real hinges or plastic hinges, or both.

*Plastic design*—A design method for continuous steel beams and frames which defines the limit of structural usefulness as the "maximum load." (The term "plastic" comes from the fact that the maximum load is computed from a knowledge of the strength of steel in the plastic range.)

*Plastic hinge*—A yielded zone which forms in a structural member when the plastic moment is applied. The beam rotates as if hinged, except that it is restrained by the plastic moment, $M_p$.

*Plastic limit load*—The maximum load that is attained when a sufficient number of yield zones have formed to permit the structure to deform plastically without further increase in load. It is the largest load a structure will support, when perfect plasticity is assumed and when such factors as instability, strain hardening, and fracture are disregarded.

*Plastic modulus*—The modulus of resistance to bending of a completely yielded cross section. It is the combined statical moment about the neutral axis of the cross-sectional areas above and below that axis.

*Plastic moment*—The resisting moment of a fully yielded cross section, $M_p$.

*Postbuckling strength*—The additional load which can be carried by a plate element or structural member after buckling.

*Proportional loading*—A loading system in which all loads increase in a constant ratio, one to the other.

*Redistribution of moment*—A process which results in the successive formation of plastic hinges until the maximum load is reached. As a result of the formation of plastic hinges, less highly-stressed portions of a structure may carry increased moments.

*Residual stress*—The stresses that remain in an unloaded member after it has been formed and erected. (Such stresses can be caused by cold bending and straightening, cooling after rolling, or by welding.)

*Service load*—See working load.

*Shape factor*—The ratio of the plastic moment to the yield moment ($M_p/M_y$) or the ratio of the plastic modulus to the section modulus ($Z/S$) for a cross section.

*Stability limit load*—Maximum (theoretical) load a structure can support when second-order instability effects are included.

*Strain-hardening modulus*—For structural steels which have a flat (plastic) region in the stress-strain relationship, the strain-hardening modulus is the initial slope of the stress-strain curve subsequent to the plastic region (see Art. 5.1).

*Stub column*—A short compression-test specimen, sufficiently long for use in measuring the stress-strain relationship for the complete cross section, but short enough to avoid buckling as a column in the elastic and plastic ranges.

*Supported frame*—A frame which depends upon adjacent braced or unbraced frames for resistance to lateral load or frame instability. (This transfer of load is frequently provided by the floor system through diaphragm action.)

*Tensile strength*—The maximum tensile stress that a material is capable of sustaining.

*Ultimate strength*—The maximum strength of a cross section.

*Unbraced frame*—A frame in which the resistance to lateral load is provided by the bending resistance of frame members and their connections.

*Unbraced length*—The distance between braced points of a member.

*Working load*—The load expected on a structure and for which it is designed; service load.

*Yield point*—The first stress in a material, less than the maximum attainable stress, at which an increase in strain occurs without an increase in stress.

*Yield moment*—In a member subjected to bending, the moment at which an outer fiber first attains the yield stress.

*Yield strength*—The stress at which a material exhibits a specified limiting deviation from the proportionality of stress to strain. The deviation is expressed in terms of strain.
Note: It is customary to determine yield strength by (1) offset method (usually a strain of 0.2% is specified), or (2) total-extension-under-load method (usually a strain of 0.5% is specified, although other values of strain may be used).

*Yield stress*—Yield point, yield strength, or yield stress level, as defined.

*Yield stress level*—It is a particular yield strength: the average stress during yielding in the plastic range. It is the stress determined in a tension test when the strain reaches 0.005 in. per in.

# APPENDIX III.—REFERENCES

## CHAPTER 1.—INTRODUCTION

1.1    Baker, J. F., Horne, M. R., and Heyman, J.,
       THE STEEL SKELETON, VOL. 2, Cambridge University Press,
       Cambridge, England, 1956.

1.2    Beedle, L. S.,
       PLASTIC DESIGN OF STEEL FRAMES, John Wiley and Sons, New
       York, 1958.

1.3    PLASTIC DESIGN IN STEEL, American Institute of Steel Construc-
       tion (AISC), New York, 1959.

1.4    Heyman, J.,
       PLASTIC DESIGN OF PORTAL FRAMES, Cambridge University
       Press, Cambridge, England, 1957.

1.5    Hodge, P. G., Jr.,
       PLASTIC ANALYSIS OF STRUCTURES, McGraw-Hill Book Co.,
       Inc., New York, 1959.

1.6    Neal, B. G.,
       THE PLASTIC METHODS OF STRUCTURAL ANALYSIS, 2nd
       ed., John Wiley and Sons, New York, 1963.

1.7    Prager, W.,
       INTRODUCTION TO PLASTICITY, Addison-Wesley Publishing
       Co., Reading, Mass., 1959.

1.8    Massonnet, C., and Save, M.,
       PLASTIC ANALYSIS AND DESIGN, VOL. 1, Blaisdell Publishing
       Co., New York, 1965.

1.9    Smith, J. O., and Sidebottom, D. M.,
       INELASTIC BEHAVIOR OF LOAD-CARRYING MEMBERS,
       John Wiley and Sons, New York, 1965.

1.10   Daniels, S. R.,
       INELASTIC STEEL STRUCTURES, University of Tennessee Press,
       Knoxville, Tenn., 1966.

1.11   Heyman, J., Leckie, F. A., *et al.*,
       ENGINEERING PLASTICITY, Cambridge University Press,
       Cambridge, England, 1968.

293

1.12    Drucker, D. C.,
        INTRODUCTION TO MECHANICS OF DEFORMABLE SOL-
        IDS, McGraw-Hill Book Co., Inc., New York, 1967.

1.13    Popov, E. P.,
        INTRODUCTION TO MECHANICS OF SOLIDS, Prentice-Hall,
        Inc., Englewood Cliffs, N.J., 1968.

1.14    Gerstle, K. H.,
        BASIC STRUCTURAL DESIGN, McGraw-Hill Book Co., Inc.,
        New York, 1967.

1.15    Tall, L., et al.,
        STRUCTURAL STEEL DESIGN, Ronald Press Co., New York,
        1964.

1.16    McGuire, W.,
        STEEL STRUCTURES, Prentice-Hall, Inc., Englewood Cliffs, N.J.
        1968.

1.17    Bresler, B., Lin, T. Y., and Scalzi, J. B.,
        DESIGN OF STEEL STRUCTURES, John Wiley and Sons, New
        York, 1968.

1.18    Drucker, D. C.,
        PLASTIC DESIGN METHODS-ADVANTAGES AND LIMITA-
        TIONS, Transactions, Society of Naval Architects and Marine Engi-
        neers, Vol. 65, 1958, p. 172.

1.19    Baker, J. F.,
        SHORTCOMINGS OF STRUCTURAL ANALYSIS, Transactions,
        North East Coast Institution of Engineers and Shipbuilders, England,
        Vol. 68, 1951, p. 31.

1.20    Kazinczy, G.,
        KISERLETEK BEFALAZOTT TARTOKKAL (Experiments with
        Clamped Girders), Betonszemle, Vol. 2, No. 4, p. 68, No. 5, p. 83, and
        No. 6, p. 101, 1914.

1.21    Hoff, N. J.,
        Discussion of AN EVALUATION OF PLASTIC ANALYSIS AS
        APPLIED TO STRUCTURAL DESIGN, by Johnston, B. G., Beedle,
        L. S., and Yang, C. H., The Welding Journal, Vol. 33, No. 1, Jan., 1954,
        p. 14-s.

1.22    Maier-Leibnitz, H.,
        CONTRIBUTIONS TO THE PROBLEM OF ULTIMATE CARRY-
        ING CAPACITY OF SIMPLE AND CONTINUOUS BEAMS OF
        STRUCTURAL STEEL AND TIMBER, Die Bautechnik, Vol. 1, No.
        6, 1927.

1.23    Van Den Broek, J. A.,
        THEORY OF LIMIT DESIGN, John Wiley and Sons, New York,
        1948.

1.24    Roderick, J. W., and Phillips, I. H.,
        CARRYING CAPACITY OF SIMPLY SUPPORTED MILD
        STEEL BEAMS, *Engineering Structures,* Academic Press, New York,
        1950.

1.25    Horne, M. R.,
        A MOMENT DISTRIBUTION METHOD FOR THE ANALYSIS
        AND DESIGN OF STRUCTURES, *Proceedings of the Institution of
        Civil Engineers,* Apr., 1954, p. 51.

1.26    Greenberg, H. J., and Prager, W.,
        LIMIT DESIGN OF BEAMS AND FRAMES, *Transactions,* ASCE,
        Vol. 117, Paper No. 2501, 1952, p. 447.

1.27    Symonds, P. S., and Neal, B. G.,
        RECENT PROGRESS IN THE PLASTIC METHODS OF STRUC-
        TURAL ANALYSIS, *Journal of the Franklin Institute,* Vol. 252, 1951,
        pp. 383–407 and 469–492.

1.28    Winter, G.,
        TRENDS IN STEEL DESIGN AND RESEARCH, *Buildings Re-
        search Congress,* Div. I, Part II, 1951, pp. 81–88.

1.29    Johnston, B. G., Beedle, L. S., and Yang, C. H.,
        AN EVALUATION OF PLASTIC ANALYSIS AS APPLIED TO
        STRUCTURAL DESIGN, *The Welding Journal,* Vol. 32, No. 5, May,
        1953, p. 224–s.

1.30    Lay, M. G.,
        THE EXPERIMENTAL BASIS FOR PLASTIC DESIGN, *Bulletin
        No. 99,* Welding Research Council, Sept., 1964.

1.31    Beedle, L. S.,
        ON THE APPLICATION OF PLASTIC DESIGN, *Proceedings,* 2nd
        Symposium on Naval Structural Mechanics, Pergamon Press, London,
        England, 1961.

1.32    Beedle, L. S., Lu, L. W., and Lim, L. C.,
        RECENT DEVELOPMENTS IN PLASTIC DESIGN PRACTICE,
        *Journal of the Structural Division,* ASCE, Vol. 95, No. ST9, Proc. Paper
        6781, Sept., 1969, p. 1911.

1.33    Driscoll, G. C., Jr., *et al.,*
        PLASTIC DESIGN OF MULTI-STORY FRAMES, Lecture Notes
        and Design Aids, *Reports No. 273.20 and 273.24,* Fritz Engineering
        Laboratory, Lehigh University, Bethlehem, Pa., 1965.

1.34    PLASTIC DESIGN CUTS COST ON PROTOTYPE HIGHRISE,
        *Engineering News-Record,* Vol. 173, No. 3, July 20, 1967.

1.35     Bigelow, R. H., and Gaylord, E. H.,
DESIGN OF STEEL FRAMES FOR MINIMUM WEIGHT, *Journal of the Structural Division,* ASCE, Vol. 93, No. ST6, Proc. Paper 5666, Dec., 1967, p. 109.

1.36     Murray, T. M., and Ostapenko, A.,
OPTIMUM DESIGN OF MULTI-STORY FRAMES BY PLASTIC THEORY, *Report No. 273.43,* Fritz Engineering Laboratory, Lehigh University, Bethlehem, Pa., May, 1966.

1.37     Toakley, A. R.,
OPTIMUM DESIGN USING AVAILABLE SECTIONS, *Journal of the Structural Division,* ASCE, Vol. 94, No. ST5, Proc. Paper 5960, May, 1968, p. 1219.

## CHAPTER 2.—BASIC PRINCIPLES

2.1     Gvozdev, A. A.,
THE DETERMINATION OF THE VALUE OF THE COLLAPSE LOAD FOR STATICALLY INDETERMINATE SYSTEMS UNDERGOING PLASTIC DEFORMATION, *Proceedings of the Conference on Plastic Deformations,* Akademiia Nauk SSSR, Moscow-Leningrad, USSR, 1938, p. 19. English translation by R. M. Haythornthwaite, *International Journal of Mechanical Sciences,* Vol. 1, No. 4, July, 1960, p. 322.

2.2     Feinberg, S. M.,
THE PRINCIPLE OF LIMITING STRESS, *Prikladnaya Matematika i Mekhanika,* Vol. 12, 1948, p. 63.

2.3     Horne, M. R.,
FUNDAMENTAL PROPOSITIONS IN THE PLASTIC THEORY OF STRUCTURES, *Journal of the Institution of Civil Engineers,* Vol. 34, Apr., 1950, p. 174.

2.4     Drucker, D. C., Greenberg, H. J., and Prager, W.,
THE SAFETY FACTOR OF AN ELASTIC-PLASTIC BODY IN PLANE STRAIN, *Transactions,* ASME, Vol. 73, 1951, pp. 371–378.

2.5     Drucker, D. C., Greenberg, H. J., and Prager, W.,
EXTENDED LIMIT DESIGN THEOREMS FOR CONTINUOUS MEDIA, *Quarterly of Applied Mathematics,* Vol. 9, Jan., 1952, pp. 381–389.

2.6     Drucker, D. C.,
PLASTICITY, *Proceedings,* 1st Symposium on Naval Structural Mechanics, Pergamon Press, London, England, 1960, p. 407.

2.7     Hrennikoff, A. P.,
THEORY OF INELASTIC BENDING WITH REFERENCE TO LIMIT DESIGN, *Transactions,* ASCE, Vol. 113, Paper No. 2334, 1948, p. 213.

2.8    Yang, C. H.,
       THE PLASTIC BEHAVIOR OF CONTINUOUS BEAMS, thesis
       presented to Lehigh University, at Bethlehem, Pa., in 1951, in partial
       fulfillment of the requirements for the degree of Doctor of Philosophy.

2.9    Lay, M. G., and Smith, P. D.,
       THE ROLE OF STRAIN HARDENING IN PLASTIC DESIGN,
       *Journal of the Structural Division,* ASCE, Vol. 91, No. ST3, Proc.
       Paper 4355, June, 1965, p. 25.

2.10   Hrennikoff, A. P.,
       IMPORTANCE OF STRAIN HARDENING IN PLASTIC DE-
       SIGN, *Journal of the Structural Division,* ASCE, Vol. 91, No. ST4,
       Proc. Paper 4424, Aug., 1965, p. 23.

2.11   Adams, P. F., and Galambos, T. V.,
       MATERIAL CONSIDERATIONS IN PLASTIC DESIGN, *Report
       No. 297.23,* Fritz Engineering Laboratory, Lehigh University, Bethle-
       hem, Pa., Nov., 1966.

2.12   Galambos, T. V.,
       STRUCTURAL MEMBERS AND FRAMES, Prentice-Hall, Inc.,
       Englewood Cliffs, N.J., 1968.

2.13   Vickery, B.,
       THE INFLUENCE OF DEFORMATIONS AND STRAIN-
       HARDENING ON THE COLLAPSE LOAD OF RIGID FRAME
       STRUCTURES, *Transactions,* Institution of Engineers, Australia,
       Vol. CE3, No. 2, Sept., 1961, p. 103.

2.14   Ang, A. H-S.,
       ANALYSIS OF FRAMES WITH NONLINEAR BEHAVIOR,
       *Transactions,* ASCE, Vol. 126, Part I, Paper No. 3189, 1961, p. 823.

2.15   Horne, M. R., and Medland, I. C.,
       COLLAPSE LOADS OF STEEL FRAMEWORKS ALLOWING
       FOR THE EFFECT OF STRAIN-HARDENING, *Proceedings of the
       Institution of Civil Engineers,* Vol. 33, Mar., 1966, p. 381.

2.16   Lay, M. G.,
       A NEW APPROACH TO INELASTIC STRUCTURAL DESIGN,
       *Proceedings of the Institution of Civil Engineers,* Vol. 34, May, 1966,
       p. 1.

## CHAPTER 3.—ANALYSIS AND DESIGN

3.1    Beedle, L. S., Thürlimann, B., and Ketter, R. L.,
       PLASTIC DESIGN IN STRUCTURAL STEEL, Lecture Notes, Le-
       high University, Bethlehem, Pa., and American Institute of Steel Con-
       struction, New York, Sept., 1955.

3.2     Dolphin, J. W., Wright, D. T., and Nelson, H. M.,
        PLASTIC DESIGN OF STEEL STRUCTURES, Royal Military Col-
        lege and Queen's University Publication, May, 1956.

3.3     Neal, B. G., and Symonds, P. S.
        THE CALCULATION OF COLLAPSE LOADS FOR FRAMED
        STRUCTURES, *Journal of the Institution of Civil Engineers,* Vol. 35,
        1950, p. 20.

3.4     English, J. M.,
        DESIGN OF FRAMES BY RELAXATION OF YIELD HINGES,
        *Transactions,* ASCE, Vol. 119, Paper No. 2715, 1954, p. 1143.

3.5     Tocher, J. L., and Popov, E. P.,
        PLASTIC ANALYSIS OF RIGID FRAMES BY MODIFIED
        LINEAR PROGRAMMING, presented at the Symposium on the
        Use of Computers in Civil Engineering, Laboratorio Nacional de En-
        genharia Civil, Lisbon, Portugal, Oct. 1–5, 1962.

3.6     Kawai, T.,
        PLASTIC ANALYSIS AND MINIMUM WEIGHT DESIGN OF
        MULTI-STORY PLANE FRAMES, *Plastic Design of Multi-Story
        Frames—Guest Lectures, Report No. 273.46,* Fritz Engineering Labora-
        tory, Lehigh University, Bethlehem, Pa., 1966.

3.7     Thürlimann, B.,
        OPTIMUM DESIGN OF STRUCTURES, *Plastic Design of Multi-
        Story Frames—Guest Lectures, Report No. 273.26,* Fritz Engineering
        Laboratory, Lehigh University, Bethlehem, Pa., 1966.

3.8     Rubinstein, M. F., and Karagozian, J.,
        BUILDING DESIGN USING LINEAR PROGRAMMING, *Journal
        of the Structural Division,* ASCE, Vol. 92, No. ST6, Proc. Paper 5012,
        Dec., 1966, p. 223.

3.9     Wang, C. K.,
        GENERAL COMPUTER PROGRAM FOR LIMIT LOAD ANAL-
        YSIS, *Journal of the Structural Division,* ASCE, Vol. 89, No. ST6, Proc.
        Paper 3719, Dec., 1963, p. 101.

3.10    Harrison, H. B.,
        PLASTIC ANALYSIS OF RIGID FRAMES OF HIGH-
        STRENGTH STEEL ACCOUNT FOR DEFORMATION EFFECT,
        *Civil Engineering Transactions,* Institution of Engineers, Australia,
        Vol. CE9, No. 1, Mar., 1967, p. 127.

## CHAPTER 4.—GENERAL PROVISIONS

4.1     Beedle, L. S.,
        BASIC CONCEPTS, Lecture 2, *Report No. 273.20, Report No. 273.24,*

Fritz Engineering Laboratory, Lehigh University, Bethlehem, Pa., 1965.

4.2 Thürlimann, B.,
MODIFICATIONS TO THE PLASTIC THEORY, *Proceedings,* AISC National Engineering Conference, 1956, p. 50.

4.3 Harris, L. A., and Newmark, N. M.,
THE EFFECT OF FABRICATED EDGE CONDITIONS ON BRITTLE FRACTURE OF STRUCTURAL STEEL, *AREA Bulletin 59(538),* 1957, pp. 247–289.

4.4 Beedle, L. S., and Tall, L.,
BASIC COLUMN STRENGTH, *Journal of the Structural Division,* ASCE, Vol. 86, No. ST7, Proc. Paper 2555, July, 1960, p. 139.

4.5 Rao, N. R. N., Lohrmann, M., and Tall, L.,
EFFECT OF STRAIN RATE ON THE YIELD STRESS OF STRUCTURAL STEELS, *Journal of Materials,* Vol. 1, No. 1, Mar., 1966, p. 1.

4.6 Desai, S.,
MECHANICAL PROPERTIES OF A572 GRADE 65 STEEL, *Report No. 343.2,* Fritz Engineering Laboratory, Lehigh University, Bethlehem, Pa., Sept., 1969.

4.7 Lim, L. C., Lu, L. W., and Beedle, L. S.,
MECHANICAL PROPERTIES OF ASTM A36 AND A441 STEEL, *Report No. 345.14,* Fritz Engineering Laboratory, Lehigh University, Bethlehem, Pa., Aug., 1969.

4.8 Adams, P. F., Lay, M. G., and Galambos, T. V.,
EXPERIMENTS ON HIGH STRENGTH STEEL MEMBERS, *Bulletin No. 10,* Welding Research Council, Nov., 1965.

4.9 Viest, I. M., Fountain, R. S., and Singleton, R. C.,
COMPOSITE CONSTRUCTION IN STEEL AND CONCRETE, McGraw-Hill Book Co., Inc., New York, 1958.

4.10 Slutter, R. G., and Driscoll, G. C., Jr.,
FLEXURAL STRENGTH OF STEEL-CONCRETE COMPOSITE BEAMS, *Journal of the Structural Division,* ASCE, Vol. 91, No. ST2, Proc. Paper 4294, Apr., 1965, p. 71.

4.11 Chapman, J. C., and Balakrishnan, S.,
EXPERIMENTS ON COMPOSITE BEAMS, *Structural Engineer,* England, Vol. 42, No. 11, Nov., 1964, p. 369.

4.12 Roderick, J. W., Hawkins, N. M., and Lim, L. C.,
THE BEHAVIOR OF COMPOSITE STEEL AND LIGHTWEIGHT CONCRETE BEAMS, *Civil Engineering Transactions,* Institution of Engineers, Australia, Vol. CE9, No. 2, Oct., 1967, p. 265.

4.13    COMPOSITE CONSTRUCTION IN STRUCTURAL STEEL AND
        CONCRETE, British Standard Code of Practice, CP117, Part 1, 1965,
        and Part 2, 1968.

4.14    Daniels, J. H., and Fisher, J. W.,
        STATIC BEHAVIOR OF CONTINUOUS COMPOSITE BEAMS,
        *Report No. 324.2,* Fritz Engineering Laboratory, Lehigh University,
        Bethlehem, Pa., Mar., 1967.

4.15    Bernard, P. R., and Johnson, R. P.,
        PLASTIC BEHAVIOR OF CONTINUOUS COMPOSITE BEAMS,
        *Proceedings of the Institution of Civil Engineers,* Vol. 32, Oct., 1965,
        p. 161.

4.16    Park, R.,
        THE ULTIMATE STRENGTH OF CONTINUOUS COMPOSITE
        T-BEAMS, *Civil Engineering Transactions,* Institution of Engineers,
        Australia, Vol. CE9, No. 2, Oct., 1967, p. 245.

4.17    AMERICAN STANDARD BUILDING CODE REQUIREMENTS
        FOR MINIMUM DESIGN LOADS IN BUILDINGS AND OTHER
        STRUCTURES, ASA A58.1, U.S.A. Standards Institute, 1955.

4.18    STEEL CONSTRUCTION, Manual of American Institute of Steel
        Construction, New York, 7th ed., 1969.

4.19    Beedle, L. S.
        INTRODUCTION, *Structural Steel Design,* by L. Tall *et al.,* Chapter
        1, Ronald Press Co., New York, 1964.

# CHAPTER 5.—VERIFICATION OF PLASTIC THEORY

5.1     Yang, C. H., Beedle, L. S., and Johnston, B. G.,
        RESIDUAL STRESS AND THE YIELD STRENGTH OF BEAMS,
        *The Welding Journal,* Vol. 31, No. 4, Apr., 1952, p. 205-s.

5.2     GUIDE TO DESIGN CRITERIA FOR METAL COMPRESSION
        MEMBERS, ed. B. G. Johnston, John Wiley and Sons, New York,
        2nd ed., 1966.

5.3     Desai, S.,
        TENSION TESTING PROCEDURE, *Report No. 237.44,* Fritz En-
        gineering Laboratory, Lehigh University, Bethlehem, Pa., Feb., 1969.

5.4     Luxion, W., and Johnston, B. G.,
        PLASTIC BEHAVIOR OF WIDE-FLANGE BEAMS, *The Welding
        Journal,* Vol. 27, No. 11, Nov., 1948, p. 538-s.

5.5     Driscoll, G. C., Jr., and Beedle, L. S.,
        THE PLASTIC BEHAVIOR OF STRUCTURAL MEMBERS AND
        FRAMES, *The Welding Journal,* Vol. 36, No. 6, June, 1957, p. 275-s.

5.6     Kim, S. W.,
EXPERIMENTS ON A572 (GRADE 65) STEEL BEAMS, *Report No. 343.4,* Fritz Engineering Laboratory, Lehigh University, Bethlehem, Pa., Aug., 1969.

5.7     Lukey, A. F., and Adams, P. F.,
ROTATIONAL CAPACITY OF WIDE FLANGE BEAMS UNDER MOMENT GRADIENT, *Journal of the Structural Division, ASCE,* Vol. 95, No. ST6, Proc. Paper 6599, June, 1969, p. 1173.

5.8     Lay, M. G., and Galambos, T. V.,
INELASTIC BEAMS UNDER MOMENT GRADIENT, *Journal of the Structural Division, ASCE,* Vol. 93, No. ST1, Proc. Paper 5110, Feb., 1967, p. 381.

5.9     Popov, E. P., and Willis, J. A.,
PLASTIC DESIGN OF COVER-PLATED CONTINUOUS BEAMS, *Journal of the Engineering Mechanics Division, ASCE,* Vol. 84, No. EM1, Proc. Paper 1495, Jan., 1958.

5.10    Yura, J. A., and Lu, L. W.,
ULTIMATE LOAD TESTS ON BRACED MULTISTORY FRAMES, *Journal of the Structural Division, ASCE,* Vol. 95, No. ST10, Proc. Paper 6840, Oct., 1969, p. 2243.

5.11    Knudsen, K. E., Ruzek, J., Johnston, E. R., and Beedle, L. S.,
WELDED PORTAL FRAMES TESTED TO COLLAPSE, *The Welding Journal,* Vol. 33, No. 9, Sept., 1954, p. 469-s.

5.12    Schilling, C. G., Schutz, F. W., Jr., and Beedle, L. S.,
BEHAVIOR OF WELDED SINGLE-SPAN FRAMES UNDER COMBINED LOADING, *The Welding Journal,* Vol. 35, No. 5, May, 1956, p. 234-s.

5.13    Driscoll, G. C., Jr.,
TEST OF TWO-SPAN GABLED PORTAL FRAME, *Proceedings,* AISC National Engineering Conference, 1956, p. 74.

5.14    Nelson, H. M., Wright, D. T., and Dolphin, J. W.,
DEMONSTRATIONS OF PLASTIC BEHAVIOR OF STEEL FRAMES, *Journal of the Engineering Mechanics Division, ASCE,* Vol. 83, No. EM4, Proc. Paper 1390, Oct., 1957.

5.15    Baker, J. F., and Roderick, J. W.,
TESTS ON FULL SCALE PORTAL FRAMES, *Proceedings of the Institution of Civil Engineers,* Jan., 1952.

5.16    Baker, J. F., and Eickhoff, K. G.,
THE BEHAVIOR OF SAW-TOOTH PORTAL FRAMES, *Proceedings,* Conference on the Correlation between Calculated and Observed Stresses and Displacements in Structures, Institution of Civil Engineers, 1955, p. 107.

5.17    Baker, J. F., and Eickhoff, K. G.,
        A TEST ON A PITCHED ROOF PORTAL, Preliminary Publication,
        5th Congress, IABSE, Lisbon, Portugal, 1956.

5.18    Blessey, W. E.,
        Personal communication, Feb. 7, 1958.

5.19    Arnold, P., Adams, P. F., and Lu, L. W.,
        STRENGTH AND BEHAVIOR OF AN INELASTIC HYBRID
        FRAME, *Journal of the Structural Division, ASCE*, Vol. 94, No. ST1,
        Proc. Paper 5759, Jan., 1968, p. 243.

5.20    Baker, J. F., and Charlton, T. M.,
        A TEST ON A TWO-STORY SINGLE-BAY PORTAL STRUC-
        TURE, *British Welding Journal*, Vol. 5, No. 5, May, 1958, p. 226.

5.21    Bryan, E. R., and El-Dakhakakhni, W. M.,
        BEHAVIOR OF SHEETED PORTAL FRAME SHEDS: THEORY
        AND EXPERIMENTS, *Proceedings of the Institution of Civil Engi-
        neers*, Vol. 29, Dec., 1964, p. 743.

5.22    Wakabayashi, M., *et al.*,
        FULL SCALE TESTS USING PORTAL FRAMES WITHOUT
        BRACING SUBJECTED TO CONSTANT VERTICAL AND
        VARYING HORIZONTAL LOAD, *Transactions*, Architectural In-
        stitute of Japan, extra, Aug., 1969.

# CHAPTER 6.—ADDITIONAL DESIGN CONSIDERATIONS

6.1     Horne, M. R.,
        THE PLASTIC THEORY OF BENDING OF MILD STEEL
        BEAMS WITH PARTICULAR REFERENCE TO THE EFFECT
        OF SHEAR FORCES, *Proceedings of the Royal Society*, London,
        Vol. 207, 1951, p. 216.

6.2     Leth, F. A.,
        THE EFFECT OF SHEAR STRESSES ON THE CARRYING CA-
        PACITY OF I-BEAMS, *Technical Report 107*, Brown University,
        Providence, R.I., 1954.

6.3     Neal, B. G.,
        EFFECT OF SHEAR FORCE ON THE FULLY PLASTIC MO-
        MENT OF AN I-BEAM, *Journal of Mechanical Engineering Science*,
        Vol. 3, 1961, p. 258.

6.4     Heyman, J., and Dutton, V. L.,
        PLASTIC DESIGN OF PLATE GIRDERS WITH UNSTIFFENED
        WEBS, *Welding and Metal Fabrication*, Vol. 22, 1954, p. 265.

6.5     Green, A. P.,
        A THEORY OF THE PLASTIC YIELDING DUE TO BENDING

OF CANTILEVERS AND FIXED-ENDED BEAMS, *Journal of Mechanics and Physics of Solids,* Vol. 3, No. 1, 1954, p. 143.

6.6 Onat, E. T., and Shield, R. T.,
THE INFLUENCE OF SHEARING FORCES ON THE PLASTIC BENDING OF THE WIDE BEAMS, *Proceedings,* 2nd U.S. National Congress of Applied Mechanics, Ann Arbor, Mich., 1954, pp. 535–537.

6.7 Drucker, D. C.,
THE EFFECT OF SHEAR ON THE PLASTIC MOMENT OF BEAMS, *Journal of Applied Mechanics,* ASME, Vol. 23, No. 4, Dec., 1956, pp. 509–514.

6.8 Hodge, P. G., Jr.,
INTERACTION CURVES FOR SHEAR AND BENDING OF PLASTIC BEAMS, *Journal of Applied Mechanics,* ASME, Vol. 24, No. 3, Sept., 1957, pp. 453–456.

6.9 Fujita, Y., Kusuda, T., and Thürlimann, B.,
INFLUENCE OF SHEAR ON THE FULL PLASTIC MOMENT OF BEAMS, *Report No. 205B.23,* Fritz Engineering Laboratory, Lehigh University, Bethlehem, Pa., 1955.

6.10 Horne, M. R.,
THE FULL PLASTIC MOMENT OF SECTIONS SUBJECTED TO SHEAR FORCE AND AXIAL LOAD, *British Welding Journal,* Vol. 5, Apr., 1958, p. 170.

6.11 Kusuda, T., and Thürlimann, B.,
STRENGTH OF WIDE-FLANGE BEAMS UNDER COMBINED INFLUENCE OF MOMENT, SHEAR, AND AXIAL FORCE, *Report No. 248.1,* Fritz Engineering Laboratory, Lehigh University, Bethlehem, Pa., 1958.

6.12 Neal, B. G.,
THE EFFECT OF SHEAR AND NORMAL FORCES ON THE FULLY PLASTIC MOMENT OF A BEAM OF RECTANGULAR CROSS SECTION, *Journal of Applied Mechanics,* Vol. 60, Dec., 1960.

6.13 Neal, B. G.,
EFFECT OF SHEAR AND NORMAL FORCES ON THE FULLY PLASTIC MOMENT OF AN I-BEAM, *Journal of Mechanical Science,* Vol. 3, 1961, p. 279.

6.14 Prager, W., and Hodge, P. G., Jr.,
THEORY OF PERFECTLY PLASTIC SOLIDS, John Wiley Book Co., London, 1951, p. 51.

6.15 Yang, C. H., and Beedle, L. S.,
BEHAVIOR OF I AND **WF** BEAMS IN SHEAR, *Report No. 205B.21,* Fritz Engineering Laboratory, Lehigh University, Bethlehem, Pa., 1951.

6.16    Hall, W. J., and Newmark, N. M.,
        SHEAR DEFLECTION OF WIDE-FLANGE STEEL BEAMS IN
        THE PLASTIC RANGE, *Transactions, ASCE*, Vol. 122, Paper No.
        2878, 1957, p. 666.

6.17    Lee, G. C., and Galambos, T. V.,
        POST-BUCKLING STRENGTH OF WIDE-FLANGE BEAMS,
        *Journal of the Engineering Mechanics Division*, Vol. 88, No. EM1,
        Proc. Paper 3059, Feb., 1962, p. 59.

6.18    Bleich, F.,
        BUCKLING STRENGTH OF METAL STRUCTURES, McGraw-
        Hill Book Co., Inc., New York, 1952.

6.19    Bijlaard, P. P.,
        SOME CONTRIBUTIONS TO THE THEORY OF ELASTIC AND
        PLASTIC STABILITY, Publication of IABSE, VIII, 1947.

6.20    Ilyushin, A. A.,
        STABILITY OF PLATES AND SHELLS BEYOND THE PRO-
        PORTIONAL LIMIT, *Technical Memorandum 1116*, NACA, Wash-
        ington, D.C., 1947.

6.21    Stowell, E. Z.,
        A UNIFIED THEORY OF PLASTIC BUCKLING OF COLUMNS
        AND PLATES, *Report 898*, NACA, Washington, D.C., 1958.

6.22    Winter, G.,
        FLANGE BUCKLING, A LIMITATION OF PLASTIC DESIGN,
        Final Report of IABSE, 1952, p. 139.

6.23    Handelman, G. H., and Prager, W.,
        PLASTIC BUCKLING OF A RECTANGULAR PLATE UNDER
        EDGE THRUST, *Technical Note 1530*, NACA, Washington, D.C.,
        1948.

6.24    Onat, E. T., and Drucker, D. C.,
        INELASTIC INSTABILITY AND INCREMENTAL THEORIES
        OF PLASTICITY, *Journal of Aeronautical Science*, Vol. 20, No. 3,
        Mar., 1953.

6.25    Haaijer, G.,
        PLATE BUCKLING IN THE STRAIN-HARDENING RANGE,
        *Journal of the Engineering Mechanics Division*, ASCE, Vol. 83, No.
        EM2, Proc. Paper 1212, Apr., 1957.

6.26    Haaijer, G., and Thürlimann, B.,
        ON INELASTIC BUCKLING IN STEEL, *Journal of the Engineering
        Mechanics Division*, Vol. 84, No. EM2, Proc. Paper 1581, Apr., 1958.

6.27    Lay, M. G.,
        THE STATIC LOAD DEFORMATION BEHAVIOR OF PLANAR

STEEL STRUCTURES, dissertation presented to Lehigh University, at Bethlehem, Pa., in 1964, in partial fulfillment of the requirements for the degree of Doctor of Philosophy.

6.28   Lay, M. G.,
       FLANGE LOCAL BUCKLING IN WIDE-FLANGE SHAPES, *Journal of the Structural Division,* ASCE, Vol. 91, No. ST6, Proc. Paper 4554, Dec., 1965, p. 95.

6.29   Adams, P. F.,
       PLASTIC DESIGN IN HIGH STRENGTH STEEL, dissertation presented to Lehigh University, at Bethlehem, Pa., in 1966, in partial fulfillment of the requirements for the degree of Doctor of Philosophy.

6.30   Fisher, J. W., Driscoll, G. C., Jr., and Schutz, F. W., Jr.,
       BEHAVIOR OF WELDED CORNER CONNECTIONS, *The Welding Journal,* Vol. 37, No. 5, May, 1958, p. 216-s.

6.31   Lay, M. G., and Galambos, T. V.,
       INELASTIC STEEL BEAMS UNDER UNIFORM MOMENT, *Journal of the Structural Division,* ASCE, Vol. 91, No. ST6, Proc. Paper 4566, Dec., 1965, p. 67.

6.32   Timoshenko, S. P., and Gere, J. M.,
       THEORY OF ELASTIC STABILITY, McGraw-Hill Book Co., Inc., New York, 1961.

6.33   Lee, G. C.,
       A SURVEY OF THE LITERATURE ON THE LATERAL IN-STABILITY OF BEAMS, *Bulletin No. 63,* Welding Research Council, Aug., 1960.

6.34   Timoshenko, S.,
       THEORY OF BENDING, TORSION AND BUCKLING OF THIN WALLED MEMBERS OF OPEN CROSS SECTION, *Journal of the Franklin Institute,* Vol. 239, 1945, pp. 201, 249, 343.

6.35   Clark, J. W., and Hill, H. N.,
       LATERAL BUCKLING OF BEAMS, *Journal of the Structural Division,* ASCE, Vol. 86, No. ST7, Proc. Paper 2559, July, 1960, p. 175.

6.36   Campus, F., and Massonnet, C.,
       RECHERCHES SUR LE FLAMBEMENT DE COLONNES EN ACIER A37, A PROFIL EN DOUBLE TE, SOLLICITEES OB-LIQUEMENT (Research on the buckling of A37 Steel H-section columns loaded obliquely), *Comptes Rendus de Recherches,* IRSIA, No. 17, Apr., 1956.

6.37   Neal, B. G.,
       THE LATERAL INSTABILITY OF YIELDED MILD STEEL BEAMS OF RECTANGULAR CROSS SECTION, *Philosophical Transactions,* Royal Society of London, Vol. 242, Jan., 1950, p. 846.

6.38    Wittrick, W. H.,
        LATERAL INSTABILITY OF RECTANGULAR BEAMS OF
        STRAIN-HARDENING MATERIAL UNDER UNIFORM BEND-
        ING, *Journal of Aeronautical Science,* Vol. 19, No. 12, Dec., 1952,
        p. 835.

6.39    Horne, M. R.,
        CRITICAL LOADING CONDITIONS IN ENGINEERING
        STRUCTURES, dissertation presented to Cambridge University, at
        Cambridge, England, in 1950, in partial fulfillment of the requirements
        for the degree of Doctor of Philosophy.

6.40    Galambos, T. V.,
        INELASTIC LATERAL BUCKLING OF BEAMS, *Journal of the
        Structural Division,* ASCE, Vol. 89, No. ST5, Proc. Paper 3683, Oct.,
        1963, p. 217.

6.41    Galambos, T. V., and Fukumoto, Y.,
        INELASTIC LATERAL-TORSIONAL BUCKLING OF BEAM-
        COLUMNS, *Journal of the Structural Division,* ASCE, Vol. 92, No.
        ST2, Proc. Paper 4770, Apr., 1966, p. 41.

6.42    Galambos, T. V., Fukumoto, Y., and Adams, P. F.,
        FURTHER STUDIES ON THE LATERAL-TORSIONAL BUCK-
        LING OF BEAM-COLUMNS, *Bulletin No. 115,* Welding Research
        Council, July, 1966.

6.43    White, M. W.,
        THE LATERAL-TORSIONAL BUCKLING OF YIELDED
        STRUCTURAL STEEL MEMBERS, dissertation presented to Lehigh
        University, at Bethlehem, Pa., in 1956, in partial fulfillment of the re-
        quirements for the degree of Doctor of Philosophy.

6.44    Kusuda, T., Sarubbi, R. G., and Thürlimann, B.,
        LATERAL BRACING OF BEAMS IN PLASTIC DESIGN, *Report
        No. 205.E11,* Fritz Engineering Laboratory, Lehigh University, Beth-
        lehem, Pa., 1960.

6.45    Prasad, J., and Galambos, T. V.,
        THE INFLUENCE OF ADJACENT SPANS ON THE ROTATION
        CAPACITY OF BEAMS, *Report No. 205H.12,* Fritz Engineering Lab-
        oratory, Lehigh University, Bethlehem, Pa., June, 1963.

6.46    Sawyer, H. A.,
        POST-ELASTIC BEHAVIOR OF WIDE-FLANGE STEEL BEAMS,
        *Journal of the Structural Division,* ASCE, Vol. 87, No. ST8, Proc. Paper
        3016, Dec., 1961, p. 43.

6.47    Lee, G. C., Ferrara, A. T., and Galambos, T. V.,
        EXPERIMENTS ON WIDE-FLANGE BEAMS, *Bulletin No. 99,*
        Welding Research Council, Sept., 1964.

6.48    Janss, J., and Massonnet, C.,
        THE EXTENSION OF PLASTIC DESIGN TO STEEL A52, Publications of IABSE, Vol. 27, 1967, pp. 15–30.

6.49    Smith, R. J., *et al.*,
        EXPERIMENTS ON WIDE-FLANGE BEAMS UNDER MOMENT GRADIENT, *Bulletin No. 142*, Welding Research Council, July, 1969.

6.50    Lay, M. G.,
        YIELDING OF UNIFORMLY LOADED STEEL MEMBERS, *Journal of the Structural Division*, ASCE, Vol. 81, No. ST6, Proc. Paper 4580, Dec., 1965, p. 49.

6.51    Massey, C., and Pitman, F. S.,
        INELASTIC LATERAL INSTABILITY UNDER A MOMENT GRADIENT, *Journal of the Engineering Mechanics Division*, ASCE, Vol. 92, No. EM2, Proc. Paper 4779, Apr., 1966, p. 101.

6.52    Lay, M. G., and Galambos, T. V.,
        BRACING REQUIREMENTS FOR INELASTIC STEEL BEAMS, *Journal of the Structural Division*, ASCE, Vol. 92, No. ST2, Proc. Paper 4785, Apr., 1966, p. 207.

6.53    Augusti, G.,
        EXPERIMENTAL ROTATION CAPACITY OF STEEL BEAM-COLUMNS, *Journal of the Structural Division*, ASCE, Vol. 90, No. ST6, Proc. Paper 4175, Dec., 1964, p. 171.

6.54    Grüning, M.,
        DIE TRAGFÄHIGKEIT STATISCH UNBESTIMMTER TRAGWERKE AUS STAHL BEI BELIEBIG HÄUFIG WIEDERHOLTER BELASTUNG (The carrying capacity of statically indeterminate steel frames subjected to arbitrarily repeated loading), Julius Springer, Berlin, Germany, 1926.

6.55    Bleich, H.,
        UBER DIE BEMESSUNG STATISCH UNBESTIMMTER STAHLTRAGWERKE UNTER BERÜCKSICHTIGUNG DES ELASTISCH-PLASTISCHEN BAUSTOFF (The design of statically indeterminate steel frames considering the elastic-plastic behavior of the material), *Bauingenieur*, Vol. 13, 1932, p. 261.

6.56    Melan, E.,
        THEORIE STATISCH UNBESTIMMTER SYSTEME AUS IDEAL PLASTISCHEN BAUSTOFF (The theory of statically indeterminate systems made of ideally plastic material), *Sitzber. Akad. Wiss.*, Vienna, Austria, Vol. 145(IIa), 1936, p. 195.

6.57    Horne, M. R.,
        THE EFFECT OF VARIABLE REPEATED LOADS IN BUILD-

ING STRUCTURES DESIGNED BY THE PLASTIC THEORY, *Proceedings,* IABSE, Vol. 14, 1954, p. 53.

6.58   Symonds, P. S.,
       THE BASIC THEOREMS IN THE PLASTIC THEORY OF STRUCTURES, *Journal of Aeronautical Science,* Vol. 17 (18), 1950.

6.59   Neal, B. G., and Symonds, P. S.,
       CYCLIC LOADING OF PORTAL FRAMES, THEORY AND TESTS, *Proceedings,* IABSE, Vol. 18, 1958, p. 171.

6.60   Neal, B. G., and Symonds, P. S.,
       A METHOD FOR CALCULATING THE FAILURE LOAD FOR A FRAMED STRUCTURE SUBJECTED TO FLUCTUATING LOADS, *Journal of the Institution of Civil Engineers,* Vol. 35, 1950, p. 186.

6.61   Neal, B. G.,
       THE BEHAVIOR OF FRAMED STRUCTURES UNDER RE-PEATED LOADING, *Quarterly Journal of Mechanics and Applied Mathematics,* Vol. 4, 1951, p. 78.

6.62   Neal, B. G.,
       PLASTIC COLLAPSE AND SHAKEDOWN THEOREMS FOR STRUCTURES OF STRAIN-HARDENING MATERIAL, *Journal of Aeronautical Science,* Vol. 17, 1950, p. 297.

6.63   Hodge, P. G., Jr.,
       SHAKEDOWN OF ELASTIC-PLASTIC STRUCTURES, *Residual Stresses in Metals and Metal Construction,* ed. W. R. Osgood, Reinhold Publishing Corp., New York, 1954.

6.64   Massonnet, C.,
       ESSAIS D'ADAPTATION ET DE STABILIZATION PLASTIQUES SUR DES POURTRELLES LAMINÉES (Tests on the behavior and plastic stability of rolled beams), *Proceedings,* IABSE, Vol. 13, 1953, p. 239.

6.65   Gozum, A. T., and Haaijer, G.,
       DEFLECTION STABILITY OF CONTINOUS BEAMS, *Report No. 205G.1,* Fritz Engineering Laboratory, Lehigh University, Bethlehem, Pa., 1955.

6.66   Popov, E. P., and McCarthy, R. E.,
       DEFLECTION STABILITY OF RIGID FRAMES UNDER RE-PEATED LOADS, *Journal of the Engineering Mechanics Division,* ASCE, Vol. 86, No. EM1, Proc. Paper 2334, Jan., 1960, p. 61.

6.67   Ghani, A. F. M. R.,
       SHAKEDOWN ANALYSIS OF NONPRISMATIC BEAMS, *Journal of the Structural Division,* ASCE, Vol. 93, No. ST6, Proc. Paper 5643, Dec., 1967, p. 25.

6.68  Fukumoto, Y., and Yoshida, H.,
      DEFLECTION STABILITY OF BEAMS UNDER REPEATED
      LOADS, *Journal of the Structural Division,* ASCE, Vol. 95, No. ST7,
      Proc. Paper 6668, July, 1969, p. 1443.

6.69  Toridis, T. G., and Wen, R. K.,
      INELASTIC RESPONSE OF BEAMS TO MOVING LOADS,
      *Journal of the Engineering Mechanics Division,* ASCE, Vol. 92, No.
      EM6, Proc. Paper 5028, Dec., 1966, p. 43.

6.70  Eyre, D. G., and Galambos, T. V.,
      VARIABLE REPEATED LOADING—A LITERATURE SURVEY,
      *Bulletin No. 142,* Welding Research Council, July, 1969.

6.71  Klöppel, K.,
      BEITRAG ZUR FRAGE DER AUSNUTZBARKEIT DER PLAS-
      TITÄT DER DAUERBEANSPRUCHTEN DURCHLAUFTRA-
      GERN (Contributions on the question of the applicability of plasticity
      to repeatedly loaded continuous beams), Final Report of the 2nd Con-
      gress, IABSE, 1939.

6.72  Popov, E. P., and Becker, E.,
      SHAKEDOWN ANALYSIS FOR TYPICAL ONE-STORY BENTS,
      *Journal of the Structural Division,* ASCE, Vol. 90, No. ST5, Proc. Paper
      4069, Oct., 1964, p. 1.

6.73  Popov, E. P., and Franklin, H. A.,
      STEEL BEAM-TO-COLUMN CONNECTIONS SUBJECTED TO
      CYCLICALLY REVERSED LOADING, *Steel Research for Con-
      struction,* AISI, Feb., 1966.

6.74  Popov, E. P., and Pinkney, R. B.,
      BEHAVIOR OF STEEL BUILDING CONNECTIONS SUB-
      JECTED TO REPEATED INELASTIC STRAIN REVERSAL—
      Experimental Data, *Report No. 67-31,* University of California at
      Berkeley, Dec., 1967.

6.75  Popov, E. P., and Pinkney, R. B.,
      BEHAVIOR OF STEEL CONNECTIONS SUBJECTED TO RE-
      PEATED INELASTIC STRAIN REVERSAL, *Report No. 67-30,*
      University of California at Berkeley, Dec., 1967.

6.76  Popov, E. P., and Pinkney, R. B.,
      RELIABILITY OF STEEL BEAM-TO-COLUMN CONNECTIONS
      UNDER CYCLIC LOADING, 4th World Conference on Earthquake
      Engineering, Santiago, Chile, Jan., 1969.

6.77  Popov, E. P.,
      PERFORMANCE OF STEEL BEAMS AND THEIR CONNEC-
      TIONS TO COLUMNS DURING SEVERE CYCLIC LOADING,
      Contributions to the expanded discussion, 8th Congress of IABSE,
      Theme III, New York, Sept., 1968.

6.78      Sherbourne, A. N.,
SOME PRELIMINARY EXPERIMENTS ON THE BEHAVIOR OF
DUCTILE STRUCTURES UNDER REPEATED LOADS, *Experimental Mechanics,* Vol. 3, No. 5, May, 1963, p. 119.

6.79      Krishnasamy, S., and Sherbourne, A. N.,
RESPONSE OF A "PLASTIC HINGE" TO LOW CYCLE ALTERNATING DEFLECTIONS, *Experimental Mechanics,* Vol. 8, No. 6,
June, 1968, p. 241.

6.80      Royles, R.,
INCREMENTAL EXTENSION OF MILD STEEL BEAMS IN
REVERSED BENDING, *Journal of Strain Analysis,* Vol. 1, No. 2,
1966, p. 133.

6.81      Hagura, H.,
RESEARCH ON THE ELASTO-PLASTIC ANALYSIS OF STEEL
SECTIONS SUBJECTED TO ALTERNATIVE LOADS, *Transactions of the Architectural Institute of Japan,* No. 125, July, 1966, p. 8.

6.82      Naka, T., *et al.,*
ULTIMATE STRENGTH OF COLUMNS IN MULTI-STORY
RIGID FRAMES, *Yawata Technical Report No. 256,* Sept., 1966, p.
82.

6.83      Naka, T., Kato, B., and Watabe, M.,
RESEARCH ON THE BEHAVIOR OF STEEL BEAM-TO-COLUMN CONNECTIONS, Laboratory for Steel Structures, University of Tokyo, Japan, 1966.

6.84      Wakabayashi, M., *et al.,*
AN EXPERIMENTAL STUDY OF THE ELASTIC-PLASTIC
STABILITY OF CROSS SHAPED STRUCTURAL SYSTEMS,
Kinki Branch of the Architectural Institute of Japan, 1967.

6.85      Wakabayashi, M.,
THE RESTORING FORCE CHARACTERISTIC OF MULTI-STORY FRAMES, *Bulletin of the Disaster Prevention Research Institute* ( Japan), Vol. 14, Part 2, Feb., 1965.

6.86      Igarashi, S., *et al.,*
PLASTIC BEHAVIOR OF STEEL FRAMES UNDER CYCLIC
LOADINGS, *Transactions of the Architectural Institute of Japan,* No.
130, Dec., 1966.

6.87      Igarashi, S., and Toga, N.,
HYSTERESIS CHARACTERISTICS AND STRUCTURAL
DAMPING OF STEEL STRUCTURES UNDER ALTERNATE
LATERAL LOADING, *Transactions of the Architectural Institute of
Japan,* No. 120, Feb., 1960.

6.88    Yokoo, Y., *et al.*,
        HORIZONTAL-FORCE-RESTRAINT PROPERTIES OF MULTI-
        STORY STEEL FRAMES, *Yawata Technical Report No. 256*, Sept.,
        1966, p. 43.

6.89    Yarimci, E.,
        INCREMENTAL INELASTIC ANALYSIS OF FRAMED STRUC-
        TURES AND SOME EXPERIMENTAL VERIFICATIONS, dis-
        sertation presented to Lehigh University, at Bethlehem, Pa., in 1966, in
        partial fulfillment of the requirements for the degree of Doctor of
        Philosophy.

6.90    Arnold, P., Adams, P. F., and Lu, L. W.,
        THE EFFECT OF INSTABILITY ON THE CYCLIC BEHAVIOR
        OF A FRAME, *Report No. 297.24*, Fritz Engineering Laboratory,
        Lehigh University, Bethlehem, Pa., Sept., 1966.

6.91    Beedle, L. S.,
        REVERSED LOADING OF FRAMES—PRELIMINARY TESTS,
        *Proceedings*, Structural Engineers Association of California, 1965,
        p. 87.

6.92    Carpenter, L. D., and Lu, L. W.,
        BEHAVIOR OF STEEL FRAMES SUBJECTED TO REPEATED
        AND REVERSED LOADS, Final Report of 8th Congress of IABSE
        at New York, Sept., 1968.

6.93    Carpenter, L. D., and Lu, L. W.,
        REPEATED AND REVERSED LOAD TESTS ON FULL-SCALE
        STEEL FRAMES, 4th World Conference on Earthquake Engineering,
        Santiago, Chile, Jan., 1969.

6.94    Hanson, R. E.,
        COMPARISON OF STATIC AND DYNAMIC HYSTERESIS
        CURVES, *Journal of the Engineering Mechanics Division*, ASCE, Vol.
        92, No. EM5, Proc. Paper 4949, Oct., 1966, p. 87.

6.95    Bertero, V. V., and Popov, E. P.,
        EFFECT OF LARGE ALTERNATING STRAINS ON STEEL
        BEAMS, *Journal of the Structural Division*, ASCE, Vol. 91, No. ST1,
        Proc. Paper 4217, Feb., 1965, p. 1.

6.96    Morrow, J.,
        CYCLIC PLASTIC STRAIN ENERGY AND FATIGUE OF
        METALS, *Special Technical Publication No. 378*, ASTM, 1965.

6.97    Benham, P. P., and Ford, H.,
        LOW ENDURANCE FATIGUE OF A MILD STEEL AND AN
        ALUMINUM ALLOY, *Journal of Mechanical Engineering Science*,
        Vol. 3, No. 2, June, 1961.

6.98    Popov, E. P.,
BEHAVIOR OF STEEL BEAM-TO-COLUMN CONNECTIONS UNDER REPEATED AND REVERSED LOADING, *Proceedings,* Summer Conference on Plastic Design, Lehigh University, Bethlehem, Pa., 1965.

6.99    Popov, E. P., and Franklin, H. A.,
STEEL BEAM-TO-COLUMN CONNECTIONS SUBJECTED TO CYCLICALLY REVERSED LOADING, *Proceedings,* 34th Annual Convention of Structural Engineering Association of California, Oct., 1965.

6.100   Popov, E. P.,
LOW-CYCLE FATIGUE OF STEEL BEAM-TO-COLUMN CONNECTIONS, RILEM International Symposium on the Effects of Repeated Loading of Materials and Structural Elements, Mexico City, Sept. 15–17, 1966.

6.101   Popov, E. P., and Pinkney, R. B.,
CYCLIC YIELD REVERSAL IN STEEL BUILDING CONNECTIONS, *Journal of the Structural Division,* ASCE, Vol. 95, No. ST3, Proc. Paper 6441, Mar., 1969, p. 327.

6.102   McNamee, B. M.,
THE GENERAL BEHAVIOR AND STRENGTH OF UNBRACED MULTI-STORY FRAMES UNDER GRAVITY LOADING, dissertation presented to Lehigh University, at Bethlehem Pa., in 1967, in partial fulfillment of the requirements for the degree of Doctor of Philosophy.

6.103   Galambos, T. V.,
DEFORMATION AND ENERGY ABSORPTION CAPACITY OF STEEL STRUCTURES IN THE INELASTIC RANGE, *Bulletin No. 8,* AISI, Mar., 1968.

6.104   Berg, G. V.,
A STUDY OF THE EARTHQUAKE RESPONSE OF INELASTIC SYSTEMS, *Proceedings,* 34th Annual Convention of Structural Engineering Association of California, Oct., 1965.

6.105   Jennings, P. C.,
PERIODIC RESPONSE OF A GENERAL YIELDING STRUCTURE, *Journal of the Engineering Mechanics Division,* ASCE, Vol. 90, No. EM2, Proc. Paper 3871, Apr., 1964, p. 131.

6.106   Goel, S. C., and Berg, G. V.,
INELASTIC EARTHQUAKE RESPONSE OF TALL STEEL FRAMES, *Journal of the Structural Division,* ASCE, Vol. 94, No. ST8, Proc. Paper 6061, Aug., 1968, p. 1907.

6.107     Kaldjian, M. J., and Fan, W. R. S.,
EARTHQUAKE RESPONSE OF RAMBERG-OSGOOD STRUC-
TURE, *Journal of the Structural Division*, ASCE, Vol. 94, No. ST10,
Proc. Paper 6196, Oct., 1968, p. 2451.

6.108     Blume, J. A.,
A RESERVE ENERGY TECHNIQUE FOR THE EARTHQUAKE
DESIGN AND RATING OF STRUCTURES IN THE INELASTIC
RANGE, 2nd World Conference on Earthquake Engineering, Tokyo,
Japan, 1960, p. 1061.

6.109     Nigam, C.,
INELASTIC INTERACTIONS IN DYNAMIC RESPONSE OF
STRUCTURES, California Institute of Technology, Pasadena, Calif.,
June, 1967.

6.110     Husid, R.,
GRAVITY EFFECTS ON THE EARTHQUAKE RESPONSE OF
YIELDING STRUCTURES, dissertation presented to California
Institute of Technology, at Pasadena, Calif., in 1967, in partial fulfill-
ment of the requirements for the degree of Doctor of Philosophy.

6.111     Bertero, V.,
INELASTIC BEHAVIOR OF BEAM TO COLUMN SUBASSEM-
BLAGES UNDER REPEATED LOADING, *Report EERC-68.2*,
Univ. of Calif., Berkeley, Calif., Apr., 1968.

6.112     Miki, S., *et al.*,
SOME PROBLEMS ON THE STRENGTH AND RIGIDITY OF
BEAM TO COLUMN CONNECTIONS IN STEEL FRAMES,
Report of the Kawasaki Dockyard Co., Ltd., Steel Structure Division,
Nov., 1964.

6.113     Popov, E. P., Bertero, V. V., and Watabe, M.,
A TEST FRAME FOR SIMULATING GRAVITY AND GROUND
MOTION ON STRUCTURAL ASSEMBLAGES, RILEM International Symposium on Methodology and Technique of Testing Structures, Bucharest, Rumania, Vol. 4, Sept., 1969, p. 53.

## CHAPTER 7.—COMPRESSION MEMBERS

7.1     Girkmann, K.,
BEMESSUNG VON RAHMENTRAGWERKEN UNTER ZU-
GRUNDELEGUNG EINES IDEAL PLASTISCHEN STAHLES
(The design of frames assuming a steel of ideal plasticity), *Sitzberichten
Akad. Wiss.*, Vienna, Austria, Vol. 140, IIa, 1931, p. 679.

7.2     Baker, J. F.,
A REVIEW OF RECENT INVESTIGATIONS INTO THE BE-
HAVIOR OF STEEL FRAMES IN THE PLASTIC RANGE, *Journal
of the Institution of Civil Engineers*, Vol. 3, Jan., 1949.

7.3     Roderick, J. W.,
        THEORY OF PLASTICITY—ELEMENTS OF THE SIMPLE
        PLASTIC THEORY, *Philosophical Magazine*, Series 7, Vol. 39, July,
        1948, p. 529.

7.4     Hendry, A. W.,
        AN INVESTIGATION OF THE STRENGTH OF CERTAIN
        WELDED PORTAL FRAMES IN RELATION TO THE PLASTIC
        METHOD OF DESIGN, *The Structural Engineer*, Vol. 28, No. 12,
        Dec., 1950.

7.5     Ketter, R. L., Beedle, L. S., and Johnston, B. G.,
        COLUMN STRENGTH UNDER COMBINED BENDING AND
        THRUST, *The Welding Journal*, Vol. 31, No. 12, Dec., 1952, p. 607-s.

7.6     Onat, E. T., and Prager, W.,
        LIMIT ANALYSIS OF ARCHES, *Journal of Mechanics and Physics
        of Solids*, Vol. 1, No. 12, Jan., 1953.

7.7     Santathadaporn, S., and Chen, W. F.,
        INTERACTION CURVES FOR SECTIONS UNDER COM-
        BINED BIAXIAL BENDING AND AXIAL FORCE, *Report No.
        331.3*, Fritz Engineering Laboratory, Lehigh University, Bethlehem,
        Pa., Aug., 1968.

7.8     Howland, F. L., Egger, W., Mayerjak, R. J., and Munz, R. J.,
        STATIC AND DYNAMIC LOAD-DEFLECTION TESTS OF
        STEEL STRUCTURES, *Structural Research Series, No. 92*, Univer-
        sity of Illinois, Feb., 1955.

7.9     Lay, M. G., and Gimsing, N.,
        EXPERIMENTAL STUDIES OF THE MOMENT-THRUST-
        CURVATURE RELATIONSHIP, *The Welding Journal*, Vol. 44, Feb.,
        1965.

7.10    Bijlaard, P. P., Fisher, G. P., and Winter, G.,
        ECCENTRICALLY LOADED, END-RESTRAINED COLUMNS,
        *Transactions*, ASCE, Vol. 120, 1955, p. 1070.

7.11    Ketter, R. L., Kaminsky, E. L., and Beedle, L. S.,
        PLASTIC DEFORMATION OF WIDE-FLANGE BEAM-
        COLUMNS, *Transactions*, ASCE, Vol. 120, 1955, p. 1028.

7.12    Galambos, T. V., and Ketter, R. L.,
        COLUMNS UNDER COMBINED BENDING AND THRUST,
        *Journal of the Engineering Mechanics Division*, ASCE, Vol. 85, No.
        EM2, Proc. Paper 1990, Apr., 1959, p. 1.

7.13    Ketter, R. L.,
        STABILITY OF BEAM-COLUMNS ABOVE THE ELASTIC
        LIMIT, *Proceedings*, ASCE, Separate No. 692, May, 1955.

7.14    Ketter, R. L.,
        FURTHER STUDIES ON THE STRENGTH OF BEAM-
        COLUMNS, *Journal of the Structural Division,* ASCE, Vol. 87, No.
        ST6, Proc. Paper 2879, Aug., 1961, p. 135.

7.15    Ojalvo, M.,
        RESTRAINED COLUMNS, *Journal of the Engineering Mechanics
        Division,* ASCE, Vol. 86, No. EM5, Proc. Paper 2615, Oct., 1960, p. 1.

7.16    Chen, W. F., and Santathadaporn, S.,
        CURVATURE AND THE SOLUTION OF ECCENTRICALLY
        LOADED COLUMNS, *Journal of the Engineering Mechanics Division,*
        ASCE, Vol. 95, No. EM1, Proc. Paper 6382, Feb., 1969, p. 21.

7.17    Massonnet, C.,
        STABILITY CONSIDERATIONS IN THE DESIGN OF STEEL
        COLUMNS, *Journal of the Structural Division,* ASCE, Vol. 85, No.
        ST7, Proc. Paper 2163, Sept., 1959, p. 75.

7.18    Austin, W. J.,
        STRENGTH AND DESIGN OF METAL BEAM-COLUMNS,
        *Journal of the Structural Division,* ASCE, Vol. 87, No. ST4, Proc.
        Paper 2802, Apr., 1961, p. 1.

7.19    Yura, J. A., and Galambos, T. V.,
        STRENGTH OF SINGLE-STORY STEEL FRAMES, *Journal of
        the Structural Division,* ASCE, Vol. 91, No. ST5, Proc. Paper 4507,
        Oct., 1965, p. 81.

7.20    Mason, R. E., Fisher, G. P., and Winter, G.,
        ECCENTRICALLY LOADED, HINGED STEEL COLUMNS,
        *Journal of the Engineering Mechanics Division,* ASCE, Vol. 84, No.
        EM4, Proc. Paper 1792, Oct., 1958.

7.21    Johnston, B. G., and Cheney, L.,
        STEEL COLUMNS OF ROLLED WIDE-FLANGE SECTION,
        Progress Report 2, AISC, New York, Nov., 1942.

7.22    STEEL COLUMN RESEARCH, Second Progress Report of the
        Special Committee on Steel Columns, *Transactions,* ASCE, Vol. 95,
        Paper No. 1789, 1931, p. 1152.

7.23    Van Kuren, R. C., and Galambos, T. V.,
        BEAM-COLUMN EXPERIMENTS, *Journal of the Structural Divi-
        sion,* ASCE, Vol. 90, No. ST2, Proc. Paper 3876, Apr., 1964, p. 223.

7.24    Prasad, J., and Galambos, T. V.,
        ULTIMATE STRENGTH TABLES FOR BEAM-COLUMNS,
        *Bulletin No. 78,* Welding Research Council, New York, July, 1962.

7.25    Chwalla, E.,
        THEORIE DES AUSSERMITTIG GEDRUCKTEN STABES AUS

316        REFERENCES

BAUSTAHL (Theory of Eccentrically Loaded Steel Columns), *Der Stahlbau*, Vol. 7, Oct. and Nov., 1934.

7.26   Von Kármán, T.,
       UNTERSUCHUNGEN UBER KNICKFESTIGKEIT (Investigation on Buckling Strength), *Mitt. u. Forschungsarbeit*, V.D.I. 81, Berlin, Germany, 1910.

7.27   Ellis, J. S.,
       PLASTIC BEHAVIOR OF COMPRESSION MEMBERS, *Journal of the Mechanics and Physics of Solids*, Vol. 6, 1958, p. 282.

7.28   Neal, B. G., and Mansell, D. S.,
       THE EFFECT OF RESTRAINT UPON THE COLLAPSE OF MILD STEEL TRUSSES, *International Journal of Mechanical Science*, Vol. 5, Feb., 1963.

7.29   Horne, M. R.,
       THE ELASTIC-PLASTIC THEORY OF COMPRESSION MEMBERS, *Journal of the Mechanics and Physics of Solids*, Vol. 4, 1956, p. 104.

7.30   Bijlaard, P. P.,
       BUCKLING OF COLUMNS WITH EQUAL AND UNEQUAL END ECCENTRICITIES AND EQUAL AND UNEQUAL ROTATIONAL END RESTRAINTS, *Proceedings*, 2nd U.S. National Congress of Applied Mechanics, Ann Arbor, Mich., 1954.

7.31   Lee, S. L., and Hauck, G. F.,
       BUCKLING OF STEEL COLUMNS UNDER ARBITRARY END LOADS, *Journal of the Structural Division*, ASCE, Vol. 90, No. ST2, Proc. Paper 3872, Apr., 1964, p. 179.

7.32   Levi, V.,
       PLASTIC DESIGN OF BRACED MULTI-STORY FRAMES, dissertation presented to Lehigh University, at Bethlehem, Pa., in 1962, in partial fulfillment of the requirements for the degree of Doctor of Philosophy.

7.33   Levi, V., Driscoll, G. C., and Lu, L. W.,
       ANALYSIS OF RESTRAINED COLUMNS PERMITTED TO SWAY, *Journal of the Structural Division*, ASCE, Vol. 93, No. ST1, Proc. Paper 5092, Feb., 1967, p. 87.

7.34   Lay, M. G.,
       THE MECHANICS OF COLUMN DEFLECTION CURVES, *Report No. 278.12*, Fritz Engineering Laboratory, Lehigh University, Bethlehem, Pa., June, 1964.

7.35   Ojalvo, M., and Fukumoto, Y.,
       NOMOGRAPHS FOR THE SOLUTION OF BEAM-COLUMN PROBLEMS, *Bulletin No. 78*, Welding Research Council, June, 1962.

7.36 Lay, M. G., and Galambos, T. V.,
END-MOMENT END-ROTATION CHARACTERISTICS FOR BEAM-COLUMNS, *Report No. 205A.36*, Fritz Engineering Laboratory, Lehigh University, Bethlehem, Pa., May, 1962.

7.37 Aglietti, R. A., Lay, M. G., and Galambos, T. V.,
TESTS ON A36 AND A441 STEEL BEAM-COLUMNS, *Report No. 278.14*, Fritz Engineering Laboratory, Lehigh University, Bethlehem, Pa., June, 1964.

7.38 Lay, M. G., and Galambos, T. V.,
EXPERIMENTAL BEHAVIOR OF RESTRAINED COLUMNS, *Bulletin No. 110*, Welding Research Council, Nov., 1965.

7.39 Hill, H. N., and Clark, J. W.,
LATERAL BUCKLING OF ECCENTRICALLY LOADED I-SECTION COLUMNS, *Transactions*, ASCE, Vol. 116, Paper No. 2462, 1951, p. 1179.

7.40 Salvadori, M. G.,
LATERAL BUCKLING OF ECCENTRICALLY LOADED I-COLUMNS, *Transactions*, ASCE, Vol. 121, Paper No. 2836, 1956, p. 1163.

7.41 Galambos, T. V.,
INELASTIC LATERAL-TORSIONAL BUCKLING OF EC-CENTRICALLY LOADED WIDE-FLANGE COLUMNS, dissertation presented to Lehigh University, at Bethlehem, Pa., in 1959, in partial fulfillment of the requirements for the degree of Doctor of Philosophy.

7.42 Fukumoto, Y.,
INELASTIC LATERAL-TORSIONAL BUCKLING OF BEAM-COLUMNS, dissertation presented to Lehigh University, at Bethlehem, Pa., in 1963, in partial fulfillment of the requirements for the degree of Doctor of Philosophy.

7.43 Miranda, C., and Ojalvo, M.,
INELASTIC LATERAL-TORSIONAL BUCKLING OF BEAM-COLUMNS, *Journal of the Engineering Mechanics Division*, ASCE, Vol. 91, No. EM6, Proc. Paper 4563, Dec., 1965, p. 21.

7.44 Fukumoto, Y., and Galambos, T. V.,
INELASTIC LATERAL-TORSIONAL BUCKLING OF BEAM-COLUMNS, *Journal of the Structural Division*, ASCE, Vol. 92, No. ST2, Proc. Paper 4770, Apr., 1966, p. 41.

7.45 Lu, L. W.,
COLUMNS, *Plastic Design of Multi-Story Frames*, Chapter 4, *Report No. 273.20 and No. 273.24*, Fritz Engineering Laboratory, Lehigh University, Bethlehem, Pa., 1965.

7.46    Birnstiel, C., and Michalos, J.,
        ULTIMATE LOAD OF H-COLUMNS UNDER BIAXIAL BEND-
        ING, *Journal of the Structural Division,* ASCE, Vol. 89, No. ST2,
        Proc. Paper 3503, Apr. 1963.

7.47    Birnstiel, C., Harstead, G. A., and Leu, K. C.,
        INELASTIC BEHAVIOR OF H-COLUMNS UNDER BIAXIAL
        BENDING, New York University, New York, Nov., 1967.

7.48    Sharma, S. S., and Gaylord, E. H.,
        STRENGTH OF STEEL COLUMNS WITH BIAXIALLY EC-
        CENTRIC LOAD, *Journal of the Structural Division,* ASCE, Vol. 95,
        No. ST12, Proc. Paper 6960, Dec., 1969, p. 2797.

7.49    Birnstiel, C., Leu, K. C., Tesoro, J. A., and Tomasetti, R. L.,
        EXPERIMENTS ON H-COLUMNS UNDER BIAXIAL BEND-
        ING, New York University, New York, Jan., 1967.

7.50    Chubkin, G. M.,
        EXPERIMENTAL RESEARCH ON THE STABILITY OF THIN
        PLATE STEEL MEMBERS WITH BIAXIAL ECCENTRICITY,
        *Analysis of Spatial Structure,* Vol. 5, Paper No. 6, G.I.L.S., Moscow,
        USSR, 1959.

7.51    Milner, H. R.,
        THE ELASTIC PLASTIC STABILITY OF STANCHIONS BENT
        ABOUT TWO AXES, dissertation presented to the University of
        London, England, in December, 1965, in partial fulfillment of the
        requirements for the degree of Doctor of Philosophy.

7.52    Chen, W. F., and Santathadaporn, S.,
        REVIEW OF COLUMN BEHAVIOR UNDER BIAXIAL LOAD-
        ING, *Journal of the Structural Division,* ASCE, Vol. 94, No. ST12,
        Proc. Paper 6316, Dec., 1968, p. 2999.

## CHAPTER 8.—CONNECTIONS

8.1     Blodgett, O. W., and Scalzi, J. B.,
        DESIGN OF WELDED STRUCTURAL CONNECTIONS, The
        James F. Lincoln Arc Welding Foundation, Cleveland, Ohio, 1961.

8.2     Blodgett, O. W.,
        DESIGN OF WELDED STRUCTURES, The James F. Lincoln Arc
        Welding Foundation, Cleveland, Ohio, 1966.

8.3     Beedle, L. S., and Christopher, R. J.,
        TESTS OF STEEL MOMENT CONNECTIONS, *Proceedings,* Struc-
        tural Engineers Association, 1963.

8.4     Toprac, A. A., Johnston, B. G., and Beedle, L. S.,
        CONNECTIONS FOR WELDED CONTINUOUS PORTAL
        FRAMES, *The Welding Journal,* Vol. 30, Nos. 7 and 8, Vol. 31, No.
        11, 1951, 1952.

8.5    Hendry, A. W.,
       AN INVESTIGATION OF THE STRENGTH OF WELDED
       PORTAL FRAME CONNECTIONS, *The Structural Engineer,* Vol.
       28, No. 10, 1950.

8.6    Wright, D. T.,
       THE DESIGN OF KNEE JOINTS FOR RIGID STEEL FRAMES,
       *BWRA No. FE 1/38,* Apr., 1954.

8.7    Fisher, J. W., Driscoll, G. C., Jr., and Beedle, L. S.,
       PLASTIC ANALYSIS AND DESIGN OF SQUARE RIGID
       FRAME KNEES, *Bulletin No. 39,* Welding Research Council, Apr.,
       1958.

8.8    Fisher, J. W., and Driscoll, G. C., Jr.,
       CORNER CONNECTIONS LOADED IN TENSION, *The Welding
       Journal,* Vol. 38, No. 11, Nov., 1959, p. 425–s.

8.9    Fisher, J. W.,
       PLASTIC ANALYSIS OF HAUNCHED CONNECTIONS, thesis
       presented to Lehigh University, at Bethlehem, Pa., in 1958, in partial
       fulfillment of the requirements for the degree of Master of Science.

8.10   Fisher, J. W., Lee, G. C., Yura, J. A., and Driscoll, G. C.,
       PLASTIC ANALYSIS AND TESTS OF HAUNCHED CORNER
       CONNECTIONS, *Bulletin No. 91,* Welding Research Council, Oct.,
       1963.

8.11   Pray, R. F., and Jensen, C. D.,
       WELDED TOP PLATE BEAM-COLUMN CONNECTIONS, *The
       Welding Journal,* Vol. 35, No. 7, July, 1956.

8.12   Graham, J. D., Sherbourne, A. N., Khabbaz, R. N., and Jensen, C. D.,
       WELDED INTERIOR BEAM-TO-COLUMN CONNECTIONS,
       AISC, New York, 1959.

8.13   Peters, J. W., and Driscoll, G. C., Jr.,
       A STUDY OF THE BEHAVIOR OF BEAM-TO-COLUMN CON-
       NECTIONS, *Report No. 333.2,* Fritz Engineering Laboratory, Lehigh
       University, Bethlehem, Pa., June, 1968.

8.14   Freeman, F. R.,
       THE STRENGTH OF ARC-WELDED JOINTS, *Proceedings of the
       Institution of Civil Engineers.* Vol. 231, 1930, pp. 322–325.

8.15   WELDING HANDBOOK, American Welding Society, New York,
       1958.

8.16   Denara, L. F.,
       SURVEY OF EXISTING PUBLISHED INFORMATION, Appen-
       dix D, Report of Weld Panel of the Steel Structures Research Com-

mittee, Department of Scientific and Industrial Research, London, England, 1938.

8.17    Higgins, T. R., and Preece, F. R.,
        PROPOSED WORKING STRESSES FOR FILLET WELD IN BUILDING CONSTRUCTION, *The Welding Journal*, Vol. 47, No. 10, Oct., 1968, p. 429-s.

8.18    Archer, F. E., Fisher, H. K., and Kitchem, E. M.,
        FILLET WELDS SUBJECTED TO BENDING AND SHEAR, *Civil Engineering and Public Works Review*, London, England, Vol. 54, No. 634, April, 1959, pp. 455-458.

8.19    Schreiner, N.,
        THE BEHAVIOR OF FILLET WELDS WHEN SUBJECTED TO BENDING STRESSES, *The Welding Journal*, Vol. 14, No. 9, 1935.

8.20    Wallaert, J. J., and Fisher, J. W.,
        SHEAR STRENGTH OF HIGH-STRENGTH BOLTS, *Journal of the Structural Division*, ASCE, Vol. 91, No. ST3, Proc. Paper 4368, June, 1965, p. 99.

8.21    Rumpf, J. L., and Fisher, J. W.,
        CALIBRATION OF A325 BOLTS, *Journal of the Structural Division*, ASCE, Vol. 89, No. ST6, Proc. Paper 3731, Dec., 1963, p. 215.

8.22    Sterling, G. H., Troup, E. W. J., Chesson, E., and Fisher, J. W.,
        CALIBRATION TESTS OF A490 HIGH-STRENGTH BOLTS, *Journal of the Structural Division*, ASCE, Vol. 91, No. ST5, Oct., 1965.

8.23    Christopher, R. J., Kulak, G. L., and Fisher, J. W.,
        CALIBRATION OF ALLOY STEEL BOLTS, *Journal of the Structural Division*, ASCE, Vol. 92, No. ST2, Proc. Paper 4768, Apr., 1966, p. 19.

8.24    Fisher, J. W., and Beedle, L. S.,
        CRITERIA FOR DESIGNING BEARING-TYPE BOLTED JOINTS, *Journal of the Structural Division*, ASCE, Vol. 91, No. ST5, Proc. Paper 4511, Oct., 1965, p. 129.

8.25    Vincent, G. S.,
        TENTATIVE CRITERIA FOR LOAD FACTOR DESIGN OF STEEL HIGHWAY BRIDGES, AISI, Feb., 1968.

8.26    Chesson, E., Faustino, N. L., and Munse, W. H.,
        HIGH STRENGTH BOLTS SUBJECTED TO TENSION AND SHEAR, *Journal of the Structural Division*, ASCE, Vol. 91, No. ST5, Proc. Paper 4512, Oct., 1965, p. 155.

8.27    Johnson, L. G., Cannon, J. C., and Spooner, L. A.,
        HIGH-TENSILE PRELOADED BOLTED JOINTS FOR DEVEL-

OPMENT OF FULL PLASTIC MOMENTS, *British Welding Journal,* Sept., 1960.

8.28 Douty, R. T., and McGuire, W.,
HIGH STRENGTH BOLTED MOMENT CONNECTIONS, *Journal of the Structural Division,* ASCE, Vol. 91, No. ST2, Proc. Paper 4298, Apr., 1965, p. 101.

8.29 Fisher, J. W.,
BEHAVIOR OF FASTENERS AND PLATES WITH HOLES, *Journal of the Structural Division,* ASCE, Vol. 91, No. ST6, Proc. Paper 4587, Dec., 1965, p. 265.

8.30 Schutz, F. W.,
STRENGTH OF MOMENT CONNECTIONS USING HIGH TEN-SILE STRENGTH BOLTS, *Proceedings,* AISC, 1959.

8.31 Bannister, A.,
BEHAVIOR OF CERTAIN CONNECTIONS INCORPORATING HIGH STRENGTH FRICTION RIP BOLTS, *Civil Engineering and Public Works Review,* London, Vol. 60, No. 711, Oct., 1965, Vol. 60, No. 712, Nov., 1965.

8.32 Yamada, M.,
BEHAVIOR OF WIDE FLANGE BEAM-COLUMN CONNEC-TIONS, Department of Architecture, Kobe University, Kobe, Japan, 1963.

8.33 Sherbourne, A. N.,
BOLTED BEAM TO COLUMN CONNECTIONS, *The Structural Engineer,* London, Vol. 39, No. 6, June, 1961.

## CHAPTER 9.—DEFLECTIONS

9.1 Knudsen, K. E., Yang, C. H., Johnston, B. G., and Beedle, L. S.,
PLASTIC STRENGTH AND DEFLECTIONS OF CONTINUOUS BEAMS, *The Welding Journal,* Vol. 32, No. 5, May, 1953, p. 240–s.

9.2 Gerstle, K. H.,
DEFLECTIONS OF STRUCTURES IN THE INELASTIC RANGE, *Journal of the Engineering Mechanics Division,* ASCE, Vol. 83, No. EM3, Proc. Paper 1290, July, 1957.

9.3 Gerstle, K. H., and Zarboulas, V.,
ELASTIC-PLASTIC DEFORMATIONS OF STEEL STRUC-TURES, *Journal of the Structural Division,* ASCE, Vol. 89, No. ST1, Proc. Paper 3419, Feb., 1963, p. 179.

9.4 Alvarez, R. J., and Birnstiel, C.,
ELASTIC-PLASTIC ANALYSIS OF PLANE RIGID FRAMES, New York University, New York, Oct., 1967.

9.5     Driscoll, G. C., Jr.,
        ROTATION CAPACITY REQUIREMENTS FOR BEAMS AND
        FRAMES OF STRUCTURAL STEEL, dissertation presented to
        Lehigh University, at Bethlehem, Pa., in 1958, in partial fulfillment of
        the requirements for the degree of Doctor of Philosophy.

9.6     Lu, L. W., and Driscoll, G. C., Jr.,
        PLASTIC STRENGTH AND DEFLECTION OF A GABLED
        FRAME, *Report No. 205D.8,* Fritz Engineering Laboratory, Lehigh
        University, Bethlehem, Pa., June, 1958.

9.7     Symonds, P. S.,
        A REVIEW OF METHODS FOR THE PLASTIC ANALYSIS
        OF RIGID FRAMES OF DUCTILE METAL, *Technical Report
        A11-S' 6/86,* Brown University to Office of Naval Research, May,
        1950, pp. 44–49.

9.8     Parikh, B. P.,
        ELASTIC-PLASTIC ANALYSIS AND DESIGN OF UNBRACED
        MULTI-STORY STEEL FRAMES, dissertation presented to Lehigh
        University, at Bethlehem, Pa., in 1966, in partial fulfillment of the re-
        quirements for the degree of Doctor of Philosophy; University Micro-
        films, Inc., Ann Arbor, Mich.

9.9     Harrison, H. B.,
        THE ELASTIC-PLASTIC ANALYSIS OF PLANE FLEXURAL
        FRAMES, *Report No. 297.16,* Fritz Engineering Laboratory, Lehigh
        University, Bethlehem, Pa., July, 1965.

9.10    Wang, C. K., and Eckel, C. L.,
        ELEMENTARY THEORY OF STRUCTURES, McGraw-Hill Book
        Co., Inc., New York, 1957, p. 243 ff.

9.11    Heyman, J.,
        ON THE ESTIMATION OF DEFLEXIONS IN ELASTIC-
        PLASTIC FRAMED STRUCTURES, *Proceedings of the Institution
        of Civil Engineers,* Vol. 19, May, 1961, p. 39.

9.12    Martin, J. B.,
        Discussion of ON THE ESTIMATION OF DEFLEXIONS IN
        ELASTIC-PLASTIC FRAMED STRUCTURES, by J. Heyman,
        *Proceedings of the Institution of Civil Engineers,* Vol. 23, Oct., 1962,
        p. 303.

9.13    Yang, C. H., Beedle, L. S., and Johnston, B. G.,
        PLASTIC DESIGN AND THE DEFORMATION OF STRUC-
        TURES, *The Welding Journal,* Vol. 30, No. 7, July, 1951, p. 348–s.

9.14    Neal, B. G.,
        DEFLECTIONS OF PLANE FRAMES AT THE POINT OF COL-
        LAPSE, *The Structural Engineer,* Vol. 38, No. 7, July, 1960, p. 224.

9.15    Jennings, A., and Majid, K.,
        AN ELASTIC-PLASTIC ANALYSIS BY COMPUTER FOR
        FRAMED STRUCTURES LOADED UP TO COLLAPSE, *The
        Structural Engineer,* Vol. 43, No. 12, Dec., 1965, p. 407.

9.16    Davies, J. M.,
        FRAME INSTABILITY AND STRAIN HARDENING IN PLAS-
        TIC THEORY, *Journal of the Structural Division,* ASCE, Vol. 92,
        No. ST3, Proc. Paper 4836, June, 1966, p. 1.

9.17    Davies, J. M.,
        THE RESPONSE OF PLANE FRAMEWORKS TO STATIC AND
        VARIABLE REPEATED LOADING IN THE ELASTIC-PLASTIC
        RANGE, *The Structural Engineer,* Vol. 44, No. 8, Aug., 1966, p. 277.

9.18    Korn, A., and Galambos, T. V.,
        BEHAVIOR OF ELASTIC-PLASTIC FRAMES, *Journal of the Struc-
        tural Division,* ASCE, Vol. 94, No. ST5, Proc. Paper 5942, May, 1968,
        p. 1119.

9.19    Wright, E. W., and Gaylord, E. H.,
        ANALYSIS OF UNBRACED MULTI-STORY RIGID FRAMES,
        *Journal of the Structural Division,* ASCE, Vol. 94, No. ST5, Proc. Paper
        5944, May, 1968, p. 1143.

9.20    Yarimci, E., Yura, J. A., and Lu, L. W.,
        TECHNIQUES FOR TESTING STRUCTURES PERMITTED TO
        SWAY, *Experimental Mechanics,* SESA, Vol. 24, No. 2, Aug., 1967,
        p. 321.

9.21    Symonds, P. S.,
        Discussion of PLASTIC DESIGN AND THE DEFORMATION OF
        STRUCTURES, by C. H. Yang, L. S. Beedle, and B. G. Johnston, *The
        Welding Journal,* Vol. 31, No. 1, Jan., 1952, pp. 33–s to 36–s.

9.22    PLASTIC DESIGN OF BRACED MULTI-STORY STEEL
        FRAMES, American Iron and Steel Institute, New York, 1968.

9.23    Takeda, T.,
        AN APPROXIMATE METHOD OF STRESS ANALYSIS OF
        MULTISTORY FRAME SUBJECTED TO HORIZONTAL FORCE
        INCLUDING CONSIDERATION OF BEAM-COLUMN CON-
        NECTIVE ZONE, Architectural Institute of Japan, Feb., 1965, p. 26.

## CHAPTER 10.—MULTISTORY FRAMES

10.1    Allison, H.,
        PLASTIC VS. ELASTIC DESIGN IN STRUCTURAL STEEL,
        *The Construction Specifier,* Construction Specifications Institute,
        Washington, D.C., Vol. 20, No. 9, Feb., 1968, p. 61–65.

10.2 Bennett, W. A.,
PLASTIC DESIGN OF A 14-STORY APARTMENT BUILDING,
*AISC Engineering Journal,* Vol. 4, No. 2, Apr., 1967.

10.3 HYBRID DESIGN CUTS STEEL USE, *Engineering News-Record,*
New York, July 10, 1969.

10.4 Lu, L. W., Armacost, J. O., III, and Driscoll, G. C., Jr.,
PLASTIC DESIGN OF MULTI-STORY FRAMES—BRACED
FRAMES, *Report No. 273.55,* Fritz Engineering Laboratory, Lehigh
University, Bethlehem, Pa., Jan., 1968.

10.5 Daniels, J. H., and Lu, L. W.,
SWAY SUBASSEMBLAGE ANALYSIS FOR UNBRACED
FRAMES, Preprint No. 717, ASCE, Oct., 1968.

10.6 Driscoll, G. C., Jr., Armacost, J. O., III, and Lu, L. W.,
PLASTIC DESIGN OF MULTI-STORY FRAMES—UNBRACED
FRAMES, *Report No. 345.2,* Fritz Engineering Laboratory, Lehigh
University, Bethlehem, Pa., June, 1968.

10.7 Armacost, J. O., III, and Driscoll, G. C., Jr.,
THE COMPUTER ANALYSIS OF UNBRACED MULTI-STORY
FRAMES, *Report No. 345.5,* Fritz Engineering Laboratory, Lehigh
University, Bethlehem, Pa., May, 1968.

10.8 Daniels, J. H., and Lu, L. W.,
APPLICATIONS OF THE SWAY SUBASSEMBLAGE METHOD,
*Report No. 338.4,* Fritz Engineering Laboratory, Lehigh University,
Bethlehem, Pa. (to be published).

10.9 Yoshida, H., and Daniels, J. H.,
MINIMUM WEIGHT DESIGN OF FRAMES USING SWAY
SUBASSEMBLAGE THEORY, *Report No. 273.65,* Fritz Engineering
Laboratory, Lehigh University, Bethlehem, Pa., Jan., 1969.

10.10 Daniels, J. H.,
COMBINED LOAD ANALYSIS OF UNBRACED FRAMES, dis-
sertation presented to Lehigh University, at Bethlehem, Pa., in 1967,
in partial fulfillment of the requirements for the degree of Doctor of
Philosophy; University Microfilms, Inc., Ann Arbor, Mich.

10.11 Hansell, W. C.,
PRELIMINARY DESIGN OF UNBRACED MULTI-STORY
FRAMES, dissertation presented to Lehigh University, at Bethlehem,
Pa., in 1966, in partial fulfillment of the requirements for the degree of
Doctor of Philosophy; University Microfilms, Inc., Ann Arbor, Mich.

10.12 Daniels, J. H., and Lu, L. W.,
DESIGN CHARTS FOR THE SUBASSEMBLAGE METHOD
OF DESIGNING UNBRACED MULTI-STORY FRAMES, *Report
No. 273.54,* Fritz Engineering Laboratory, Lehigh University, Bethle-
hem, Pa., Nov., 1966.

10.13    FULLY RIGID MULTI-STORY WELDED STEEL FRAMES, Joint
         Committee Report, Institution of Structural Engineers, London,
         England, Dec., 1964.

10.14    Majumdar, S. N., et al.,
         APPROXIMATE INELASTIC ANALYSIS OF SHEAR WALL-
         FRAME STRUCTURES, Proceedings, 8th Congress, International
         Association for Bridge and Structural Engineering, New York, Sept.
         1968.

10.15    Adams, P. F., and MacGregor, J. G.,
         DESIGN OF SHEAR WALL-FRAME STRUCTURES, presented
         at the ASCE Annual Meeting held at Pittsburgh, Pa., Oct., 1968.

10.16    Yura, J. A.,
         THE STRENGTH OF BRACED MULTI-STORY FRAMES,
         Report No. 273.28, Fritz Engineering Laboratory, Lehigh University,
         Bethlehem, Pa., Sept., 1965.

10.17    Galambos, T. V.,
         LATERAL SUPPORT FOR TIER BUILDING FRAMES, AISC
         Engineering Journal, Vol. 1, No. 1, Jan., 1964.

10.18    Lu, L. W.,
         A SURVEY OF LITERATURE ON THE STABILITY OF
         FRAMES, Bulletin 81, Welding Research Council, Sept., 1962.

10.19    Adams, P. F.,
         LOAD-DEFORMATION RELATIONSHIPS FOR SIMPLE
         FRAMES, Report No. 273.21, Fritz Engineering Laboratory, Lehigh
         University, Bethlehem, Pa., Dec., 1964.

10.20    Lu, L. W.,
         INELASTIC BUCKLING OF STEEL FRAMES, Journal of the
         Structural Division, ASCE, Vol. 91, No. ST6, Proc. Paper 4577, Dec.,
         1965, p. 185.

10.21    Moses, F.,
         INELASTIC FRAME BUCKLING, Journal of the Structural Divi-
         sion, ASCE, Vol. 90, No. ST6, Proc. Paper 4169, Dec., 1964, p. 105.

10.22    Sapp, D. H.,
         INELASTIC STABILITY OF RECTANGULAR STEEL FRAMES,
         dissertation presented to the University of Illinois, at Urbana, Ill., in
         1964, in partial fulfillment of the requirements for the degree of Doctor
         of Philosophy; University Microfilms, Inc., Ann Arbor, Mich.

10.23    Lu, L. W.,
         STABILITY OF FRAMES UNDER PRIMARY BENDING
         MOMENTS, Journal of the Structural Division, ASCE, Vol. 89, No.
         ST3, Proc. Paper 3547, June, 1963, p. 35.

10.24   Chu, K. H., and Pabacius, A.,
ELASTIC AND INELASTIC BUCKLING OF PORTAL FRAMES,
*Journal of the Engineering Mechanics Division,* ASCE, Vol. 90, No.
EM5, Proc. Paper 4094, Oct., 1964, p. 221.

10.25   Yen, Y. C.,
ELASTIC AND PARTIAL PLASTIC INSTABILITY OF MULTI-
STORY FRAMES, dissertation presented to Lehigh University, at
Bethlehem, Pa., in 1966, in partial fulfillment of the requirements for
the degree of Doctor of Philosophy; University Microfilms, Inc., Ann
Arbor, Mich.

10.26   Majid, K. I.,
ELASTIC-PLASTIC STRUCTURAL ANALYSIS, dissertation presented to Manchester University, at Manchester, England, in 1963, in
partial fulfillment of the requirements for the degree of Doctor of
Philosophy.

10.27   Galambos, T. V.,
INFLUENCE OF PARTIAL BASE FIXITY ON FRAME STA-
BILITY, *Transactions,* ASCE, Vol. 126, Part II, Paper No. 3256, 1961,
p. 929.

10.28   Lu, L. W.,
COMPRESSION MEMBERS IN FRAMES AND TRUSSES,
*Structural Steel Design,* Chapter 10, Ronald Press Co., New York,
1964.

# AUTHOR INDEX[a]

---

[a]Reference numbers are in bold-face type. The numbers following a reference number
indicate the pages on which the reference is cited.

327

# SUBJECT INDEX